Conservation of Building and Decorative Stone

Volume 1

Butterworth–Heinemann Series in Conservation and Museology

Conservation of Building and Decorative Stone

Volume 1

Editors

John Ashurst DArch FSA(Scot)
Principal Architect, Research and Technical Advisory Service,
Historic Buildings and Monuments Commission for England;
Chairman Standing Joint Committee on Natural Stones (UK)

Francis G. Dimes MSc BSc MIGeol FGS
Private Consultant
Formerly Institute of Geological Sciences, Geological Museum, London

Butterworth–Heinemann
London   Boston   Singapore   Sydney   Toronto   Wellington

First published 1990

Chapter 1 © Ian Bristow, 1990
Chapter 2–6 © F.G. Dimes, 1990
Chapter 7 © Butterworth-Heinemann Ltd, 1990

British Library Cataloguing in Publication Data

Conservation of building and decorative stone.—
(Butterworth's series in conservation and museology)
1. Stone buildings. Conservation
I. Ashurst, John, *1937—*
II. Dimes, Francis G.
721'.0441

ISBN 0–7506–1268–1

Library of Congress Cataloging-in-Publication Data

Conservation of building and decorative stone/editors,
John Ashurst, Francis G. Dimes
p.   cm.—(Butterworths series in conservation and museology)
Bibliography: v. 1, p.
Includes index.
1. Stone buildings—Conservation and restoration. 2. Stone.
I. Ashurst, John. II. Dimes, Francis G. III. Series.
TH1201.c66 1989
691'2—dc19

Laserset by Scribe Design, Gillingham, Kent
Printed and bound by Hartnolls Ltd, Bodmin, Cornwall

Series Editors' Preface

The conservation of artefacts and buildings has a long history, but the positive emergence of conservation as a profession can be said to date from the foundation of the International Institute for the Conservation of Museum Objects (IIC) in 1950 (the last two words of the title being later changed to Historic and Artistic Works) and the appearance soon after in 1952 of its journal *Studies in Conservation*. The role of the conservator as distinct from those of the restorer and the scientist had been emerging during the 1930s with a focal point in the Fogg Art Museum, Harvard University, which published the precursor to *Studies in Conservation, Technical Studies in the Field of the Fine Arts* (1932–42).

UNESCO, through its Cultural Heritage Division and its publications, had always taken a positive role in conservation and the foundation, under its auspices, of the International Centre for the Study of the Preservation and the Restoration of Cultural Property (ICCROM), in Rome, was a further advance. The Centre was established in 1959 with the aims of advising internationally on conservation problems, co-ordinating conservation activities and establishing standards and training courses.

A significant confirmation of professional progress was the transformation at New York in 1966 of the two committees of the International Council of Museums (ICOM), one curatorial on the Care of Paintings (founded in 1949) and the other mainly scientific (founded in the mid-1950s) into the ICOM Committee for Conservation.

Following the Second International Congress of Architects in Venice in 1964 when the Venice Charter was promulgated, the International Council of Monuments and Sites (ICOMOS) was set up in 1965 to deal with archaeological, architectural and town planning questions, to schedule monuments and sites and to monitor relevant legislation.

From the early 1960s onwards, international congresses (and the literature emerging from them) held by IIC, ICOM, ICOMOS and ICCROM not only advanced the subject in its various technical specializations but also emphasized the cohesion of conservators and their subject as an interdisciplinary profession.

The use of the term *Conservation* in the title of this series refers to the whole subject of the care and treatment of valuable artefacts both movable and immovable, but within the discipline conservation has a meaning which is distinct from that of restoration. *Conservation* used in this specialized sense has two aspects: firstly, the control of the environment to minimize the decay of artefacts and materials; and, secondly, their treatment to arrest decay and to stabilize them where possible against further deterioration. Restoration is the continuation of the latter process, when conservation treatment is thought to be insufficient, to the extent of reinstating an object, without falsification, to a condition in which it can be exhibited.

In the field of conservation conflicts of values on aesthetic, historical, or technical grounds are often inevitable. Rival attitudes and methods inevitably arise in a subject which is still developing and at the core of these differences there is often a deficiency of technical knowledge. That is one of the principal *raisons d'être* of this series. In most of these matters ethical principles are the subject of much discussion, and generalizations cannot easily cover (say) buildings, furniture, easel paintings and waterlogged wooden objects.

A rigid, universally agreed principle is that all treatment should be adequately documented. There is also general agreement that structural and decorative falsification should be avoided. In addition there are three other principles which, unless there are overriding objections, it is generally agreed should be followed.

The first is the principle of the reversibility of processes, which states that a treatment should normally be such that the artefact can, if desired, be returned to its pre-treatment condition even after a long lapse of time. This principle is impossible to apply in some cases, for example where the survival of an artefact may depend upon an irreversible process. The second, intrinsic to the whole subject, is that as far as possible decayed parts of an artefact should be conserved and not replaced. The third is that the consequences of the ageing of the original materials (for example 'patina') should not normally be disguised or removed. This includes a secondary proviso that later accretions should not be retained under the false guise of natural patina.

The authors of the volumes in this series give their views on these matters, where relevant, with reference to the types of material within their scope. They take into account the differences in approach to artefacts of essentially artistic significance and to those in which the interest is primarily historical or archaeological.

The volumes are unified by a systematic and balanced presentation of theoretical and practical material with, where necessary, an objective comparison of different methods and approaches. A balance has also been maintained between the fine (and decorative) arts, archaeology and architecture in those cases where the respective branches of the subject have common ground, for example in the treatment of stone and glass and in the control of the museum environment. Since the publication of the first volume it has been decided to include within the series related monographs and technical studies. To reflect this enlargement of its scope the series has been renamed the Butterworth–Heinemann Series in Conservation and Museology.

Though necessarily different in details of organization and treatment (to fit the particular requirements of the subject) each volume has the same general standard which is that of such training courses as those of the University of London Institute of Archaeology, the Victoria and Albert Museum, the Conservation Center, New York University, the Institute of Advanced Architectural Studies, York, and ICCROM.

The authors have been chosen from among the acknowledged experts in each field, but as a result of the wide areas of knowledge and technique covered even by the specialized volumes in this series, in many instances multi-authorship has been necessary.

With the existence of IIC, ICOM, ICOMOS and ICCROM, the principles and practice of conservation have become as internationalized as the problems. The collaboration of Consultant Editors will help to ensure that the practices discussed in this series will be applicable throughout the world.

Preface

In presenting this book, John Ashurst and I have many people to thank, particularly Ian Bristow for his admirable introduction to the subject of conservation on which successive contributors have built; and David Honeyborne, whose name has long been associated with pioneering work in the field of stone weathering. Many others are owed much, and it is a debt which cannot adequately be repaid.

For my part I must thank John Ashurst, first and foremost for the constant aid and encouragement he has given. Without him the shoe leather would not have hit the pavement carrying the wearer to yet another building to add to the record. Chapters 2 to 6 owe much to Murray Mitchell, one of Britain's foremost geological editors, who spent many hours reading the script, correcting it, improving it and removing the double-negatives. The script was better for it. Especial thanks are due also to a friend and former colleague, Gilbert Green, for his great patience in straightening out my understanding of Bath Stone. The section on that stone owes much to him.

My erstwhile colleagues at the Geological Museum have helped, probably more than they realize, in answering the questions asked of them. Ron Roberts, Alan Timms, Peter Clough, Alan Jobbins and Robin Sanderson all had the kindness not to plead other engagements when they saw the question coming.

Inevitably Chapters 2 to 6 of Volume 1 are to some degree a compilation of existing, scattered knowledge. Many of the examples given are quoted from other books. They are listed in the References. There are examples, however, which may be said to be in the public domain. Should any of my friends have passed an example to me and I have not acknowledged it, I offer them my apologies.

It has not been possible to check every example given of the use of stone. I should be grateful, therefore, if any reader would let me know of any which are incorrect and, indeed, I should be pleased to learn of new outstanding uses. None of this might

Donovan Purcell

have happened but for one person to whom both John Ashurst and I must express the deepest debt of gratitude. Sadly he is no longer with us. Donovan Purcell, a former Surveyor to the Fabric of Ely Cathedral, a friend in all senses of the word, gently taught me what it was that an architect wanted to know from a geologist. To both John and me he demonstrated what limitless enthusiasm for a material could achieve. As founder chairman of the Standing Joint Committee on Natural Stones he opened a dialogue again between the masonry trade, the quarrying industry, the training establishments and architects and surveyors, contributing in no small way to a new unity of interest and purpose which has been foundational to the revival of the stone industry of the United Kingdom. To a great extent this book is part of his memorial.

John Ashurst and I have learned much from the band of dedicated people who have made their knowledge available and who have contributed largely to Volume 2. John particularly remembers with great pleasure the many discussions with these contributors on the philosophy of repair, consolidation and conservation. That this book is in two volumes is simply a matter of convenience. There is no division between an understanding of the nature of stone and the study of its repair and conservation in buildings.

Finally I must thank Janet, who came into the life of this book – too late! – and Margaret, who has lived with this book – too long!

Francis G. Dimes
Kingston Vale,
September 1990

Contents

1

An introduction to the restoration, conservation and repair of stone

Ian Bristow

Introduction

> Whoever expects to find a stone that will stand from century to century, deriding alike the frigid rains and scorching solar rays, without need of reparation, will indeed search for 'the philosopher's stone'.[1]

As C.H. Smith, who delivered these lines at a lecture to the Royal Institute of British Architects in 1840 realized, stone, despite its image as the eternal material, has a limited life. Its decay may be caused by a number of factors, including polluted acidic atmospheres, which lead to surface erosion, flaking, and exfoliation. Eventually this may impair the aesthetic appearance of a building or affect its structural stability, and proper remedial measures will be needed.

The traditional method of repair has been to cut out and renew all weathered or otherwise defective stones, but in the case of historic buildings this process is, in effect, destructive both of the ancient fabric, with its archaeological interest and, no less importantly, of the character of age such a structure will inevitably possess. The loss of either will concern equally those who are interested in the history of a building and those to whom the qualities of its age are important. It is therefore necessary to adopt a special attitude to the repair of historic stonework, soundly based on a carefully considered philosophy. The approach adopted in any given case will vary, but should spring from consideration of a number of points, most importantly:

1. the age and character of the building;
2. the structural function of the individual stone in question, and the nature and cause of its defect;
3. a careful assessment of its rate of decay, taken in the context of the building as a whole.

The last of these, the much overlooked dimension of time, is in many ways the most difficult. It needs experience and an outlook which is foreign to many architects and building contractors, especially today; but it was much neglected too in the nineteenth century, and many churches received over-drastic restoration as a result.

The first essential in approaching an historic building in need of repair is to determine the cause of decay, and, where possible, remove it or minimize its effect. If surface disruption is caused by acidic air pollution, there is little the individual can do, although governmental action in a national or international context could be of the very greatest importance. Poor selection or incorrect bedding of stones is also without simple remedy, but it is sometimes possible to improve poor detailing without alteration to the appearance of a building, as, for example, by the provision of a drip on the underside of a projecting window sill. Where a material change in appearance would result, however, it is often necessary to accept the defect and any consequent tendency to decay in order to preserve the integrity of the historic fabric.

The effects of overloading can, on the other hand, often be remedied inconspicuously. For example, the detached marble shafts employed in thirteenth-century churches and nineteenth-century buildings of the same style often become overcompressed through settlement of the more frequently jointed adjoining masonry, and the stress may be simply relieved by sawing out their joints and repointing. To remedy the spalling resulting from concave beds, or the decay caused by juxtaposition of incompatible stones is, however, more problematical; but action can be taken to control plant growth in masonry, rusting and contingent expansion of iron cramps or window ferramenta, damage caused by mason bees, leaking gutters and rainwater goods, rising damp, and unsuitable uses and human activities.

In practice, one of the most important responsibilities of anyone faced with the care of an historic building is to anticipate trouble before it happens. Not only must maintenance, especially the cleaning out of gutters and downpipes, be carried out thoroughly and regularly, but potential trouble spots should be eliminated. If a bend can be removed from a rainwater pipe it will lessen the chances of a blockage; and where there is important internal masonry, such as a carved freestone or marble wall monument, any exterior downpipe should be resited as far away from it as possible. Care should also be taken to ensure that any repointing is carried out in a suitable mix, and that impervious paints and plasters, which will inhibit the free evaporation of moisture, are not used to the detriment of the masonry. Heating pipes should be sited well away from historic carving or wall bases in order to avoid rapid decay through increased evaporation of moisture within the fabric.

The birth of a conservative approach to repair

The need for careful maintenance was recognized by the fifteenth-century Florentine architect Leone Battista Alberti, who exclaimed that he was often filled with the highest indignation when he saw buildings going to ruin owing to the carelessness of their owners.[2] From the mid-sixteenth century, however, the growing English fashion for Italianate architecture led to a contempt for the Gothic style, and its consequent neglect. The seventeenth-century diarist John Evelyn, for example, spoke disparagingly of Henry VII's chapel at Westminster, as being composed of 'lame *Statues, Lace* and other *Cut-work* and *Crinkle Crankle*';[3] and at the same period many mediaeval churches, already despoiled by puritanical fanaticism, fell into poor repair. The Civil War too brought in its wake a toll of destruction to many castles, and a large number were slighted to prevent their continued use for military purposes.

The resulting ruins, together with those of classical Italy, soon became a poignant reminder of the past; and their fascination to the eighteenth-century mind is splendidly revealed in the following lines from David Mallet's poem *The Excursion* of 1726:

> Behind me rises huge an awful *Pile,*
> Sole on this blasted Heath, a Place of Tombs,
> Waste, desolate, where *Ruin* dreary dwells,
> Brooding o'er sightless Sculls, and crumbling
>   Bones.
> Ghastful *He* sits, and eyes with stedfast Glare
> The Column grey with Moss, the falling Bust,

The Time-shook Arch, the monumental Stone,
Impair'd, effac'd, and hastening into Dust.[4]

The particular qualities of ruins eventually became incorporated formally into aesthetic theory. In the 1750s, the philosopher Edmund Burke had postulated two characters, the Sublime and the Beautiful, the latter expressed by smooth outline and flowing lines, the former by jagged outline and grandeur of scale, a quality with which ruins would no doubt have been identified.[5] By the 1790s, however, this simple duality had come to seem unsatisfactory, and Sir Uvedale Price added a third character, the Picturesque, describing the way a beautiful building with its smooth surface and even colouring was converted by time into a picturesque ruin:

> First, by means of weather stains, partial incrustations, mosses, &c. it at the same time takes off from the uniformity of its surface, and of its colour; that is, gives it a degree of roughness, and variety of tint. Next, the various accidents of weather loosen the stones themselves; they tumble in irregular masses upon what was perhaps smooth turf or pavement, or nicely trimmed walks and shrubberies; now mixed and overgrown with wild plants and creepers, that crawl over, and shoot among the fallen ruins. Sedums, wall-flowers, and other vegetables that bear drought, find nourishment in the decayed cement from which the stones have been detached: Birds convey their food into the chinks, and yew, elder, and other berried plants project from the sides; while the ivy mantles over other parts, and crowns the top.[6]

The late eighteenth and early nineteenth century greatly enjoyed the qualities offered by decay of this nature, and the preoccupation with its pleasing character is well expressed in engravings of the period, such as that of St. Giles's Church, Little Malvern, Worcestershire (*Figure 1.1*). In it may be seen the evident pleasure of the artists in the ivy-clad ruins at the east end and on the southern side of the chancel of this fifteenth-century building, besides the truncated tower with its pyramidal roof which replaced the earlier parapet.

In parallel with this enthusiasm for the aesthetic qualities of ruins, an academic interest in the study of the remains of mediaeval architecture developed. The eighteenth-century classical architect Sir William Chambers, for example, made a plea in his *Treatise on the Decorative Part of Civil Architecture* (1791) for 'a correct elegant publication of our own cathedrals, and other buildings called Gothick, before they totally fall to ruin',[7] which was answered rapidly by a whole series of publications. Under the auspices of the Society of Antiquaries, John Carter

Figure 1.1 Pleasing decay. A view of St Giles's Church, Little Malvern, Worcestershire. (Engraving by J.le Keux from a drawing by J.P. Neal in their *Views of the most interesting Collegiate and Parochial Churches in Great Britain* (1824-1825), volume 2)

produced his superb folios of measured drawings of cathedrals, including those of Durham, Exeter, Gloucester, and York, and the abbeys of Bath and St. Alban's; whilst in 1811 John Milner published his *Treatise on the Ecclesiastical Architecture of England*, a work followed in 1817 by Thomas Rickman's *Attempt to discriminate the Styles of Architecture in England*, which formed the foundation of nineteenth-century scholarship. Perhaps the most prolific publisher of the period was John Britton, whose *Architectural Antiquities*, which contained splendid engravings of ancient buildings, appeared in five volumes between 1807 and 1826, and whose series of *Cathedral Antiquities*, which dealt with fourteen English cathedrals, was produced between 1814 and 1835. The latter volumes were distinguished by containing, besides a selection of general views and details, carefully executed measured drawings of the buildings. This was also a feature of the vitally important volumes of *Specimens* and *Examples of Gothic Architecture* produced by Augustus Pugin in 1819–1822 and 1828–1838 respectively. Together with others, these formed primary source books for the revival of mediaeval architectural styles, a subject outside the scope of the present chapter, but brilliantly charted by Charles Eastlake in his *History of the Gothic Revival* (1872). It had, though, an important parallel which

is of great moment in the present context, the revival by the Tractarians of the ancient dignity of Christian worship.

In 1827, the author of *Notes on the Cambridgeshire Churches* wrote:

> The dilapidation of churches is a delicate subject to speak of … but when the archdeacons abandoned their duty … peculation, ruin, and desolation stalked abroad… and corruption and decay withered all around… The established places of worship have become unfit and unsafe for Christians to meet in; the churches are cold, comfortless, unhealthy; the haunts of colds, catarrhs, and rheumatism; the receptacle frequently of filth, and the abode of toads and reptiles. Congregations… are deterred from entering… by the dread of the fevers and consumption that they know lurk within… [and] are driven into dissenting places of worship.[8]

A few years later, Augustus Pugin's son, Augustus Welby Northmore Pugin, complained that the font at Selby Abbey, Yorkshire, was disused. The transept chapels were filled with rubbish, one even being used as a coal hole, and the eastern aisle windows were disfigured by having two large stove pipes carried through them.[9] The engraving of the interior

Figure 1.2 The neglected state of St Peter's, Cambridge, in the early nineteenth century (provenance unknown)

of St. Peter's Church, Cambridge, illustrated in *Figure 1.2*, shows the appearance of just such a neglected church; and it was not long before a concerted effort was made to remove the offending bric-a-brac from them, to repair their roofs and restore their damaged masonry in order to permit seemly and proper worship within. A large number of churches had, of course, been refitted in the eighteenth century, most generally by the installation of box pews, a reredos, pulpit, and galleries; and certain major structures, such as Milton Abbey, Winchester and Salisbury Cathedrals and Henry VII's Chapel, had been restored by architects such as James Wyatt, whose thoroughgoing approach had been the subject of controversy at the time.[10] To those who wished to revive the ancient dignities of worship, however, such crass alterations were anathema, and the resulting movement to put matters to rights led in 1839 to foundation of the Cambridge Camden Society. This event was of profound significance and was soon to have a devastating effect on ancient structures throughout the length and breadth of Britain.

The Society was formed by a group of undergraduates, notable amongst whom was J.M. Neale, who dedicated themselves not only to the study of

mediaeval ecclesiastical structures, but, most importantly, to undertake their restoration. They started their programme for the latter in a small way with the font at Coton, a village church very close to Cambridge,[11] and in 1841 reported their repair of the font at St. Peter's. This had been broken into pieces, some of which had been lost;[12] the restored bowl with its sculpture pieced-in by the Society can still be seen in the church today. In June 1840, they paid to have the rough-cast removed from the tower of St. Bene't's, Cambridge, in order to expose 'the interest of its Anglo-Saxon construction',[13] and the following year embarked on their largest project, the 'thorough restoration' of the Church of the Holy Sepulchre,[14] which, on account of the impact it was to have elsewhere, is worth considering in a little detail. The opportunity for the Society's involvement was provided by the collapse of part of the vault of the circular aisle, caused by settlement of the perimeter wall which had been undermined by grave-digging. This had occasioned movement in the round tower, and the remedial measures instigated in 1841, under the direction of the architect Anthony

Figure 1.3 Church of the Holy Sepulchre, Cambridge, before restoration (from John Britton, *The Architectural Antiquities of Great Britain* (1807-1826) volume 3 (1812), plate facing page 90)

Salvin, involved not only rebuilding the wall and vault, but also the removal of the upper storey of the tower which had been added to the Romanesque structure in the fifteenth century (*Figure 1.3*). In addition, 'Plain single Norman lights' were 'substituted for the unsightly Perpendicular insertions which disfigured, as well as weakened, the walls of the circular Aisle'. The liaison in this statement between a return to a structurally perfect condition and restoration to an earlier physical state is significant; and in parallel with this, the box pews and other later furnishings were removed from the interior.

Such an approach typified a large number of later restorations at other churches inspired by the activities of the Cambridge Camden Society, the nineteenth-century debate surrounding which has been ably charted by Stephan Tschudi Madsen in his recent book *Restoration and Anti-Restoration* (Oslo, 1976), to which the reader is referred for greater detail of this important issue. From the point of view of the present chapter, however, the most important facet of the Holy Sepulchre restoration was the smoothing and redressing of the remaining ancient stonework both within and without, a matter the Society reported with enthusiasm.[15] The transformation effected by the works may be seen in the post restoration photograph (*Figure 1.4*), the final product, bereft of patina and 'scraped' clean, presenting a tidy and perfect face to the world, thus testifying to its new found health in the care of what was seen by its authors as a revitalized Christian witness.

Although the Cambridge Camden Society was disbanded in 1846, it was refounded the following year in London as the Ecclesiological Society and continued its activities, which included publication of the periodical, the *Ecclesiologist* (1841–1868). Through this, the principles of restoration advocated by the Society swept the country, and church after church was subjected to thoroughgoing works of the kind seen at the Holy Sepulchre. The enthusiasm of the clergy, which stands in marked contrast to their general apathy towards historic buildings today, ranged unchecked over ancient fabric; and gradually the picturesque face of the English parish church became transformed into a scraped and tidy blandness, scarred too with the harshness of new stone which was often cut with a soulless precision unknown in the Middle Ages. Restoration thus came inevitably into conflict with artistic sensibilities, and, furthermore, with archaeological interests as genuine mediaeval work disappeared in favour of somebody's more or less scholarly notion of what seemed correct.

The most notable reaction to this process was that of John Ruskin, who was horrified at the destruction of ancient fabric which was taking place. In 1849 he expressed his concern with considerable force in the 'Lamp of Memory', which formed Chapter VI of the *Seven Lamps of Architecture*. He characterized restoration as 'a Lie from beginning to end' and wrote:

> You may make a model of a building as you may of a corpse, and your model may have the shell

Figure 1.4 A nineteenth-century photograph showing the Church of the Holy Sepulchre, Cambridge, after restoration

of the old walls within it as your cast might have the skeleton… but the old building is destroyed.

To lose the original surface, albeit weathered, was tragic; and its replacement totally unsatisfactory. How could one, he demanded, copy a surface that had been worn half an inch down, since the whole finish was in the half inch that had gone. The old, he insisted, still had some life, some mysterious suggestion of what it had been, and of what it had lost. All in all, he remarked:

> Neither by the public, nor by those who have the care of public monuments, is the true meaning of the word *restoration* understood. It means the most total destruction which a building can suffer.[16]

In both the *Seven Lamps* and the *Stones of Venice*, which succeeded it a few years later in 1851–1853, Ruskin showed himself to be not only an extremely sensitive observer and draughtsman of the patina of decay, but also an astute analyst of mediaeval fabric. The irregularities of setting out which he discovered at Pisa and elsewhere were just the sort of thing liable to be missed and made uniform by a restorer,[17] and the almost unique way in which he combined picturesque artist *and* archaeological scholar was quite remarkable.

The force of his arguments come to be accepted only gradually, to the great regret of many architectural historians today, but by 1861 the architect William Butterfield was writing in connection with his restoration of the tower of the Chapel at Winchester College:

> I should carefully save and reuse every old moulding and surface stone which is at all likely to last, even though it may be in some respects in an imperfect state;[18]

whilst about five years later George Edmund Street, faced at Monkland, Herefordshire, with tufa 'so rough, and… so rude, that most men would have proposed to build an entirely new church', rebuilt the nave 'with every wrought stone put back in its old place'.[19] One of the most revealing of these later restorations was the *anastylosis*, carried out by Sir Gilbert Scott in about 1875, of the fragments of the shrine of St. Alban which had been discovered in 1873. This was later praised even by such a critic as E.S. Prior, who remarked that we are

> fortunate in the taste and good sense with which the remains have been put together and treated, as such monuments should be, with the sole intention of the preservation of the beauties they have left.[20]

Scott himself wrote that the Shrine was, 'by the ingenuity of the foreman and the clerk of the works,

Figure 1.5 St Alban's Abbey, Hertfordshire, the shrine of St Alban after reconstruction in the 1870s. (From *Architecture*, volume 2 (1897), p. 77)

set up again, exactly in its old place, stone for stone, and fragment for fragment: the most marvellous restitution that ever was made'.[21] The illustration (*Figure 1.5*) shows the result, with no attempt to replace missing features, nor, most importantly, to renew damaged or defective stones. Of it, Gilbert Scott's son, George Gilbert Scott wrote:

> In that one structure, as it now stands, is summed up the history of english church architecture as a living fact, and of the death which finally overtook it. The one is seen in the exquisite finish and beauty of the monument thus recovered from its ruins; the other in the marks, which it bears upon it, of the crowbar-blows which shattered it into splinters, starring the finely-wrought marble, as ice is shivered by a mattock.[22]

In this passage a profound change from the attitude of the Ecclesiological Society may be noted. No longer is it necessary to present perfection of form as a living testimony to the Christian witness, its continued life is asserted *despite* the damage inflicted by the wreckers of the past.

Nevertheless, restorations of earlier type continued, notably under the direction of Lord Grimthorpe (formerly Sir Edmund Beckett Denison, QC). In 1877 matters came to a head over Tewkesbury Abbey, where the aged Scott, despite the sensitivity he could bring to mediaeval masonry, proposed to remove the seventeenth-century furnishings. To a younger generation, they too were part of the building's history, and over this issue William Morris founded the Society for the Protection of Ancient Buildings and published its *Manifesto*. This important document, which still forms the basis of the Society's policy, represents a milestone in thinking about the repair of historic buildings, and has dominated attitudes in England for over a century. It has also had considerable influence abroad. In it, Morris proscribed the restoration of a building to an earlier stage of its development, as had been done at the Holy Sepulchre and vast numbers of other mediaeval churches, and emphasized the need for careful and consistent maintenance, or 'daily care'. He stressed too the need to preserve the patina of age. However, unlike Ruskin, whose total opposition to tampering with historic fabric had led him to prefer demolition to repair,[23] Morris, in the *Manifesto*, implicitly acknowledged the need for renewal of decayed stone; but, he insisted, where this was done the new should be clearly distinguishable from the old.

The working out of this dictum in practice has been a matter of concern to many architects. In fact, the idea was not completely new, and in restoring the arch of Titus in the Forum Romanum in the early nineteenth century, the architect Giuseppe Valadier had distinguished his new architectural mouldings by omitting the enrichments, and by simplifying the new Ionic capitals whilst retaining the overall form of the antique survivors.[24] A similar approach was adopted about 1880 in the reconstruction of the shrine of St Frideswide in Christ Church Cathedral, Oxford (*Figure 1.6*), where the piers supporting the fragments of the canopy are uncompromisingly cut to show their status as new elements. Other examples of this may be seen on the exterior of many buildings, most notably where sculptured corbel-tables or label stops have been renewed but left uncarved as simple projecting blocks of stone. For plain areas of masonry, on the other hand, a convention arose of replacement, not in stone, but with tile, in order to differentiate the repair from

Figure 1.6 Christ Church Cathedral, Oxford, the shrine of St Frideswide as reconstructed about 1880 (F.H. Crossley/ Courtauld Institute)

Figure 1.7 Buttress repaired by the tile method, St Mary's Church, Higham, Kent

surviving mediaeval work. An example may be seen in the detail illustrated of a buttress at St Mary's Church, Higham, Kent (*Figure 1.7*), and the technique became widely used in the early years of the present century. Brick had often been employed for the same purpose but for different reasons in the eighteenth century, and it was no doubt felt that the use of tile would result in a similarly pleasing patchwork. Soon, however, it became clear that the character of large areas of mediaeval masonry was being transformed in a way just as assertive as insensitively inserted new stone; and an alternative was therefore developed in which the tile was recessed half an inch from the wall face, and its surface rendered to provide a closer colour match to the adjoining old masonry. The revised method was strongly advocated by A.R. Powys, who, in his book *Repair of Ancient Buildings* (1929), from which *Figures 1.8 to 1.11* are taken, linked it especially with the work of William Wier.[25] The first two illustrations show repairs carried out in this way to a buttress, and the second pair the same technique employed in the repair of a mediaeval window at Limpsfield Church, Surrey, in 1927.

Closely related to this method is the use of 'plastic stone', a specially constituted mortar reinforced and

keyed back to sound stone with copper wire or dowels used to make up defective areas. This too, was widely used between the wars, but has problems of its own, and shares with the rendered tile method a tendency to discoloration over a comparatively short period of years, so that even if there is a good match with the old stone when first completed and dried out, it will often weather to produce a disfiguring piebald appearance. The material also requires great care in mixing to avoid being too strong and impervious, and whilst in skilled hands it can be a useful solution in some circumstances, it has acquired a poor reputation amongst many architects since where the mix is too strong it will eventually crack away from the backing stone owing to the effects of salt action. When this happens (*Figure 1.12*) it will often pull away a further inch or more of old stone with it. For success, the mixture must thus be quite weak; and the material cannot, therefore, be used for the repair of structural or weathering elements. Indeed, it has always been best used for the simple filling of cavities, rather on the principle adopted by the dental profession. In this connection it is interesting to see that Powys seems to have acknowledged that the rendered tile method too was unsuitable for weathering elements, since in his drawing showing the repair of a buttress (*Figure 1.8*) he shows a new stone for one of the water-tablings. Undoubtedly, however, the greatest danger in the use of plastic stone is the tendency for every blemish, however tiny, in a wall to be 'repaired'; and examples may be found where masonry has been so over-treated with the material that it has lost the patina of age, and thus presents an unpleasant smoothness to the observer.

Attitudes towards the repair of stonework today

From the chronological résumé above it will be seen that the repair of masonry has a history of its own, and is not simply a mechanical operation which can be tackled in a purely utilitarian way. Rather, the architect must educate himself to understand the art-historical and archaeological importance and character of the particular structure with which he is concerned, and develop a sensitivity towards the preoccupations of the different groups and disciplines interested in its continued preservation. Inevitably too, he will come to see his own operation not only in the historical perspective of the individual building, but also in the context of the philosophical developments of the last two or three hundred years.

Perhaps the greatest lesson to be learned from the observation of work carried out during the eighteenth and nineteenth centuries is that the least

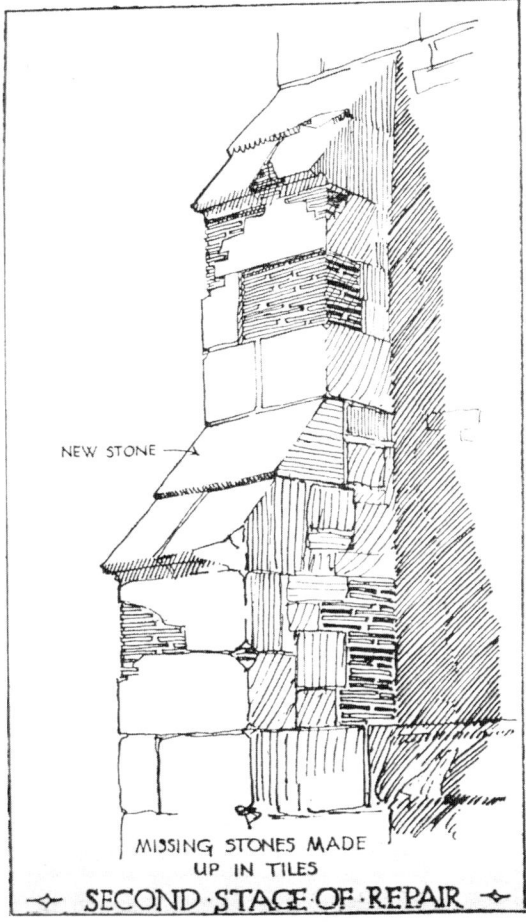

Figures 1.8 and 1.9 Rendering of tiles; diagrams showing stages in the repair of a buttress. (From A.R. Powys, *Repair* *of Ancient Buildings*, figures 11 and 12. Reproduced by kind permission of Mrs Eleanor Walton)

possible amount of stone renewal, whatever material is selected to replace it, makes for the fewest problems and greatest preservation of historical material. The crucial decision to be made is what to repair and what to leave alone, a critical matter which must be approached in a careful and organized way and not simply left to be made at the last moment by someone on site. Just as an elegant mathematical proof will do only what is *necessary* *and sufficient*, so too the historic-buildings architect should adopt the same criteria with respect to aged masonry. The first stage, as emphasized in the first section of this chapter, is a painstaking survey leading to historical appreciation of the structure and careful and thorough diagnosis of any defects which are found. These, as stressed, have to be set into the context of the building as a whole, in dimensions of

both space and time. Obviously too, any major structural movements which are progressive must be attended to at an early stage; but even here careful thought is necessary, and where cracks are the result of movement which took place early in a building's history and have since remained static there may be no need for action, obviating any need to disturb the archaeological integrity of the wall or its foundations. Where work is necessary, on the other hand, it is important it should be carried out using a method which will involve the least damage to historic fabric, not necessarily by the cheapest available. Thus, the use of bored rather than driven piles may avoid damage through vibration; or in instances where facework has become detached from the main mass of a wall and is bulging, a method of tying it back *in* *situ* (with, for example, resin anchor bolts concealed

Figures 1.10 and 1.11 Limpsfield Church, Surrey. A window in the north wall during and after repair in 1927. (From A.R. Powys, *Repair of Ancient Buildings*, figures 14 and 15. Reproduced by kind permission of Mrs Eleanor Walton)

Figure 1.12 Plaxtol Church, Kent. A failed cement repair to the belfry window

in the joints) will often be preferable to taking the face down and rebuilding it. Again, it is often possible to avoid rebuilding dangerously leaning walls by jacking them back into a vertical position or by stabilizing them with concealed reinforced concrete members. For examples where this has been successfully done, the reader is referred to *Old Churches and Modern Craftsmanship* by A.D.R. Caroe (1949), *The Care of Old Buildings* by Donald W. Insall (1958), and the same author's *The Care of Old Buildings Today* (1972).

Once the problems presented by such major structural faults have been resolved, the wall may be looked at in terms of its individual components. The architect should consider each defective stone in turn, asking if it is doing its job in the wall as a load-bearing or weathering member. Just because the face of a stone is weathered it does not mean it has become incapable of supporting the masonry above: after all, it may have lost half an inch of its face in the course of one or more centuries, but there may well be considerable substance remaining which could be allowed to weather further for a material period before renewal becomes necessary. Even where a stone is fractured, this does not mean of itself that it is no longer fulfilling its function and must be cut out and replaced. A cracked lintel in the Temple of Zeus at Athens has been cited as an instance of this: the fractured block of marble now acts as an arch rather than a beam and thus remains structurally completely stable.[26] Other fractures are often caused by the rusting of buried iron dowels or cramps which can be carefully removed and the disrupted stone repaired by gluing the broken pieces together using a suitable masonry adhesive.

The special techniques now available for the consolidation of decaying architectural sculpture are discussed in Volume 2, but these are not always applicable to ordinary building elements. Nevertheless, a conservative approach may still be adopted for structural members even when they have failed. Thus, it may be possible to flash the pitted upper surface of an eighteenth-century cornice with lead in order to restore its weathering capabilities, or use the same method to provide a drip at its leading edge when that on the soffit of the corona has decayed. Other defective stones may be carefully pieced in to avoid the need to renew the whole, although the situations in which this can be done successfully must be chosen with care in order not to introduce a distracting pattern of fresh joint-lines into the masonry. A good example of the technique in practice is the work recently completed on the western towers of St. Paul's Cathedral, London. Here (*Figure 1.13*) the corona had weathered, but the mouldings of the cornice which it had sheltered were in good condition. Rather than renew the whole cornice, it was therefore decided to renew only its upper half, making a new joint in the angle beneath the corona where it was concealed in shadow. A similar instance may be found in the 'half-and-half' technique for the repair of window mullions and tracery which have weathered where exposed to the elements. In such instances, it is often possible simply to cut back the decayed stone to the glazing line, and dowel or glue back a new outer face to the old inner half. This technique was used in St. Anselm's Chapel at Canterbury Cathedral at some date prior to 1845,[27] and has been used recently with great success in the Lady Chapel and western tower at Ely (*Figure 1.14*). Here too, the new joint is concealed, this time by the glazing groove.

This careful approach, seeking always to retain every old element that can possibly continue to do its job, is the hallmark of the competent historic-buildings architect, and contrasts strongly with the attitude commonly displayed by the inexperienced.

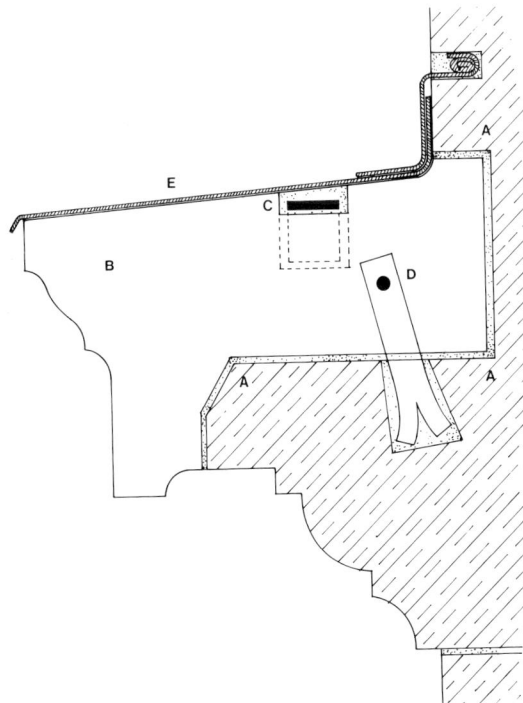

Figure 1.13 Section through a cornice, St Paul's Cathedral, London, showing the method of renewing the decayed corona. (Illustrated by kind permission of Robert Potter) (*a*) Original stonework cut back; (*c*) new stone; (*c*) stainless steel dog cramp across each joint; (*d*) stainless steel fishtail cramp and dowell; (*e*) lead weathering

Figure 1.14 The half-and-half technique used for repair of a mullion, west tower, Ely Cathedral. (Architects: Donovan Purcell and Peter Miller)

Figure 1.15 Decayed but sound masonry, south porch of St Michael's Church, East Peckham, Kent

Figure 1.16 Repaired drip mould, west window of south aisle, St John's Church, Wateringbury, Kent. (Architects: Purcell Miller Tritton and Partners).

For example, some years ago, a restoration of the fine fifteenth-century doorway of the south porch of St Michael's Church, East Peckham, Kent (*Figure 1.15*) was proposed. Looking critically at the masonry, however, and asking whether each stone was still capable of doing its job showed not only that the arch, although weathered, was structurally sound, but also that the drip provided by its label mould was in a fully functioning state. In this instance there was therefore no need for any stone repair, with a consequent saving not only to parish finances but, most importantly, to the historical integrity of the masonry and its wonderful state of picturesque decay. At St John's Church, Wateringbury, Kent, on the other hand, the drip mould of the west window of the south aisle had decayed to a point where renewal was necessary for the preservation of the window masonry beneath; but at the same time it was clear replacement could be restricted to parts of this element only (*Figure 1.16*). Furthermore, no attempt was made to repair the weathered tracery beneath, beyond careful pointing of its open joints and a few unimportant fractures.

The decision to renew any stone must in every case be taken on an individual basis, and only after a close inspection has been made. One should never think in terms of *areas* for renewal. Final decisions about stones at high levels can, accordingly, only be taken once the necessary scaffolding has been erected, and the repair specification must be written with this in mind. There is no place in historic-buildings work for the architect or other professional who remains on the ground, since defects will very often appear in a totally different light once close access is possible, and decisions over renewal should never be delegated. It has also been stressed above that the need for renewal must be assessed in the context of the building as a whole, seen both in its own timescale and that of the progress of its weathering, that is, its overall rate of decay. It must constantly be kept in mind that the purpose of repair is to hand down to the next generation the maximum possible quantity of historic fabric, not to put all defects or potential defects in the masonry to rights and obtain a textbook example of sound construction. Frequency of access, however, plays an important part in decisions over what is 'necessary and sufficient' at any given time, and when the expense of scaffolding is involved it is common to plan for an anticipated period of, say, fifty years before further repairs are needed; whilst for masonry at lower levels it is easy to go back and do a little more in ten or twenty years should this become necessary. The condition of stones on a tall spire or high parapet may, therefore, be rather more critically assessed than those on parts of the building to which more frequent access is possible.

Looking at a building and its decay in both space and time also means that there will be a different assessment of need for renewal of individual stones in a ruin, such as the east wall of Tynemouth Priory, Northumberland (*Figure 1.17*), where erosion is part of the character of the building, and in an eighteenth-century ashlar façade in good condition. As suggested above, the ruin may be considered to reflect Burke's character of the Sublime; whilst in the case of the ashlar façade, its smoothness, corresponding with his notion of beauty, is paramount. Both are

Figure 1.17 Eroded masonry as part of a ruined character. Tynemouth Priory, Northumberland

becomes necessary, and it is the ability to differentiate this from rapid decay which is important. The expertise required for historic-buildings work is thus very different from that needed in ordinary architectural practice. Much damage has been done to historic fabric by inexpert misjudgement and unnecessarily panicky action. The inexperienced individual, faced with the repair of a masonry structure for the first time, should have no qualms about obtaining a second opinion from an experienced architect.

When a decision has been made to replace a particular stone, it will either be cut out completely or to a certain depth. Once the destruction of historic fabric which this involves has taken place, it seems, perhaps, a little academic to consider what is selected to go in its place. Nevertheless, a great deal of discussion over this matter has taken place in the past; and a case can be made out for each of the methods reviewed. Today the choice rests generally between natural and 'plastic' stone, since the use of tiles is generally out of fashion although renewed interest has been shown by one or two individuals over the last few years. Some of the practical considerations affecting the choice between the genuine and the artificial product have been outlined above, the most important undoubtedly being that 'plastic' stone cannot be used for structural or weathering purposes, and can only be used to fill cavities. In many instances, therefore, it may be appropriate to employ both new and 'plastic' stone on the same job, using the former where necessary for structural reasons, and the latter to enable the minimum of old stone to be cut away where a little 'dentistry' will suffice.

Much of the nineteenth- and twentieth-century opposition to the use of new stone has come not merely from over-renewal, but also from its often hard appearance in a weathered wall. Mid-nineteenth-century masonry in particular often exhibits this insensitive character, and it is important that the architect should learn, by observation of old work, to specify replacements correctly. Mediaeval stonework was often comparatively crudely set out, especially in curved work, and the contrast between work of this nature and that of the nineteenth century may be seen clearly in the arcade running round above the wall benches in the Romanesque chapter house and vestibule at Bristol Cathedral (*Figure 1.18*). Early stonework was, moreover, dressed by hand from the rough block, and it is virtually impossible to obtain the same effect by taking a modern piece sawn die square and tooling or 'distressing' its surface and arrises (*Figure 1.19*). Of particular importance is the bed joint, which in mediaeval times was often only very roughly dressed, so that as the face of the stone weathers gently back an irregular, undulating joint line is constantly

characteristics whose retention should be sought, and whilst there would be little point in renewing any of the drip mouldings at Tynemouth in an attempt to slow down the overall rate of decay, there would be a very good case for renewing a defective stone in an ashlar façade if this would help to prevent the imminent decay of the stone below. Similarly, a nineteenth-century church or extension to an eighteenth-century house will have a character of its own which will call for sensitivity in its preservation. The architect must train himself to respond to this by constant visiting and observation (perhaps aided by drawing or photography) of a wide range of historic buildings.

Altogether, the most important judgement an architect must bring to bear is his assessment of the rate of decay of an individual element. This requires experience, often gained by the quinquennial survey and resurvey of churches under the Inspection of Churches Measure 1955, and there is no quickly available substitute, although the comparison of old photographs with the state of the structure today can often be helpful. Often, slow decay may be left to take its course for a few more years before repair

Figure 1.18 Irregular setting out of Romanesque work (right) compared with the nineteenth-century renewal (left). Chapter House, Bristol Cathedral

Figure 1.19 The unsatisfactory appearance of distressed masonry, Jumièges Abbey, Normandy

exposed rather than the hard, mathematically precise network which would result from flat, truly-sawn beds and perpends. The point may be appreciated instantly in connection with paving if the old slabs in a London street, with their hand-dressed edges, are compared with new sawn replacements (*Figure*

1.20). It is vital that the architect learn to recognize that such irregularities have nothing to do with weathering, and are a product of the original craftsmanship; when looking at a wall with a view to its repair, the two must constantly be distinguished. The stones illustrated in *Figure 1.21* for example, were laid in 1410, and still bear their original tooling, although it is slightly eroded by time. In no way would a modern piece of the same stone weather to the same appearance in five or six centuries if finished with a sawn or rubbed face, and it is not good enough, therefore, to slap in a new stone and hope that it will weather to match the old. Careful attention must be paid to the specification of finishes on both face *and* joints so that the character of the old masonry is matched and the new blends happily and unobtrusively with the old even before weathering has commenced.

Even after great care has been taken with specification, it is essential that the detailed attention which must be given to individual stones is borne upon the contractor and carried through into execution. The way the masonry trade is organized today, however, makes this extremely difficult to achieve since stone is seldom dressed on site. Instead, one man will visit the building to take measurements and profiles which are transferred to cards showing the banker mason the shape and dimensions of the new stone required. The latter will then dress the stone in a shop which may be miles from the building under repair, without ever having visited the site himself, and is thus completely unable to gain any feeling for the character of the masonry and its individual needs. The stone will be fixed by a third man, who all too often is not a mason, and may simply regard the stone as an inconveniently large form of brick. This is a most unsatisfactory state of affairs, but one not easily resolved in many instances. In the case of a large and important historic building, however, a directly employed team of craftsmen may be available, whilst for smaller jobs it may be possible to employ a small local firm who can bring the necessary individual attention to bear.

Great care is also necessary in the specification and execution of pointing, not just from the point of view of mortar mixes, but also on account of the impact the style of pointing will have on the final appearance of the work. Where one or two individual stones are to be replaced it should not necessarily be assumed that the entire wall needs to be repointed, and just as conservative an approach should be brought to bear here as in the renewal of stone. After all, the mortar is as much a part of the archaeology of the building as the building block. In such cases, the aim should be to match the original pointing as closely as possible, and experiments and sample panels for approval should be allowed for in the specification. The same is true where a whole

(a)

(b)

Figure 1.20 (*a*) Hand-dressed edges of old York stone
paving, City of London; (*b*) sawn edges of new York stone
paving

wall has to be repointed, but here, if the existing pointing is at variance with the character of the building, there is an opportunity to change to another style. This is most commonly done where a building was furnished with 'ribbon' or 'snail-creep' pointing in the nineteenth century, and a change to a more seemly variety is desired. For many mediaeval walls this replacement may be of the 'Ancient Monuments' type, where the mortar is kept back slightly from the faces of the stones to allow their arrises to read fully; but this is not always appropriate, and the architect should familiarize himself with the whole range of alternatives, both modern and historical. Above all, he should be aware of the damage that can be done to masonry in the removal of old pointing, especially where Portland cement has been used in it, and avoid the use of terms such as 'hack out' in his specification. Where possible, the

Figure 1.21 Weathered tooling of 1410, St Bartholomew's Church, Tong, Shropshire

term 'rake out' should be employed; but where forced by the hardness of the pointing to use the expression 'cut out' the architect should stipulate that this is to be done with a hammer and chisel used along the direction of the joint and not across it, in order to avoid damage to the arrises.

Finally, a word must be said about the desirability of preparing record drawings of any wall of archaeological importance both before and after repair. Record drawings may, in any case, be a vital prelude in approaching repair, especially where renewals and alterations have been carried out in the past, and will enable a proper understanding by the architect of the historic masonry under consideration. It may, indeed, lead him to stay his hand in certain particularly sensitive areas; or, conversely, indicate where repair can be carried out with impunity. It is only recently, for example, that a proper study has been made of the city walls at Canterbury, Kent. Comparison of the photograph (*Figure 1.22*) with the record drawing (*Figure 1.23*) will show how features overlooked for centuries have been revealed. Besides the plotting of the individual stones making up the wall, their types were also determined, and examination was extended to the mortars used in the different phases of the wall's construction. The most notable discovery has been the row of early battlements which are believed to be of Roman date, repaired in the early Norman period, and later built into the nave wall of the twelfth-century church of St Mary Northgate. Many more items of interest have been revealed by careful studies of this nature.[28]

The post-repair drawing, on the other hand, will be of the very greatest value to those who follow fifty years or a century later, enabling historians to distinguish replacements from old stone with great ease and providing valuable information to whomsoever has the job of supervising the next round of repairs. It may also, incidentally, be useful when

Figure 1.22 The north wall of the twelfth-century nave of St Mary's Church, Northgate, Canterbury, Kent, built on the earlier city wall (*Kentish Gazette*)

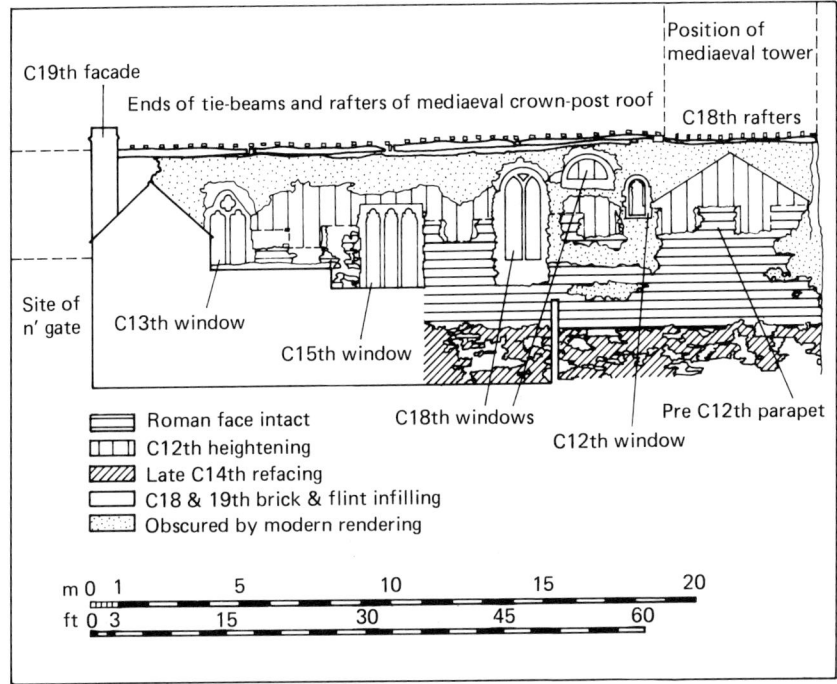

Figure 1.23 Interpretation of the wall shown in *Figure 1.22* (Canterbury Archaeological Trust)

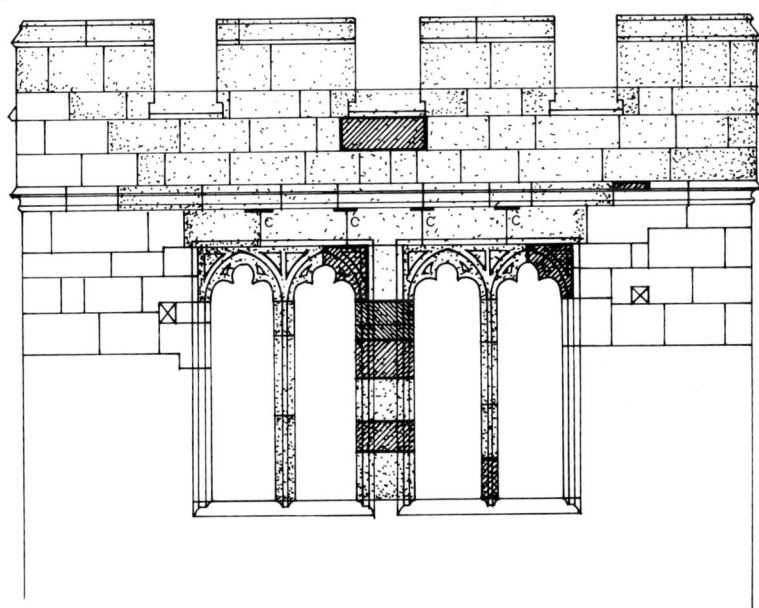

Figure 1.24 Head of the tower, north face, St Margaret's Church, Horsmonden, Kent. Areas dismantled and rebuilt are shown dotted; new stones are hatched;   'C' marks positions of concealed stainless steel cramps (By kind permission of Purcell Miller Tritton and Partners)

explaining to a client where his money has been spent, since in a good repair the renewals should blend into the wall and be difficult to see. Although in many ways the greatest compliment that can be paid to an architect is that the building after repair looks no different than before work commenced, he may still be concerned that there is little to show for what may have been considerable expenditure. Record drawings of this nature need not be particularly elaborate or costly to produce. Those made when the parapets and facings of the upper part of the tower of St Margaret's Church, Horsmonden, Kent, was dismantled and rebuilt in 1971 (*Figure 1.24*), for example, were prepared as a matter of routine during the course of the contract. They show not only the areas of masonry taken down, but also the locations of the new stainless steel ties and cramps inserted and the very small number of new stones which had to be used.

Altogether, it must be stressed, historic buildings are important artifacts, which provide a wealth of data about past habits, manners, techniques, and aspirations. In some cases they may be the only documents left by a defunct civilization. It is essential, therefore, that the architect entrusted with their repair neither seeks to leave his mark upon them nor forces them to conform with modern standards and practices, but labours instead to preserve, without distortion, the full range of evidence and enjoyment they can provide. An ill-considered refacing of the stretch of the Canterbury City wall illustrated in *Figure 1.22*, for example, would have completely destroyed the archaeological evidence it contained, leaving it bereft of its historical interest and the life given it by antiquity. In the same way, poorly-matched renewals can be equally destructive of the homogeneity of an eighteenth-century wall (*Figure 1.25*). The repair of masonry

should accordingly never be undertaken in a wanton manner, but must be a carefully considered process aimed at the preservation of both archaeological data and the aesthetic qualities of the building, including those owing to its age.

References

1. Smith, C.H., 'Lithology; or, Observations on Stone used for Building', *Transactions of the Royal Institute of British Architects*, **1**, Pt. 2, 1842, 129
2. *The Architecture of Leon Battista Alberti* (tr. James Leoni), **2**, f.99*v*, 1726
3. John Evelyn, *A Parallel of the Antient Architecture with the Modern*, 2nd edn., 1707, 'An Account of Architects and Architecture', p. 10
4. *Op.cit.,* 1728, p.23
5. Edmund Burke, *A Philosophical Enquiry into the Origin of our Ideas of the Sublime and the Beautiful*, 1757
6. Price, Uvedale, *An Essay on the Picturesque*, new edn, 1796, pp. 62-63
7. *Op.cit.,* p. 24
8. *Op. cit.,* pp.11–13
9. Pugin, A.W.N.,*Contrasts,* 2nd edn, 1841, p. 74
10. *Vide* Eastlake, C.L., *A History of the Gothic Revival,* 1872, p. 120 sqq.
11. *Report of the Cambridge Camden Society for MDCCCXL*, Cambridge, 1840, pp. 9, 15
12. *Report of the Cambridge Camden Society for MDCCCXLI*, Cambridge, 1841, p. 40
13. *Ibid,* p. 39
14. *Report of the Cambridge Camden Society for MDCCCXLII*, Cambridge, 1842, p. 23
15. *The Ecclesiologist*, **1**, 1841–2, pp. 5, 29, 143
16. *Op.cit.,* pp. 179, 180
17. *Ibid.*, p. 144 sqq.
18. Letter in Winchester College archives from Butterfield to Sir William Heathcote dated 1st or 17th June 1861 (quoted from Paul Thompson, *William Butterfield,* 1971, p. 416)
19. *The Ecclesiologist,* No. CLXXV, August 1866. p. 212
20. Prior, E.S., *A History of Gothic Art in England,* 1900, p. 289
21. Scott, Sir Gilbert, *Personal and Professional Recollections* (ed. G. Gilbert Scott), 1879, p. 325
22. Scott, George Gilbert, *An Essay on the History of English Church Architecture,* 1881, p. 147b
23. Ruskin, John, *The Seven Lamps of Architecture,* 1849, p. 180
24. *Vide* Linstrum, Derek, 'Giuseppe Valadier et l'Arc de Titus'. *Monumentum* **25**, No. 1, 43–71, March 1982
25. *Op. cit.,* p. 77
26. Heyman, Jaques, 'The Gothic Structure', *Interdisciplinary Science Reviews,* **2**, No. 1, 151–164, March 1977, fig. 23 (p. 163)
27. Willis, Robert, *The Architectural History of Canterbury Cathedral,* 1845, p. 116
28. Tatton-Brown, Tim, 'Canterbury', *Current Archaeology,* **6**, No. 3, 78–83, June 1978

Figure 1.25 Poor piecing in an eighteenth-century ashlar wall

2

The nature of building and decorative stones

Francis G. Dimes

Introduction

Stone, the primary building material taken from the crust of the Earth, has been used since the earliest times for convenience, endurance and visual impact. Its use began when man gave up the nomadic lifestyle of a hunter-gatherer and began to build permanent setttlements.

Much of the history of the world's civilizations is recorded in stone. In many instances it is almost the only remaining tangible evidence of a past occupation. The monuments include for instance, the great four-mile long, grey granite menhir avenues of Carnac, the gneiss monoliths of Callanish, the sandstone trilithons of Stonehenge and the volcanic tuff and scoria colossi of Easter Island.

The Egyptians were the earliest people to use stone in large quantities for building.[1] The pyramids are estimated to contain more than two million blocks of limestone each weighing approximately 2.5 tonnes. Stone was considered to be so important that at one time all the quarries were in royal ownership. Granite, limestone, dolerite, quartzite, schist and breccia are some of the stones used to construct the tombs, temples and palaces along the valley of the Nile.

From the early masonry achievements in Egypt, commencing before 3000 BC and extending over three millennia, an impressive catalogue can easily be assembled which demonstrates clearly the importance of stone to man in his building endeavours. There are the alabaster and limestone reliefs and sculptures of Assyria; the alabaster blocks of the Minoan palaces; the marble and limestone architecture of Greece and Rome. Many stones were

Figure 2.1 The coarsely foliated nature of gneiss is well displayed in the monoliths of Callanish, Isle of Lewis, Scotland. (Photo: John Ashurst)

19

Figure 2.2 The Parthenon, on the Acropolis, Athens, Greece. Parian marble, from the Isle of Paros was used for the roof (courtesy of R.H. Roberts)

Figure 2.3 The sculptured wall by the Terrace of the Leper King, Ankor Wat, Cambodia (now Kampuchea) is built of sandstone and of laterite (courtesy of E.A. Jobbins)

exploited during the expansion of the Roman Empire and the building of the great frontier wall of China. There is a profusion of stone buildings and trachyte sculpture left by the Mayan culture as well as the incomparable close-fitting masonry of Cuzco, the Inca capital of Peru. The Angkor Wat (*Figure 2.3*) and other vast laterite and sandstone buildings of the Khmers of Cambodia are covered with narrative reliefs. Nearly 15 000 tons of drystone walling carved with chevron patterns form the palace site on the granite hill known as Zimbabwe. The cathedrals and fortifications of medieval Europe, Russia and Scandinavia and of Saracenic Syria, North Africa, Turkey and India involve almost every building and decorative stone known. Stone was the material for the great houses and palaces of the Renaissance and the Classical and Gothic revivals which followed them. These styles were often used for public buildings, industrial buildings and churches in North America, Australia and South Africa as well as in Europe. Even modern buildings are frequently clad in thin stone facings in a way which the Assyrians, Romans or Moguls would have understood.

The repair, maintenance and preservation of this vast heritage of stone is an enormous and sometimes costly business. There are also major problems associated with decay and weathering with which this book is largely concerned. However, the principal characteristics of stone emerging from a study of masonry buildings are those of durability, versatility and of beauty. When man built, and indeed builds, for permanence and for impact, stone is the material chosen.

Definitions

Dimension stone is the term used for a rock that can be quarried, cut and worked to a specified size or shape for use in a building as a structural unit or for use purely as decoration. In this sense the term rock is defined in the dictionary as the solid part of the Earth's crust and the term stone is defined as any piece of rock which has been detached from the Earth's crust. All rocks are aggregates of minerals. Thus such materials as clay, coal and sand are recognized geologically as rocks.

Minerals, in strict scientific definition, are natural inorganic substances with symmetrical crystal forms which reflect internal atomic structures and which have defined chemical compositions. Over 2500 minerals have been identified and named. Many of them are rare. Only about twenty-five, either singly or in association, make up the physical bulk of most rocks used for building.[2]

Criteria for use

Three criteria may be considered to determine whether stone should be used in any particular situation. Firstly, it should be sufficiently durable for the intended purpose. In the past the durability of a stone was discovered from experience of its use, a method of assessment which should not be forgotten today. Now physical and chemical tests can provide valuable additional indications of likely durability (see Chapter 10). Secondly, it should be economically available and easily quarried and worked to the desired profiles. This criterion is still important but is less critical now than in the past because of improvements in transport systems and increasing sophistication of cutting equipment. Thirdly, it should be pleasing to the eye. Because stone is a natural material all types may claim to satisfy this criterion, although it may be noted that some man-made juxtapositions of stone are not aesthetically pleasing.

It may usually be assumed that in the past availability was of paramount importance. Other historical factors relating to political boundaries, ownerships, trade agreements and conditions of instability and war have obviously influenced the use and choice of particular stones.

Geological factors

Geological factors now decide whether a stone may be used within the determined criteria. Geology is the fundamental science which determines not only the scenery of any region but also its architecture. It is the science of the prime natural materials used for building and is the determining factor of regional forms of building. It is immediately apparent that the shape and size of flint, whether used as 'field flint', 'cobble' or 'squared flint', largely dictates the method of construction and is a major influence on the style of building. The main factor limiting the construction method and determining the appearance is the size of the flint blocks that can be obtained and used. The size of these blocks is a direct reflection of the mode of formation, or the genesis, of flint. Similarly, other building stones can only be obtained in sizes which are a reflection of their geological history. It follows, therefore, that any stone chosen for building must be obtainable in blocks large enough for the desired purpose. It should be free from fractures. It should be sufficiently tough and free of minerals which may break down chemically or by weathering. Hardness is not necessarily a requisite, although when a stone is to be used for paving or steps resistance to abrasion is a desirable quality. The distinction between toughness and hardness should be noted. A tough stone is not necessarily hard.

In some instances, for example where stone is to be used for internal decorative facing, it should be capable of taking a polish. The colour of the stone and its 'figuring' then become important characteristics. Depending upon the architectural detailing of a building, low water absorption, and a macroporous structure may be desirable qualities. It should be noted particularly that no two blocks of stone, even if quarried side by side, are absolutely identical any more than, for example, two planks of oak are. The differences may not be discernible and may be of no practical importance; but they may be substantial. The differences may also contribute greatly to the attractiveness and beauty of the stone and can be exploited to show the material to its best advantage.

Distribution

A purely superficial glance at the geological map of Great Britain[3] shows that the country has a great variety of rocks. This is a reflection of the geological history of the country. All rocks have been used in one manner or another for building purposes. The vast variety of rock types and the sometimes restricted area in which some occur and were used precludes mention of them all; a meaningless catalogue would result. Discussion has been confined, therefore, to those stones which have been used on any scale for building and to those which have

Figure 2.4 In an area without a supply of rock suitable for building, any stones available may be used. The 'conglomerate wall' enclosing the Nursery, Battersea Park, London, in addition to bricks and tiles has been built of many pieces of different types of stone, mostly gathered from around London's docks

particular qualities worthy of note. Many of the stones discussed here are from British sources. But, because Britain is made up of rocks which belong to the majority of all the known types, the geological considerations discussed may be applied world-wide.

On the Geological Map of the United Kingdom, published by the Ordnance Survey for the British Geological Survey, a sedimentary formation is shown as one colour throughout the length of its outcrop. This must not be interpreted as indicating that the type of rock is consistent throughout that outcrop. This is because the map shows the *age* of the formation, not necessarily its lithology. The type of stone in any area cannot be identified by reference to the map alone.

Classification

Despite the apparently bewildering variety of rocks, any one can be placed into one of three groups; all rocks within any one group have common characteristics which are unique to that group. The groups are igneous, sedimentary and metamorphic rocks.

Igneous rocks

The rocks within the lithosphere (the solid outer shell of the Earth, which includes the crust) are normally solid. They melt only when there is a decrease of pressure or there is an addition of other material. The molten rock material then formed is termed *magma* and it may originate at different levels within the Earth. It is essentially a fluid silicate melt with water-vapour and other volatiles. In geologically favourable conditions, magma may rise through the crust, becoming lighter through expansion and increasingly mobile. On cooling, at whatever level in the Earth, it forms an *igneous* rock. Some of the magma may have poured out on the surface as *lava* during a volcanic eruption and the resultant rock is known as *volcanic* or *extrusive* igneous rock. Magma which cools and consolidates within the Earth is termed an *intrusive* or *plutonic* igneous rock and is seen only when the encompassing *country rock* has been weathered away. No matter where they are found, igneous rocks have characteristics directly arising from the cooling and consolidation of magma. The form, or shape, will depend on where the magma came to rest. The rate of cooling also depends, to a great extent, upon the position of the magma within the Earth. If poured out onto the surface the magma will cool rapidly and glassy or very finely crystalline volcanic igneous rocks will result. Many cubic kilometres of magma within the lithosphere may be contained in chambers. It cools slowly and coarsely crystalline plutonic rocks result, the crystals of which normally can be individually distinguished by eye. In some instances, the magma cooled at variable rates and large crystals,

Table 2.1 Classification of igneous rocks

Position of emplacement	*Chemical composition*			
	Acid	*Intermediate*	*Basic*	*Ultra-basic*
Volcanic (extrusive) (glassy or very fine-grained)	Normally these rocks are glassy or too fine-grained for individual crystals to be seen			
	←————————————— Tuff —————————————→			
	Pumice Obsidian* Rhyolite	Andesite	Basalt*	
Minor intrusions (fine-grained or medium-grained)	Quartz obviously present	Some quartz may be present	No quartz seen	No quartz seen
	Quartz-porphyry	Porphyry*	Dolerite†	
Plutonic (medium grained or coarse-grained)	Granodiorite* Granite*	Diorite* Syenite*	Gabbro*	Serpentinite* Peridotite

*The geological names of rocks which have been used on any scale for building, either structurally or decoratively
†Quartz dolerites do exist

termed *phenocrysts* were formed first. The remaining magma cooled more slowly and the phenocrysts may be surrounded by smaller crystals.

Igneous rocks, therefore, can be classified using the position of emplacement as the criterion. However, this does not take account of the chemical composition of the original magma, which can be deduced from the chemical composition of the minerals which crystallize from it.

Igneous rocks are essentially assemblages of silicates. When they are chemically analysed the proportion of silicon dioxide (SiO_2) present may be used as a basis of classification. Those rocks yielding a high percentage of SiO_2 are termed *acid*. These rocks contain the mineral quartz, the crystal form of silica. The term acid refers to the chemical composition of the rock and does not imply that the rocks have a corrosive quality.

Rocks which yield a low percentage of SiO_2 are known as *basic* and as *ultra-basic*. The terms basic and ultra-basic refer only to the chemical composition of the rocks and not to their origin.

Purely arbitrary limits may be set for the percentage of silica present. A common classification is shown below:

Rock type	Per cent SiO_2
Acid	>65
Intermediate	55–65
Basic	45–55
Ultra-basic	<45

It should be noted, however, that there may be a continuous mineral variation in igneous rocks. Rocks which are genetically related may fall, therefore, into different divisions of a classification.

Nevertheless, using the criteria of emplacement and of chemical composition, a classification can be constructed to accommodate most igneous rocks (*Table 2.1*).

Sedimentary rocks

The geological processes of weathering and of erosion produce sediments, the raw material of sedimentary rocks. All rock types when exposed to the atmosphere are susceptible to weathering, the mechanical or chemical breakdown of the rock, and to erosion, the process of removal and of transport of the products of weathering.

The material of the sediments, often reworked many times through the long period of geological time, originated from igneous rocks which formed the first primitive crust of the Earth. The processes can be illustrated by considering the weathering of a granite, an acid plutonic igneous rock. By definition, for a rock to be termed granite, three essential minerals must be present: feldspar, mica and quartz.

The mineral quartz is hard. It is not easily cleaved and is highly resistant to chemical attack. It becomes broken into smaller and smaller fragments; the size depends on the length of time during which the fragments are exposed to the mechanical processes of weathering.

Mica is the name given to a family group of silicate minerals, which differ from each other in detailed chemical composition. They are individually named. Examples include biotite mica and muscovite mica. Mica is not very hard and is brittle. It has perfect cleavage which enables it to split into very thin plates, and is resistant to chemical attack and to weathering. It breaks down into smaller and smaller flakes until eventually they are of sub-microscopic size.

Feldspar is the name for a group of minerals with the general formula of $X(Al,Si)_4O_8$ where X = Na, K, Ca or Ba. They are named depending on their chemical composition, e.g. Orthoclase, Plagioclase. The feldspars are the most abundant of all the minerals. Feldspar, especially when acted upon by slightly acid water, breaks down to give soluble salts of potassium (K), sodium (Na), and calcium (Ca) with a clay mineral, kaolinite, hydrous aluminium silicate ($Al_4Si_4O_{10}(OH)_8$). It is the breakdown of feldspar which releases the grains of quartz and mica.

Basic igneous rocks weather in much the same manner, but more soluble material is produced and, under certain conditions, more clay. However, no quartz grains will be produced (see *Table 2.2*).

The weathering products may not be transported any distance and may remain to blanket the bedrock from which they were derived. More normally, however, they are transported and during transport are reduced in size by abrasion. They are more or less changed during their journey and finally deposited as a layer or bed (if very thin, *laminae*) of sediment (*Figure 2.5*). Running water is the most common transporting medium. Most, but not all, sediments come to rest in the oceans. Water movement sorts the sediments and tends to concentrate similar materials together.

The small, insoluble flakes are deposited as beds of *mud*; the quartz grains as beds of *sand*. The salts are added to the water where some may reach sufficiently high concentrations for them to be chemically precipitated, to form for example, a *lime mud*.

Sedimentation is not continuous; thus a series of beds of sediment is built up. The sediments are converted into sedimentary rocks, by the process of lithification, either shortly after deposition or at a later stage. Lithification includes dewatering, compaction, welding of the constituent particles and the natural cementation of the grains by other mineral matter. The form of a sedimentary rock and its unique characteristic is a roughly horizontal layer or *bed*. The major cementing minerals are calcium

Table 2.2 Classification of sedimentary rocks

Rock type	Name	Main constituents	Remarks
Rudaceous (rubbly rocks mainly composed of large fragments of older rocks)	Breccia	Large fragments of any rock type	Broken, *angular*, mostly unworn fragments set in finer material and held together by natural cement; often a cemented scree.
	Conglomerate	Large fragments of any rock type	*Rounded* fragments in finer material and held together by natural cement; a cemented gravel.
Arenaceous (sandy rocks)	Sandstone*	Quartz grains	Bedded, composed of rounded quartz grains, fine to medium grained, usually with grains cemented.
	Grit (stone)*	Quartz grains	Bedded, composed of angular quartz grains, usually medium to coarse grained. May contain small pebbles. Generally coarsely bedded.
	Flagstone*	Quartz grains and mica flakes	Finely bedded, fine-grained rounded quartz, with layers of mica flakes lying along bedding planes.
	Arkose*	Quartz grains and feldspar, commonly partly decomposed	Sandstone or grit, medium to coarse grained containing over 25% feldspar. Mostly terrestrial deposits.
	Quartzite*	Quartz grains	Composed almost entirely of quartz grains, closely fitting and naturally cemented with silica.
Argillaceous (clayey rocks)	Clay	Clay mud	Very fine-grained, flaky minerals, structureless.
	Mudstone	Clay mud	Clay with much water squeezed out; very fine grained, massive and structureless.
	Shale	Clay mud	Laminated, commonly finely compacted mudstone. Splits along laminae which are in the direction of the original bedding.
Calcareous (carbonate rocks mainly of calcium and magnesium carbonate) Some calcareous rocks are chemically precipitated.	Limestone*	Calcium carbonate, (calcite)	Bedded, composed essentially of calcium carbonate
	Oolitic limestone*	Ooliths of calcium carbonate	Limestone composed mostly of small spheroidal calcareous grains.
	Magnesian limestone*	Magnesium carbonate and calcium carbonate	Limestone, with a high proportion of dolomite; massive, granular, saccharoidal.
	Tufa*	Calcium carbonate	Deposited from saturated limey waters; friable, porous (spongy) structure.
	Travertine*	Calcium carbonate	Similar to tufa, but more compact, more dense, not friable.
Organic	Coal Lignite Peat	Organic remains	Bedded rocks formed from vegetable matter.
Evaporites	Gypsum (includes Alabaster*)	Hydrated calcium sulphate	Chemically precipitated from evaporating waters
	Anhydrite	Calcium sulphate	
	Rock salt	Sodium chloride	
Chemical precipitates	Chert *† Flint* Jasper (some limestones are chemical precipitates)	Silicon dioxide with greater or lesser amounts of impurities	

*The geological names of those rocks which have been used on any scale for building, structurally or decoratively
†There is geological controversy about the origin of chert and allied rocks which are listed here as chemical precipitates

Figure 2.5 Well marked horizontal bedding in alternating shales and limestones of the Lower Lias, Jurassic. Southerndown bay, Glamorgan

which ,are most commonly used for building or decoration are marble (contact metamorphism) and schist (regional metamorphism).

Contact or thermal metamorphism is a matter of simple baking. When subjected to heat and contained by other rocks, particles of limestone ($CaCO_3$) and fossils are gradually recrystallized into roughly similar-sized interlocking crystals of the mineral calcite. The rock is then known as *marble*. If the limestone was not confined by other rocks the calcium carbonate of the limestone would disassociate following the reaction $CaCO_3$ + heat → CaO (lime) + CO_2 (carbon dioxide).

A limestone with little or no mineral matter other than calcium carbonate converts into a pure white granular marble. However, if other mineral matter is

carbonate, especially in the form of calcite, the crystalline form of calcium carbonate ($CaCO_3$); silica, commonly in the form of quartz (SiO_2); iron, commonly as limonite ($2Fe_2O_3 \cdot 3H_2O$); and the calcium magnesium carbonate, dolomite ($CaMg(CO_3)_2$). Groundwater circulating through the sediments before or after lithification, may take mineral matter existing in the sediment into solution and re-deposit it, normally around some kind of nucleus to form a *concretion*.

It is possible, by using grain size and the nature of the constituent grains of a sediment as criteria, to construct a classification (*Table 2.2*). It should be remembered, however, that few sediments are composed exclusively of one type of constituent grain.

Metamorphic rocks

Any rock within the Earth's crust may be affected and modified by natural heat or by intense pressures, or both, generally resulting from stresses generated when large plates of the lithosphere move against each other. The mineral matter of the rocks may be re-formed to produce larger crystals of the original mineral or it may be recrystallized to form new minerals that are stable in the new environment. It is important to note that the rocks remain essentially solid during these processes and may retain some of their original characteristics. There are two categories of metamorphism which are of interest. The first type is that caused by heat alone from, for instance, an igneous intrusion. This is termed *contact metamorphism*. The second type is caused by high temperatures or by great stresses or both, generated within great fold belts found within the Earth's crust. This is termed *regional metamorphism*. In general the type of metamorphism is of little practical importance when considering types of building stones. Products of the two types of metamorphism

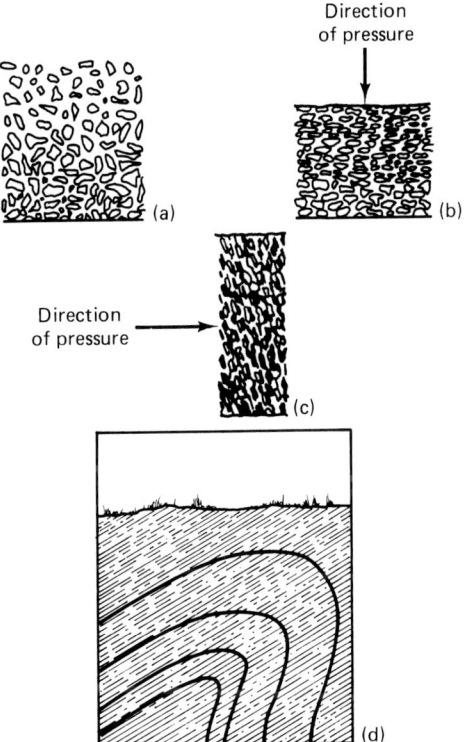

Figure 2.6 When first deposited, the submicroscopic flaky clay minerals are arranged in random order (a). With increasing pressure they tend to turn to be at right angles to that pressure (b). When regional pressure is applied the flakes tend to reorientate at right angles to the new applied pressure. Some mineral matter rearranges itself to form new minerals which grow at right angles to the pressure and slaty cleavage is imposed. If the beds of clay were folded before metamorphism, the slaty cleavage may have a direction different from that of the original bedding. The difference between bedding and cleavage should be noted. (© Nat. Mus. Wales, reproduced by permission)

present in the original limestone, it too is altered to develop new minerals which give the colour and figuring to many marbles. Marbles produced solely by thermal metamorphism are not of major importance. However, calcareous rocks subjected to regional metamorphism taking place over extensive areas recrystallize to produce fine-grained marbles. The coarseness of grain is dependent on the degree of metamorphism.

Regional metamorphism is widespread and takes place in areas of mountain building. Two factors control the processes; heat and pressure. Each of these may be acting alone or in any combination.

If a clay is subjected to sustained regional pressure at low temperature, the flaky materials present tend to reorientate at right angles to the direction of strong stress. Some recrystallization also occurs and small flakes of new minerals, mostly mica, and chlorite, a hydrated silicate of aluminium, iron and magnesium, $((Mg,Fe,Al)_6(Si,Al)_4O_{10}(OH)_8)$, grow at right angles to the direction of principal stress. A new rock, termed a *slate*, is formed and it has a parallel orientation of planar minerals impressed upon it. It has *slaty cleavage* along which the rock may be easily split. This is not the same as bedding of sedimentary rocks (see *Figure 2.7*).

The form of metamorphic rocks depends on the form of the original rocks from which they were

Figure 2.7 The parallel arrangement of sheet-shaped minerals enable the rock to be split easily along the direction of slaty cleavage. Penrhyn Quarry, Caernarvonshire. (Courtesy of R.H. Boyle)

derived. Any pre-existing rock may be metamorphosed. Characteristically all metamorphic rocks have a foliated structure. This may not always be observed on a macroscopic scale, but may possibly be seen on a microscopic scale. The rough alignment of the interlocking crystals of calcite in a marble (*Figure 2.8*) is one example.

Table 2.3 Classification of metamorphic rocks

Sedimentary origin	Regional metamorphism			Contact metamorphism
	Low grade	Medium grade	High grade	
Pelitic rocks (from argillaceous or muddy sediments)	Slate*	Schist[1]	Gneiss[2]	Hornfels
Psammitic rocks (from arenaceous, or sandy sediments)	Quartz-schist	Quartzite[3]*	Quartzite*	Quartzite*
Calcareous rocks (from calcareous, or limey, sediments)	Marble*	Marble*	Marble*	Marble*

Igneous origin	
Basic rocks (dolerites, basalts)	Schists[1] and Gneisses[2]
Acid rocks (granites)	

[1]Finely crystalline, commonly with much mica and will split relatively easily in one direction
[2]Coarsely crystalline, with crystals roughly streaked out in one direction
[3]The term quartzite is descriptive and does not indicate mode of origin
*The geological names of rocks which have been used on any scale for building, either structurally or decoratively

Figure 2.8 A coarse foliation in marble seen in a roadside section on Mount Jagro, Carrara, Italy, is picked out and emphasized by vegetation

The degree of metamorphism to which a rock was subjected is expressed by its *grade*. Complicated classifications can be constructed to take account of the many variables. Here (*Table 2.3*) a classification adapted from H.H. Read and J. Watson.[4] based on the original nature of the rock is used.

Joints

The size of a block which can be wrought from the quarry is controlled by *joints*, the chief structural feature of any rock. A joint is a parting plane within the rock which separates or tends to separate the contiguous mass into two parts. Groups of parallel joints form a *joint set* and intersecting sets of joints form a *joint system*. Joints may be only a short distance apart (*close jointed*) or may be a considerable distance apart (*wide jointed*). Persistent joints which are maintained over considerable distances are *master joints*. One or two sets of joints provide the master joints. The others are interrupted and normally are not continuous although they retain their essential parallelism. A joint is distinguished from a fault, which is a fracture within the rock mass along which the rock on one side has been displaced relative to the rock on the other side. Displacements up to thousands of metres are known.

All consolidated rocks are jointed. The joint system controls not only the shape of the quarry but also the shape and size of the blocks which can be extracted. Joints and joint systems are themselves a direct reflection of the mode of formation of the rocks in which they are found and are best considered and discussed under the major classifications of igneous, sedimentary and metamorphic rocks.

Joints in igneous rocks

Discussion on joints in igneous rocks may conveniently be divided into those found in volcanic rocks and those found in plutonic rocks.

Volcanic rocks are those poured out originally as lava sheets on the Earth's surface. The molten lava sheet cannot contract overall, and thus shrinkage commonly takes place around equidistantly spaced centres which, because they are in a more-or-less geometrical system, lead to a regular pattern. These joints usually occur at right angles to the cooling surfaces and thus the sheet is divided into hexagonal columns. The pattern is produced by contraction towards roughly equally spaced centres. Horizontal cross joints are developed to lesser extent and these divide the columns into shorter lengths. One of the most spectacular manifestations of hexagonal jointing is seen in the columnar jointing of the fine-

Figure 2.9 Weathering has accentuated the widely spaced joints in the granite of Hay Tor, Dartmoor, Devon

grained basalt of the Giants' Causeway in Northern Ireland.

Minor intrusions, commonly in the form of sills and of dykes (*Figure 2.10*) show a similar, but usually not so well developed, style of jointing. Columns, if produced, are at right angles to the cooling surfaces; the joint system is regularly arranged with respect to the walls containing the magma.

Major plutonic intrusions show a complex joint system caused by the interaction of contraction on cooling, stresses caused by emplacement and by pressure release when the overlying rocks are removed by weathering. When the cooling mass of magma reaches a sufficient state of rigidity, joints are formed in patterns related to the form of the intrusive mass.

Three sets of joints are developed. Two are vertical and roughly at right angles, while the third,

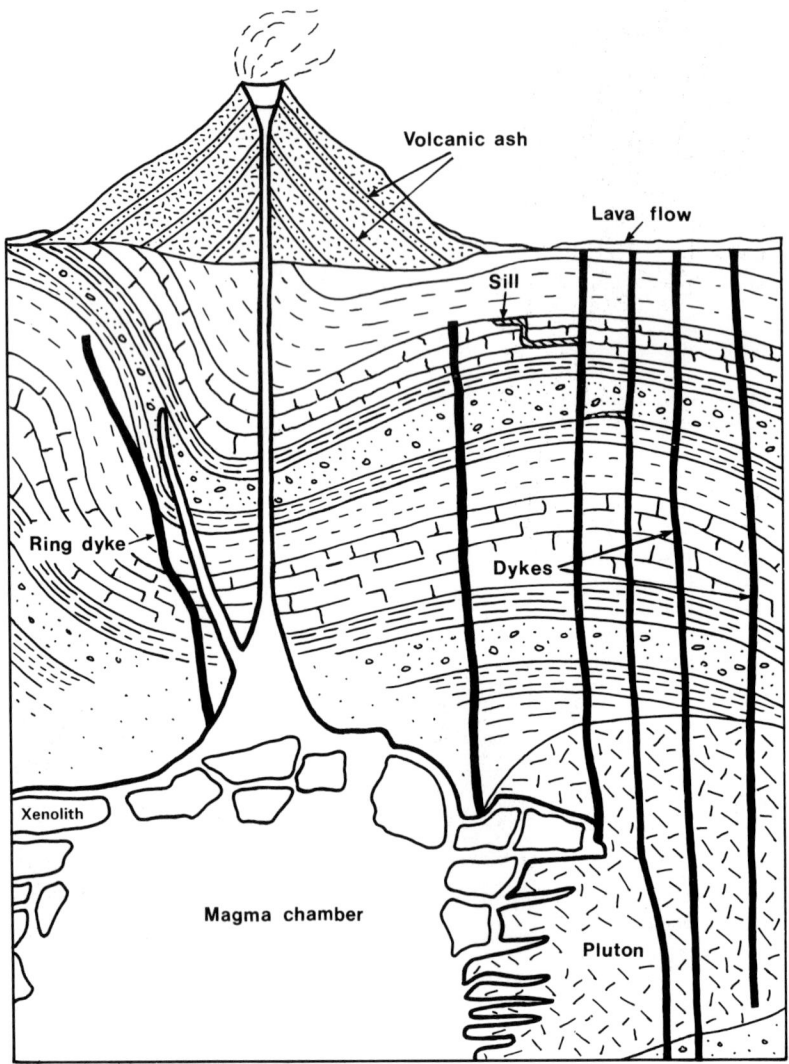

Figure 2.10 Igneous intrusion masses

termed *sheet jointing*, is horizontal, and follows the average contour of the ground surface.

Most granites, when worked in a quarry, will exhibit a direction along which the rock shows a tendency to split more easily than along other directions. This plane is known as the *rift*. Its origin is obscure; it may be due to a rough alignment of the constituent minerals of the rock or it may be a reflection of a rough orientation of the cleavage planes of the constituent minerals. A plane approximately at right angles to that of the rift and along which the rock will break with an ease second only to that of the rift, is known as the *grain*. The rift and grain follow the two intersecting vertical joint sets. When exposed to the natural agencies these joints normally are opened by weathering. Incipient joints, however, which are still mineralogically continuous may manifest themselves as thin, dark, discontinuous lines most easily distinguished on polished slabs.

Joints in plutonic igneous rocks can be widely spaced. The Duke of Argyll offered a monolithic shaft of the Ross of Mull granite 150 feet (45.7 m) long as a memorial obelisk to the Prince Regent.[5] Cleopatra's Needle in London, 68 feet 5½ inches (20.9 m) long, is one of the longest unjointed stones known.[6] An incompletely quarried obelisk at Aswan, Egypt, is 137 feet (41.7 m) long (*Figure 3.13*).

Joints in sedimentary rocks

The unique feature of sedimentary rocks is the bed. Each bed is the product of a single episode of sedimentation. A bed is bounded by two surfaces, one at the top and one at the bottom, called *the bedding planes*.

A bedding plane indicates a pause or change in the main sedimentation. During that pause the surface of the bed may have been marked by ripples, be rain pitted, dry and show sun-cracks or lie quietly under or above water level where very fine material will settle on it to form a thin layer.

Because the bed below and the bed above differ, if only very slightly, in composition, compaction, or grain size, they will not be exactly similar. The upper surface of each bed forms a plane of separation, the

Figure 2.12 Vertical joints, roughly at right-angles, determine the width and depth of block that can be extracted at Weldon Quarry near Corby, Northamptonshire. The height on bed can vary considerably

Figure 2.11 Joint system in Portland stone is well displayed on the bedding-plane surface. Portland Bill, Isle of Portland, Dorset

Figure 2.13 Markedly cross-bedded (false-bedded, current-bedded) sandstones of the Coal Measures Carboniferous, exposed in cliffs near Seaton Delaval, Northumberland

bedding plane. With the deposition of successive beds a series is built up which is called the *bedding* or *stratification*. Most sedimentary rocks consist of sediments laid down on the sea floor, and thus, the bedding is essentially horizontal. However, some sedimentary rocks result from the deposition of sediments in deltaic environments, sand banks, along the edges of lakes or seas, or from wind blown material. In these instances the bedding is at often acute angles to the general overall horizontal structure of the formation. This bedding, which may be conspicuous, is termed variously *false bedding*, *current bedding*, *cross bedding* or *dune bedding* (*Figures 2.13 and 2.14*). It is an important original

Figure 2.14 Massively bedded Millstone Grit, Carboniferous, is exposed in Johnsons' Wellfield Quarry near Huddersfield, Yorkshire. The Millstone Grit was deposited in deltaic conditions and as a result wedge-bedding can be seen

which arises from the nature of the sedimentation. It is due to the currents which deposited the sediment.

As a sediment dries out, *shrinkage joints* develop because it is physically impossible for a bed of sediment to shrink overall laterally. The shrinkage joints are limited by the bedding planes. Commonly, two joint sets are produced, approximately at right angles to each other and at right angles to the bedding planes. Irregular, subordinate joints may be developed at an angle to the main joint sets to give irregularly shaped blocks. Some joint sets are produced by tectonic movements and result from stresses imposed upon the rocks. Commonly these joints are strongly developed and persistent and cross several beds. They are termed *master joints*. The shrinkage joints are subservient to the master joints. Generally master joints run in two sets and may be the main factor which determines the manner in which sedimentary rocks are quarried.

Joints are found in all sedimentary rocks except for some of the most recent. They control not only the height on bed of the block of stone that may be quarried but also its width and depth. The nature and spacing of the joints, therefore, is of economic significance. Well jointed rocks are more easily extracted.

Joints in metamorphic rocks

Metamorphic rocks arise from the change of existing rocks caused by heat or stress or the action of chemically active fluids, normally during the complex processes of mountain building. The rocks remain essentially solid during these processes. To a greater or lesser extent they retain their pre-existing joint patterns, but in addition have joints which result from the extreme stresses of tectonic movements imposed upon them. Complex joint systems may result. The important and, indeed, fundamental structure however, is *foliation*, the more or less parallel arrangement of the minerals.

Metamorphic rocks in which the mineral grains are roughly orientated are said to show a *schistose* texture. The foliation of a schist, the most common metamorphic rock, is seen as discontinuous layers. Some schists are the product of the metamorphism of clays. A succession may be traced from a clay, to a slate, to a schist.

If the minerals are coarse grained and segregated into rough bands the rock is termed a *gneiss*. A gneiss shows a lesser tendency to split along the bands than does a schist.

Marble results from the metamorphism of limestone. The presence of carbon dioxide apparently aids the formation of a granular structure and a rough, microscopic schistosity may be imposed. Because

the calcite grains develop an interlocking structure, large blocks, the desired feature for building purposes, may be extracted from between the pre-existing joint system in areas which are not otherwise tectonically disturbed. The alignment of the calcite grains normally is not seen in pure marbles, but other coloured mineral matter may give an indication of a foliation.

Metamorphic rocks, therefore, are chosen for two contrasting characteristics. For example, slate is used because it will cleave into thin sheets and, marble is chosen because it may be obtained in large, homogeneous blocks.

Jointing and quarrying

As has been seen, the joints in any of the three major types of rock determine not only the size of the block extracted but also its shape. Because joints and bedding planes are the planes along which rocks will most easily part, their spacing and frequency are a determining factor in the quarrying of rock for dimension stone.

Stone has been extracted in many ways, including pulling out blocks, 'jumping' and digging out. However, two main methods are employed; plugs and feathers are used to quarry all types of stone, and flame-cutting is used for some igneous rocks.

For the first method a series of holes is drilled in a line parallel with one of the joint sets, and, with igneous rocks, parallel with the sheet jointing direction. The diameter of the holes, their depth and their distance apart differ from quarry to quarry and will depend on the nature of the rock being quarried and, mostly, on experience. A pair of 'feathers', shaped, semi-circular steel pieces, is inserted into the holes. A wedge-shaped 'plug' is driven between the 'feathers'. Normally the 'feathers' are shaped so that as the plug is driven down by a sledge-hammer the 'feather' stays parallel with the side of the hole, thus exerting even pressure along its length. The 'plugs' are driven in in sequence until eventually the stone splits along the line of the holes (*Figure 2.15*).

Flame-cutting (*Figure 2.17*), used only for igneous rocks, depends on the spallability of the rock. Heat will cause certain rocks to spall and the degree to which they will do so has been determined to depend on:

1. Large linear thermal expansion at temperatures below $700\,°C$;
2. High thermal diffusivity at temperatures below $400\,°C$;
3. The presence of an equigranular interlocking structure with little or no fine-grained clay or mica alteration products;

(a)

(b)

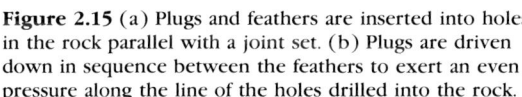

(c)

Figure 2.15 (a) Plugs and feathers are inserted into holes in the rock parallel with a joint set. (b) Plugs are driven down in sequence between the feathers to exert an even pressure along the line of the holes drilled into the rock.

Eventually the rock splits along the line of the holes. (c) Plugs and feathers may also be used to lift a block of stone along the line on the bedding-plane

Figure 2.16 Plugs and feathers have been used in holes drilled parallel to the widely spaced joints in granite at Merrivale Quarry, Dartmoor to produce blocks which can be handled by quarry machinery

4. The lack of significant amounts of soft, low-melting, or elastic minerals or materials which yield after thermal decomposition.[7]

The method uses a long blowpipe through separate conduits in which oxygen, fuel (usually hydrocarbons such as paraffin, kerosene or fuel oil but acteylene and propane have been used for concrete surface treatment); and water are passed to a burner. An exhaust flame with a temperature between 3500 and 5000 °F (1900–2800 °C) is produced with a velocity of about 5300 ft./s (1600 m/s). The high velocity of the flame wash clears the spalled pieces of rock. The water cools the nozzle of the burner and the rock surface around the flame and helps remove spallings.

Flame cutting has distinct advantages in producing a 'free end' in a widely jointed granite mass. The channel, however, is best aligned with one of the

Figure 2.17 Flame-cutting is used to produce a 'free-end' in widely jointed granite at De Lank Quarry, St Breward, near Bodmin, Cornwall (courtesy of G.H. Setchell)

joint sets. The noise level of the process is up to 120 dB and this has been regarded as a disadvantage.[8]

The colour of rocks

The colour of a rock may be its most striking visual characteristic. Colour depends on the reflection of some of the vibrations of white light seen by the human eye. It is one of the most difficult characteristics to describe. Nevertheless, it may well be the deciding factor in the choice of a stone, particularly for decorative purposes. The description of a stone as 'light salmon-coloured, coarsely crystalline, having a slightly mottled appearance' conveys little.

Increasingly used by geologists is the *Rock-Color Chart*.[9] Any given hue (colour) is expressed in terms of value (property of lightness) and chroma (degree of saturation). Both are numbered and thus a colour may be given a numerical designation. For example, pale greenish yellow is 10Y8/2; that is, hue 10Y, value 8, saturation 2. The *Rock-Color Chart* was prepared by the Geological Society of America. It uses the terms pale and light to quantify colours. Except where direct quotation is made from this chart, pale will be used here to refer to colour. The term light will be used to refer to weight.

If the accurate expression of a rock colour is desired it is recommended that the *Rock-Color Chart* is used. It must be remembered, however, that because rocks are a product of natural processes, they will rarely be uniform in colour overall. Stone from the same bed in a quarry may provide a variety of hues. Colour changes or variations, which may be marked as with 'blue-hearted' stones, should be considered early in the planning stages of a building and provision made to accommodate them. Stones capable of being polished may show a highly accentuated hue or, indeed, appear entirely different from the unpolished stones.

Names of rocks

The object of giving a name to any substance whether animal, vegetable or mineral is that when that name is used it is immediately and universally recognized as relating to a defined material with identifiable characteristics which distinguish it from all other materials. The name should be unique to the substance. Unfortunately, in the stone trade many stones are given names which do not accord with that principle and which also do not accord with geological scientific nomenclature.

For example, 'Ingleton Granite' of the stone trade is actually a grit (a sedimentary rock) from Yorkshire. 'Onyx' is a name which has been used for at least three widely different materials.[10] 'Pearl', 'Pearl Granite' or 'Blue Pearl Granite' is a syenite from Norway. Verde Issorie and Tinos which are advertised as marbles, are serpentinites.

The scientific name of a stone is of importance as was recognized by J.G.C. Anderson[5] some years ago when he wrote

> ... for purely commercial purposes a nomenclature more in accordance with strictly scientific practice would be an advantage. It is being realized that the properties of a rock are, to a considerable extent, functions of its mode of formation, composition and texture—factors that are taken into account in petrological nomenclature. If, therefore, the latter is made use of in industry, the purchaser giving a particular specification stands a better chance of getting the type of rock best

suited for his purpose, while the quarry owner is enabled to supply the product most likely to prove satisfactory.

In Chapters 2 to 6, in order to maintain geological integrity the names used are those which are scientifically appropriate with the popular name given in parenthesis if it differs widely from scientific usage.

Seasoning of rocks

The importance of allowing a stone to season, that is letting the blocks stand for some time before use, has been commented upon since early days. '...let the stone be got out two years before, not in winter, but in summer, and let it lie and stay in exposed places', wrote Vitruvius in 1 BC.[11] It is well recorded that Wren insisted that the blocks of Portland Stone used to rebuild St. Paul's Cathedral, after the Great Fire of London in 1666, should be seasoned for at least three years.[12] Most stones when first taken from the quarry contain, to a greater or lesser extent, groundwater or *quarry sap*. In this condition the stone is known as *green*. This water contains small amounts of mineral matter in solution. It was thought that when the stone was exposed to the atmosphere the water evaporated and the mineral matter was deposited between the grains within the surface layers and so acted in small degree as an additional natural cement.

Such experimental work as has been undertaken shows that the variability in specimens makes it difficult to come to definite conclusions. Recent investigations now show that the degree of cementation is not significant. For Portland Stone the reduction in pore space is less than 0.09 per cent. However, there is no doubt that the uniaxial compressive strength of a block of stone increases as the block dries out. It becomes more difficult to work after seasoning, when it is often said by masons and others to have 'hardened'. Even granite is reputed to work more easily when first extracted from the quarry. As the 'hardening' is not due to the chemical processes of cementation, it is evidently due to a physical change. The 'hardened' (sometimes called 'case-hardened') nature of 'old blocks' is commonly used as a reason for not re-using blocks already used in a building. There is, however, no evidence to indicate that second-hand stones or 'old blocks' are in any way inferior to newly quarried stone; it may be that they are just more difficult to work.

Hardness of rocks

Hardness is an important physical property of materials and each specific material has a hardness

Table 2.4 Mohs' scale of hardness

Hardness*		Notes
10	Diamond	Diamond is the hardest mineral but artificial substances harder than diamond are now known 9½ Boron carbide 9¼ Carborundum
9	Corundum	
8	Topaz	
7	Quartz	Quartz will scratch window glass. Flint may be used for quartz
6	Feldspar	A good pocket knife blade will scratch feldspar but not quartz
5	Apatite	
4	Fluorite	A copper coin will just scratch fluorite
3	Calcite	A knife blade easily scratches calcite
2	Gypsum	2½ A fingernail will scratch gypsum, but fingernails differ in hardness
1	Talc	Softest mineral

*When performing a hardness test several precautions should be observed:

1. The point of a sharp blade should be used; a definite scratch must be produced. Wet the scratch to remove the powder then use the edge of a finger-nail to feel the scratch;
2. A pocket knife may leave a line on the harder mineral if the blade has been scratched in the test;
3. In granular rocks such as sandstone the individual grains may have only been disturbed, but not scratched;
4. Some minerals may have broken because of their brittleness and not because of their hardness.

which is defined as its resistance to abrasion. It may be measured quantitatively by the diamond indentation method. Hardness (H) is the product of the packing structure of the atoms, and it is expressed by a number on Mohs' scale of hardness. In 1812 Friedrich Mohs arranged ten minerals in such an order that each one would scratch those lower in the scale. The scale, with explanatory notes, is given in *Table 2.4*. It must be noted that the scale does not advance in any regular steps; it is quite arbitrary.

It is difficult to express the hardness of some rocks because rocks are aggregates of minerals, and each mineral has a specific hardness. In granite, the mineral quartz has a hardness of 7, feldspar about 6, and mica about 2.5. The actual hardness depends on the type of feldspar and of mica. It is thus only possible to define the hardness of a rock in relative terms. Granite appears hard because quartz ($H=7$) is the mineral which binds the others together. It should be noted that hardness should not be equated with the difficulty of breaking. Many hard materials are brittle.

Eras	*Periods*	*Age in million years* *	*Notes*	*Orogenies and major intrusions of igneous rocks*
Quaternary	Holocene		Recent = Today	
	Pleistocene	1.6	The Ice Age	
Tertiary	Pliocene			
	Miocene			Alpine: Widespread basalt lava flows. Large deep seated igneous intrusions, e.g. in Skye, Mull, Mourne Mountains and Lundy
	Oligocene			
	Eocene			
	Palaeocene	60		
Mesozoic	Cretaceous	135		
	Jurassic	205	New Red Sandstone	
	Triassic	250		
Palaeozoic	Permian	290		
	Carboniferous: Coal Measures		In USA: Pennsylvanian	Hercynian: Devon and Cornwall granites[†]
	Carboniferous: Millstone Grit		Mississippian	
	Carboniferous: Carboniferous Limestone	365		
	Devonian	409	Includes Old Red Sandstone	Caledonian: Newer Granites, Cairngorms, Aberdeenshire, Galway, Donegal and Lake District
	Silurian	439		
	Ordovician	505		Volcanic rocks of Lake District and Wales
	Cambrian	570		
Precambrian		c. 3800		Older Granites Volcanic rocks of Charnwood, Grampians and elsewhere

*Based on *The Phonerozoic Time Scale,* Geological Society, London.
[†] It is possible to date any given specimen of granite rock. But as the mass was injected in a fluid state over a period of time, specimens taken from the mass give ages ranging from about 254 my to 303 my.

List of building Stones adapted from reference 14.

Figure 2.18 Geological time scale

Geological age of some building stones

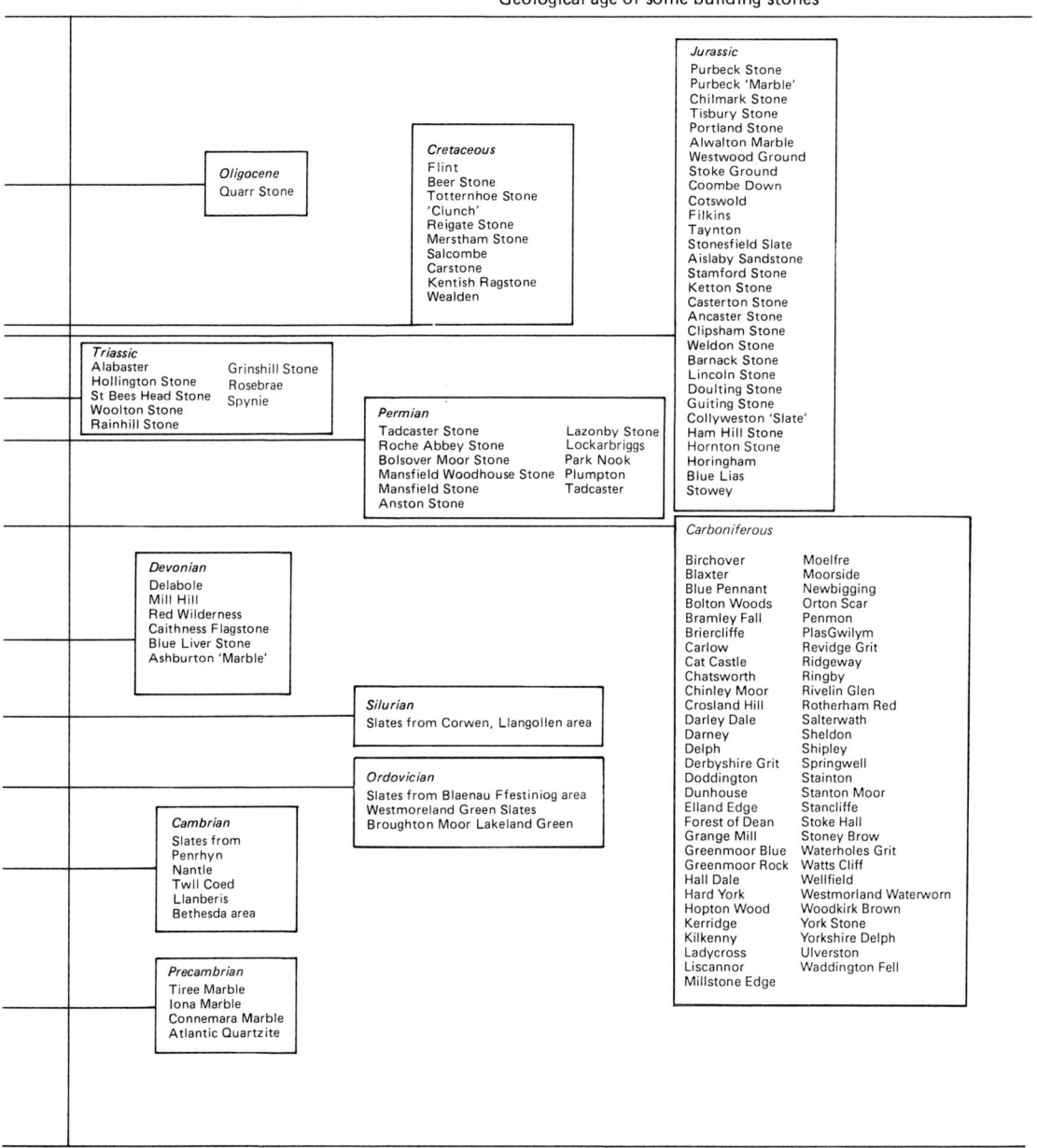

Jurassic
Purbeck Stone
Purbeck 'Marble'
Chilmark Stone
Tisbury Stone
Portland Stone
Alwalton Marble
Westwood Ground
Stoke Ground
Coombe Down
Cotswold
Filkins
Taynton
Stonesfield Slate
Aislaby Sandstone
Stamford Stone
Ketton Stone
Casterton Stone
Ancaster Stone
Clipsham Stone
Weldon Stone
Barnack Stone
Lincoln Stone
Doulting Stone
Guiting Stone
Collyweston 'Slate'
Ham Hill Stone
Hornton Stone
Horingham
Blue Lias
Stowey

Oligocene
Quarr Stone

Cretaceous
Flint
Beer Stone
Totternhoe Stone
'Clunch'
Reigate Stone
Merstham Stone
Salcombe
Carstone
Kentish Ragstone
Wealden

Triassic
Alabaster   Grinshill Stone
Hollington Stone   Rosebrae
St Bees Head Stone Spynie
Woolton Stone
Rainhill Stone

Permian
Tadcaster Stone   Lazonby Stone
Roche Abbey Stone   Lockarbriggs
Bolsover Moor Stone   Park Nook
Mansfield Woodhouse Stone Plumpton
Mansfield Stone   Tadcaster
Anston Stone

Carboniferous

Birchover	Moelfre
Blaxter	Moorside
Blue Pennant	Newbigging
Bolton Woods	Orton Scar
Bramley Fall	Penmon
Briercliffe	PlasGwilym
Carlow	Revidge Grit
Cat Castle	Ridgeway
Chatsworth	Ringby
Chinley Moor	Rivelin Glen
Crosland Hill	Rotherham Red
Darley Dale	Salterwath
Darney	Sheldon
Delph	Shipley
Derbyshire Grit	Springwell
Doddington	Stainton
Dunhouse	Stanton Moor
Elland Edge	Stancliffe
Forest of Dean	Stoke Hall
Grange Mill	Stoney Brow
Greenmoor Blue	Waterholes Grit
Greenmoor Rock	Watts Cliff
Hall Dale	Wellfield
Hard York	Westmorland Waterworn
Hopton Wood	Woodkirk Brown
Kerridge	York Stone
Kilkenny	Yorkshire Delph
Ladycross	Ulverston
Liscannor	Waddington Fell
Millstone Edge	

Devonian
Delabole
Mill Hill
Red Wilderness
Caithness Flagstone
Blue Liver Stone
Ashburton 'Marble'

Silurian
Slates from Corwen, Llangollen area

Ordovician
Slates from Blaenau Ffestiniog area
Westmoreland Green Slates
Broughton Moor Lakeland Green

Cambrian
Slates from
Penrhyn
Nantle
Twll Coed
Llanberis
Bethesda area

Precambrian
Tiree Marble
Iona Marble
Connemara Marble
Atlantic Quartzite

The distinction between hardness and toughness also should be observed. Some limestones are described as hard. But all limestones are made up essentially of calcium carbonate in the form of calcite. The hardness of all limestones, therefore, is about $H = 3$, which is relatively soft on Mohs' scale of hardness. But some limestones are friable, some are compact and it is this quality which determines the ease with which they can be worked—their apparent hardness. A sandstone made up of grains of quartz ($H = 7$), and thus hard may appear soft because the grains are not well cemented and the rock can be powdered in the hand. Toughness, or the ability to resist abrasion generally, is a more desirable quality than hardness. An old, simple but nevertheless effective and quick test may easily be performed to give an indication of the hardness of a rock. Rub a piece of the rock on an old file. A soft rock will leave much powder on the file and will make little noise; a hard rock will leave little (if any) powder and will screech.

It does not follow that a hard rock will be better suited for building purposes than a soft rock. The crushing strength of a rock is a preferred guide to its suitability for building purposes, but the geological factors of the rock *in situ* must always be borne in mind.

The age of rocks

Geological time is the expression used to denote the period since the formation of the Earth, some 4800 million years ago. The oldest rock so far found is a pebble of volcanic ash in a conglomerate in Greenland. The pebble is about 3824 million years old.[13] During that time, sediments have been laid down, life has emerged and evolved, mountains have been built and destroyed. Obviously, all this did not occur at the same time. From the apparently simple observation that one bed of sediment overlies another and therefore must be younger, a sequence of events was established and a *relative* time-scale was developed. The sediments deposited during geological time differ one from the other but it is possible to group together sequences of deposits which have some common characteristics of lithology or of fossils. A universally applicable system of time and rock divisions has been agreed. This geological time scale, or geological column, is given (*Figure 2.18*).

Since the discovery of the radioactivity of the element uranium in 1896, it has been realized that the decay of unstable elements could be used to give rocks an *absolute age* in terms of years. These ages have been added to the geological column in *Figure 2.18*.

The geological column is the fundamental reference document of the geologist. If a building is described as Georgian, it may be concluded that it was built after Elizabethan buildings and before those of Classical Revival. The building has been given a relative age and it may be implied that it will also have a certain style of architecture with specific characteristics. In the same manner, if a rock is described as Permian it can immediately be concluded that it was laid down after a series called Carboniferous and before a series of rocks called Triassic. It has been given a relative age. It can be implied also that it will have certain forms of fossils and other characteristics which, if the rocks are used as building stones, will determine to greater or lesser degree its value as a building stone and also the architectural style in those regions where the rock is found.

References

1. Bromehead, C.E.N., 'Geology in Embryo (up to 1600 AD)', *Proc. Geol. Assoc.*, **56**, Pt. 2., 1945
2. Anon. *Glossary of Terms for Stone used in Building*. British Standard 2847, British Standards Institution, London, 1957
3. British Geological Survey *Geological Map of the United Kingdom*: 1 : 625,000, Ordnance Survey, Southampton, 1979
4. Read, H.H. and Watson, J., *Introduction to Geology*, Volume 1, Macmillan & Co. Ltd. London, 1962
5. Anderson, J.G.C., 'The Granites of Scotland', *Memoirs of the Geological Survey, Special Reports on the Mineral Resources of Great Britain*, **33**, HMSO, Edinburgh, 1939
6. Burgess, S.G. and Schaffer, R.J., 'Cleopatra's Needle', *Chemistry and Industry*, **30**, pp. 1026–29, 1952
7. Rolseth, H.C. and Kohler, R.H., 'Rocket-jet burners cut time and costs in granite quarries', *Mining Engineering*, **21**, no. 7, 1969
8. Anon., 'Jet channelling at Hantergantick', *Mine and Quarry Engineering*, **28**, No. 8, 1962
9. Rock-Color Chart Committee, *Rock-Color Chart*, Geological Society of America, Boulder, Colorado, 1979
10. Dimes, F.G., 'What is Onyx?' *Stone Industries*, **12**, No. 5, pp. 14–16, 1977
11. Vitruvius, *De Achitectura* quoted in Bromehead, C.E.N., 'Geology in Embryo (up to 1600 AD)', *Proc. Geol. Assoc.*, **56**, Pt. 2, 1945
12. Watson, John, *British and Foreign Building Stones*, University Press, Cambridge, 1911
13. Thackray, J., *The age of the Earth*. HMSO, London, 1980
14. Anon., *Natural Stone Directory, 7th edition, 1987*, Stone Industries, Ealing Publications Ltd, Maidenhead, 1987

3

Igneous rocks

Francis G. Dimes

Introduction

The style of a national architecture may evidently depend, in a great measure, upon the nature of the rocks of the country.
John Ruskin, *The Stones of Venice*

Good quality stone is still one of the most permanent of all building materials, as it is beyond doubt the most beautiful and, where local material is used, the most congenial to the surrounding landscape.
Alec Clifton-Taylor, *The Pattern of English Building*

The accuracy of Ruskin's observation may be demonstrated with little difficulty. The soft nature of the limestone known as the Chalk allowed the exuberance of carving seen in the Lady Chapel of Ely Cathedral, Cambridgeshire (*Figure 3.1*). Tough and intractable Kentish Ragstone led to random walls, or walls roughly

Figure 3.2 Because of its tough, intractable nature little decorative work was undertaken in Kentish Ragstone. As a result flat walls with the stone brought roughly to courses are seen as at Knole House, Sevenoaks, Kent. The obtrusive repairs are of Portland Stone

Figure 3.1 Ease of working allowed elaborate carving of Chalk used in The Lady Chapel, Ely Cathedral. Purbeck 'marble' was used for the columns of the arcade

brought to courses (*Figure 3.2*). The tough and hard nature of the granites of south-west England is apparent in the square, undecorated churches of the area (*Figure 3.3*). The easily worked red sandstone of Cheshire was used in large blocks, even for cottages.

When there was a local supply of suitable stone, it was natural for it to be used for all building. Aberdeen is for ever associated with granite; Burford, Oxfordshire and the villages around, with Costwold Stone; Buxton, Derbyshire, with limestone and with grit. The buildings themselves are a reflection of the geological diversity of the country. Geology provided the very material of the buildings and the material determined the nature of the architectural style of the cities and of the villages. The manner in which stone was and is used is a manifestation of its genesis. It follows that the nature of the stone is of prime importance. In discussion of examples and uses,

Figure 3.3 Little decorative carving is found on granite which because of its intractable nature led to square, blocky buildings. The castellation of St Sennon Church near Land's End, mimics the castellated weathering of the Land's End granite mass. The wall around the church is of granite boulders—moorstones—picked up off the surrounding moors

therefore, consideration is given under each of the three main groups of rocks, following the classification given in Chapter 2. This chapter will concentrate on igneous rocks as building stones. Building stones from sedimentory and metamorphic rocks will be discussed in Chapters 4 and 5.

Basalt is probably the most abundant extrusive igneous rock occurring on the *surface* of the Earth. It forms the large plateaux of Northern Ireland and the Deccan of India and it covers most of Iceland, much of Washington State, USA and elsewhere. Yet in relation to its abundance, it has been little used for building, primarily because of its close-jointed nature.

In contrast, granite and closely allied rocks, which comprise about 95 per cent of the intrusive igneous rocks *within* the Earth's crust, have a limited outcrop. Nevertheless they are undoubtedly the most widely used of the igneous rocks.

Acid plutonic igneous rocks

Granite is the one rock name known to all. The grenadiers of the Consular Guard were so called because at the battle of Marengo in 1800, when the French had given way, they stood like granite. It is the connotation for all that is hard, resistant and durable. The name granite probably is more misused in the stone trade than any other rock name. Petit Granit, or, as it is known in Germany, Belgian Granite, is a limestone which is cut and polished and sold as marble! Granit de Rocq is a limestone from

France; Granito Nero a Swiss marble; Andes Black Granite is a gabbro; Black Diamond Granite, from South Africa, is a syeno-gabbro; Swedish Black Granite is a gabbro; and Blue Pearl Granite and all the other varieties of Imperial Pearl, Dark Pearl and Light Pearl, is a syenite from Norway. Blue Granite from Guernsey, much used in the past in London for kerbs, paving and steps, is a quartz-diorite. The list is seemingly endless and the names are not synonyms. The desirability of calling these stones by their proper, scientific names, is immediately apparent.

Granite is a strictly defined rock. It is an acid plutonic igneous rock, which has a fairly limited range of composition. The granite family includes members which contain varying proportions of quartz, acid plagioclase feldspar, potash feldspar and a dark-coloured ferromagnesian mineral, which is generally either biotite mica or hornblende. A granite containing a fair amount of hornblende is known as a hornblende-granite. Other accessory minerals may be present, but never in great amounts, unless as purely local concentrations.

Granites contain a high proportion of pale-coloured minerals. Quartz usually is found to be colourless. However, in the main mass of the rock, it appears to be grey, although it may sometimes have a pale purple hue. The dark brown mica, biotite, is evenly scattered throughout the mass and, if the pale-coloured mica, muscovite, is present, it is distinguished by a silvery appearance.

The mineral present in the greatest quantity is feldspar. Two varieties of feldspar are common, orthoclase and plagioclase. They may occur together in the same rock, but plagioclase is less common when quartz is present. Orthoclase is usually white to flesh pink but may be red; plagioclase is white to grey or, more rarely, yellowish, brown, or pink. Because feldspar makes up the bulk of the rock, this mineral determines the overall colour of the stone. It is possible, by detailed mineralogical study of hand specimens, to suggest the provenance of some granites. Muscovite is commonly found in association with biotite in the granite of Devon and Cornwall, England. It is unusual to find muscovite in granites of western Scotland. The mineral sphene occurs particularly in granite from Dalbeattie. Large, rounded, brownish potassic feldspar, mantled with white-coloured oligoclase feldspar, is characteristic of Baltic Brown granite from Finland. It has what is known geologically as a Rapakivi texture.

Although some granites are considered to have been formed by ultrametamorphism, most are found in the form of huge, intrusive masses, called batholiths, in the cores of old, eroded mountain chains. The outcrop of granite, consequently, is limited and is defined geographically. It is considered here on that basis.

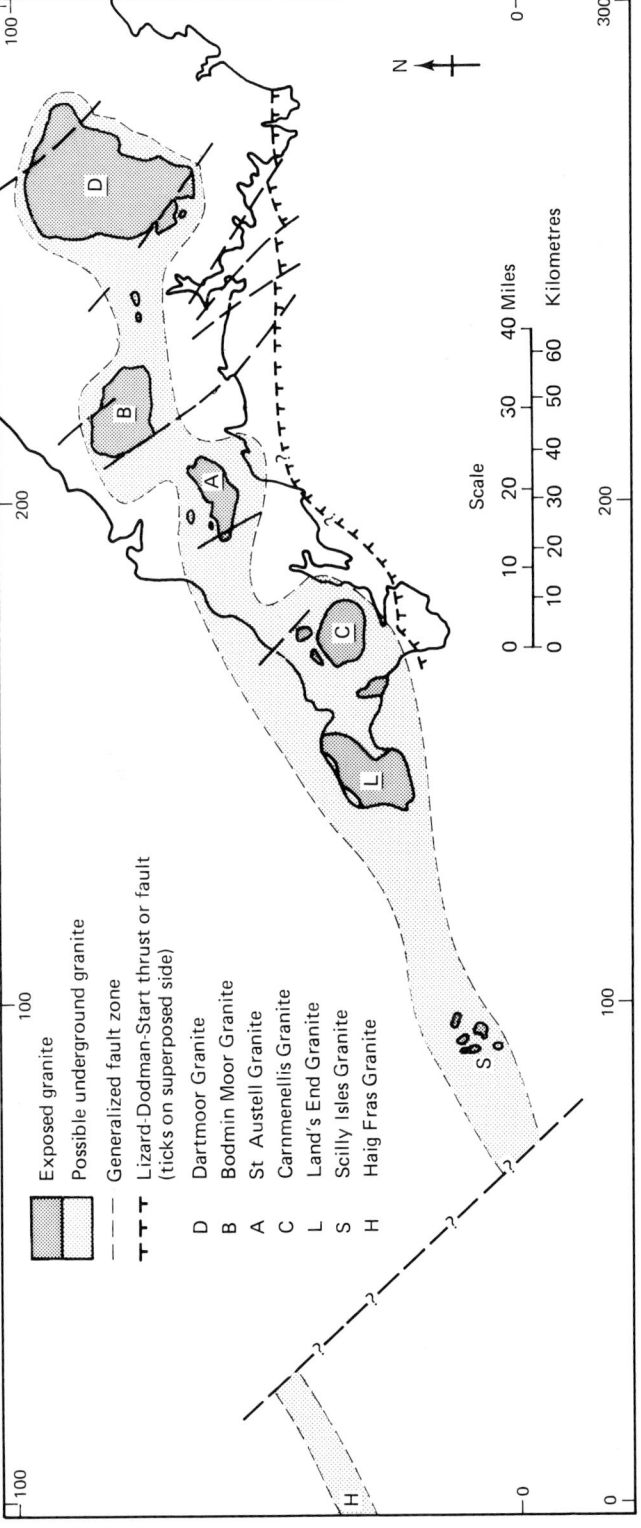

Figure 3.4 South-west England batholith. (From E.A. Edmonds *et al.*, *British Regional Geology: South-west England*, 4th edn, HMSO, 1975. Crown copyright, reproduced by permission of the Controller, HMSO)

South-west England granites

The series of granite outcrops in south-west England, which stretch from Dartmoor westwards to the Isles of Scilly, are the visible tops of bosses rising from a single, elongated batholith (*Figure 3.4*). All the granites quarried in the region are genetically related. Generally they are chemically and mineralogically in accord, although, in some areas, the rock may be slightly more acid (SiO_2–rich) than in others. All the varieties contain quartz, feldspar and mica, which is predominantly brown biotite, with some white muscovite. Tourmaline is a common accessory mineral. The texture of the granite may range from fine-grained to coarse-grained, or 'giant'-granite. Coarse-grained granites, which contain conspicuous, large feldspar crystals, up to 7 inches (175 mm) long, are termed megacrystic varieties[1,2]. The large crystals probably grew within the solid rock[3]. All granites quarried now and in the past differ principally in the abundance of feldspar megacrysts. All stone currently quarried is an overall silver-grey in colour. At one time, a pink stone was extracted at Cheesewring quarry, near Liskeard, Cornwall, and a red-coloured granite occurs in the St Austell mass.

Iron Age structures of granite are known, but, because the rock is hard and was difficult to work, most buildings constructed in the early days were of blocks picked up off the moor. These were more or less rectangular in shape, as a consequence of the joint system. The name Moorstone was given to these stones. Unfortunately, the name is also used in non-granite areas for other types of stone. The name Surface Granite is also used, particularly in Cornwall.

In general terms, granite may be described for building purposes as a compact, crystalline rock, with a generally uniform structure. It has a range in colour, is hardwearing, resistant to polluted air, impervious to water and is capable of taking a high polish. This is a specification that few, if any, other materials can meet.

In the country around Dartmoor granite is used almost without exception for the churches, but, because of its hardness, elaborate working and carving was difficult in the early days. The carving on the church at Plympton St Mary, Devon and on Launceston church, Cornwall, is remarkable, because such carving would have demanded considerable money and time. Not until the development of power tools in the middle of the eighteenth century was it possible to work granite on any scale. Since then, granite from south-west England has been widely used, much of it for civil engineering purposes. An interesting use was in the 'forgotten granite railway'. Between 1820 and about 1860, stone was sent from Hay Tor Quarry on Dartmoor, near Bovey Tracey, Devon, to London. The stone was taken from the quarry, loaded onto barges at Teigngrace, then

Figure 3.5 Flanged granite blocks were used to guide horse-drawn wagons carrying blocks of granite from quarries near Hay Tor, Devon, on the first stage of their journey to London

taken to Teignmouth, where it was transhipped for London. The 'railway' line from the quarry is made of granite blocks up to 8 feet (2.5 m) long, with an inside flange, which is normally on the wheel, on the blocks (*Figure 3.5*). In London, the stone was used in the National Gallery, in the British Museum and for London Bridge[3]. Stone from Princetown Quarry, Dartmoor, was also used for the 1831 London Bridge and for its widening in 1902. Another famous landmark in London, Nelson's column, is built of Dartmoor granite taken from the Foggintor quarries. A markedly megacrystic variety quarried by convicts from the Prison quarry, Dartmoor, was used for Norman Shaw's New Scotland Yard (1888-1899), on The Embankment, London (*Figure 3.6*). Stone from the nearby Merrivale Quarry which, although no distance from the Prison Quarry, yields a poorly

(a)

(b)

Figure 3.6 Norman Shaw's New Scotland Yard (1888–99) (a) used granite from the Prison Quarry, Dartmoor. (b) Commonly the megacrystic feldspar crystals are 'zoned' and contain small amounts of other minerals which outline the crystal shape

megacrystic stone was used to clad the present (1967) New Scotland Yard in Victoria Street. This has now been replaced by stainless steel. Stone from this quarry was used also for part of Unity House, Euston Road (1914) and more recently, for British Petroleum House and Ashdown House, both in Victoria Street, London and for the polished parapets of the new (1973) London Bridge. In the quarry, distances of up to 16 feet (5 m) between joints have been measured, with 8 feet (2.5 m), or more, between the sheet jointing.

The Cornish granite masses of St Austell and Land's End are characteristically megacrystic, while those of Bodmin Moor and Carnmenellis are poorly so. Cornwall, however, is best known for its giant crystal granite, exemplified by stone from Cheesewring Quarry, near Liskeard, which is now no longer in production. It was used for major civil engineering works, such as the piers of Westminster Bridge; for Tower Bridge (with repairs in 1981 in Merrivale granite); and for the Duke of Wellington's tomb in St Paul's Cathedral. The bases of the statues at the Guards Monument of the Crimean War, Waterloo Place, London, are also in stone from this quarry.

Carnsew Quarry, near Penryn, supplied a medium grained stone for the plinth of the railings at the British Museum, Bloomsbury. In the dressing yards at Penryn in 1956 rough stone for monumental work

and for ashlar was first shaped up by hand. The operation was known locally as 'taking the wind out of the stone'. The Cornish granites are so similar that most geologists, when asked to identify the granite in *situ* on a building, will say only that it is south-west England granite. Also, it is not easy to determine the provenance of hand specimens, without detailed microscopic study. Granite quarry workers, however, claim to be able to distinguish between granites from different quarries. Because of the similarity of the stone from one quarry to another, several quarries would operate together in supplying stone for large contracts and stone from a number of quarries might well be worked in a common yard. Many quarries in Cornwall are now supplying stone for the new town of Milton Keynes[4].

Stone from the De Lank Quarry, near St Breward, Bodmin, is renowned for its use for the Eddystone Lighthouse (1756) and the Beachy Head Lighthouse (1828). It has also been used elsewhere, for example, for the plinth of the Nurse Cavell Monument, Charing Cross Road, London (1922) and for the plinth of the Churchill Memorial, Parliament Square, London. It may be seen as polished slabs cladding the Marks and Spencer store in Sheffield. Both the De Lank Quarry and its immediate neighbour, the Hantergantick Quarry, produce coarse-grained granite, with small megacrysts, which show a foliation

defined by a generally planar disposition of feldspar and mica[2]. Stone from Hantergantick Quarry may be seen on the ABN Bank, Threadneedle Street, London.

Pelastine granite, quarried at Mabe, was taken to Penryn for dressing. It has also been used for civil engineering works; between 1949 and 1958, much was used for the South Bank wall of the River Thames. It was also used for cladding, as on the Bank of England, King Street, Leeds.

Edwin Lutyens' Castle Drogo, Drewsteignton, Devon, 'the last granite castle' (*Figure 3.7*) was built entirely in granite, including some of the bathroom furniture! It has walls 2 m (6.5 ft.) thick to the Chapel. Stone from a quarry opened in nearby Whiddon Park was used, with some stone from Pew Tor, south-west of Merrivale[5].

To some extent, all the South-west England granite masses were altered when extremely hot solutions and gases were squeezed out during the last stages of cooling and consolidation. These chemically very active, mobile emissions penetrated fissures in the consolidating granite and the surrounding rocks. Complex chemical changes took place and most of the granite mass was either kaolinized, a change that led in extreme cases to china clay, or was gneissened, a process that led to a quartz-mica rock, with some topaz and feldspar, or tourmalinized. By and large, the changes are of little interest when dealing with building and decorative stones. However, around Luxulyan, Cornwall*, tourmalinization has produced a highly decorative rock, named Luxullianite. Originally, the granite contained large crystals of feldspar; the rock now has pink-coloured feldspar megacrysts

The Ordnance Survey Atlas of Great Britain, published by Ordnance Survey/Country Life Books 1982, has been taken throughout as the authority for the spelling of place names. Spellings found elsewhere do not always agree with this source.

Figure 3.7 The architect Edwin Lutyens used granite structurally for Castle Drogo, Devon. In places the walls are 2 metres thick

in a purplish-black background consisting mostly of dark-coloured tourmaline. Apparently the only use of the stone is for the sarcophagus of the Duke of Wellington in St Paul's Cathedral, London[3,7,8]. This fact is often recorded.

Closely associated with the granites is a series of quartz-porphyry dykes with a few sills, the well known elvans. One granite in the region stands out geologically as an oddity, the mass that makes up most of Lundy Island. It has been age-dated at 50 to 55 million years, which is middle Eocene (see *Figure 2.18*). It is considerably younger than the granites so far considered. The stone is light grey in colour and varies from fine- to coarse-grained, with some large feldspar crystals. The sheet-jointing is conspicuous. Between 1864 and 1870, it was much used in the Embankment, London. The island quarry was re-opened to rebuild the Marisco Tavern (the old hotel building) and to build the Agent's bungalow in the traditional Lundy manner in 1983.

Welsh granites

Wales, which is a geologically complex region in some parts, has a tradition of building with stone. Granite masses, however, are not a major component and the stone has had little impact. Note may be made of Trevor granite, from the Eifl quarry, Clwyd, which is used for curling stones.

Igneous rocks from Leicestershire

An igneous mass at no great distance from London, in an area of mostly poorly consolidated sedimentary rocks is bound to assume an importance which might be regarded as out of proportion to the size of its outcrop. So it is with the igneous rock masses which occur in Charnwood, north of Leicester. At Markfield, Groby and Bradgate, a geologically interesting type of syenite, named Markfieldite, was quarried, but of more interest for building is the granite from Mount Sorrel. In geological terms, this stone is actually a granodiorite. The distinction is a mineralogical one; in granite *sensu strictu*, the amount of orthoclase feldspar (a potassium, aluminium silicate) is more than that of plagioclase feldspar (a sodium, calcium, aluminium silicate). In granodiorite, plagioclase exceeds orthoclase. The rock, however, belongs to the granite family. This stone was used locally for building[9], but developed a much greater reputation for use as setts, which Elsden and Howe[7] record were not used until the later part of the eighteenth century in London's roads. The so-called 'Euston Pavement' was of setts 3 inches square by 4 inches deep of Mount Sorrel granite. A drawback, however, of some of the more compact, tougher stones used for this purpose is that they develop a slippery surface when subjected to heavy wear. Mount Sorrel stone varies in colour from grey to dark red-brown and contains large, pale crystals of feldspar.

Cumbrian granites

Shap granite, from another small outcrop of only three square miles (8.7 square km), is one of the most widely known of the British granites because it is easily recognizable. Although there are many other granite intrusions in the Lake District area, the one known above all others is that from the Shap Quarries, Cumbria. This granite contains many accessory minerals, but it is immediately recognized visually by the distinctive megacrysts of pink feldspar, set in a much finer groundmass. Two varieties may be distinguished, Dark Shap and Light Shap, which are seen to grade one into the other. The dark variety occurs in bands 2.5–16 feet (0.75–5 m) wide on each side of the master joints. The megacrystic pink feldspar crystals are prominent and, apparently, were unaltered when hot vapours penetrated the master joints after consolidation of the granite and altered the minerals of the groundmass. Characteristic of Shap granite is the number of dark dots, varying in size and shape and which may have very ill-defined margins. They are known by the quarrymen as 'heathens', or, less frequently, as 'foreigners' and are geologically termed xenoliths (*Figure 3.8*). They are incompletely assimilated fragments of pre-existing rocks, which were caught up by the magma before it solidified. All stages from 'fresh' to almost completely digested fragments may be seen. These blotches are an original feature of the granite. They are not flaws, nor do they in any way affect the quality of the stone. Most granites will be found to contain xenoliths and these add character and interest to the stone.

Figure 3.8 Monolithic bollards, some of which contain xenoliths, are used to surround St Paul's Churchyard, London. Feldspar and quartz crystals may be seen in the xenolith indicating that magmatic fluids had permeated the fragment of country rock

It is apparent that the San Grita granite from Poland which clads the National Westminster Bank, Brompton Road, London, was chosen because of the effect created by the xenoliths. Shap granite has been used in villages around Shap for quoins and lintels. However, because there is little local demand, it has been used far more widely outside its own area. Fine blocks of Dark Shap for the Tyme (formerly Jean Renet) shop on the corner of Bond Street and Piccadilly, London; dark and light varieties for the columns to the hotel entrance portico, St Pancras Station, London; monolithic bollards, some with excellent xenoliths, around the west entrance of St Paul's Cathedral, London; columns for the Irish Life Assurance Company building, King Street, Manchester; and in the west portal of St Mary's Cathedral, Edinburgh, are a few examples. An unusual use is for large paving slabs in the entrance to the Central Library, St Peter's Square, Manchester.

Scottish granites

Scotland is rich in granite. It has been used widely in Scotland and it has been exported to neighbouring England and to many countries overseas. Large masses crop out in the Grampian Highlands, the Southern Uplands, the Western Isles and in the Northern Highlands. The granites range in age from Precambrian to Tertiary. Most of them, however, are associated with the Devonian-Carboniferous Caledonian orogeny, which was marked by the production of large granite masses, known as the Newer Granites. Within the Grampian Highlands, an important series of these masses crop out in a semi-circle, stretching southwards from about Inverness to the Cairngorm Mountains, eastwards, via Hill of Fayne, to Aberdeen and north-west to Peterhead and to Strichen. The chief rock type is a biotite-granite, with little, or no, muscovite, although muscovite does appear in the Kemnay granite in the northern part of the Hill of Fayne mass. Aberdeen was, at one time, the granite centre of the world, but it is, perhaps, the Peterhead granite which is more widely known and the most famous.

Most of the stone taken from the Peterhead mass is coarse-grained and dark or pale flesh-coloured. It consists mainly of quartz and orthoclase feldspar, with only a little biotite mica. Hornblende may be present and, in some places, it completely replaces the mica. The stone is noted for its characteristic dark-coloured xenoliths. It was used widely in its own area, and is responsible for the 'gleaming red' town of Peterhead. With the development of the railways in the 1880s, it was exported in vast quantities to the rest of Britain. Fine columns of this stone may be seen in the East Carriageway, St Pancras Station, London, and the Duke of York's column, (except for the base), provides an outstanding

Figure 3.9 Flesh-coloured Peterhead granite was used for this fine example of a drinking fountain near the Royal Exchange, London

Figure 3.10 Peterhead granite matched with Rubislaw granite, a favourite combination of the Victorians, used here for the Baynard Castle public house, Queen Victoria Street, London

example. Pillars of the stone can be seen in the entrance hall of the Fitzwilliam Museum, Cambridge and stone from the Stirlinghill Quarry, which is known for its fine xenoliths, was used for the base of the main building (1906) of Strathclyde University, Glasgow. The lower floors of the Midland Hotel, St Peter's Square, Manchester, provides another example. There the stone is matched with bands of Dark Shap. In some areas of the Peterhead mass, the stone is dark grey in colour and is fine-grained, with scattered irregular, larger crystals of pale-coloured feldspar. Strictly, it is a granodiorite. Cairngall Quarry was the best known of those quarries supplying this grey stone, which is commonly called Blue Peterhead. It may be seen in the plinth of the statue of Wellington, Queen Street, Glasgow; in the base of the fountains, Trafalgar Square, London; and is renowned for supplying a 30-tonne block for the sarcophagus of the Prince Consort at Frogmore, Windsor, Berkshire. Eight 20 foot (6 m) high polished columns in St George's Hall, Liverpool, are each made of one block of the stone. Another dark grey-coloured, medium-grained stone quarried at Rora, about one mile north of Aberdeen, was used for ornamental work. Pillars of it are recorded at Cambridge[6].

Aberdeen, the city of the 'glitter of mica at windy corners', typifies a city built of granite. The enormous 155 m (380 ft.) deep hole, Rubislaw Quarry, which is said to date back to 1721 and which supplied the stone to build much of Aberdeen, is now surrounded by the city. The stone from Rubislaw is blue-grey in colour, medium-grained, and contains orthoclase, plagioclase, quartz, much biotite and a little muscovite, with xenoliths. The biotite mica flakes in it have a marked orientation. If the stone is cut to be polished, the cut should be at right angles to the orientation. If the mica flakes lie parallel with the exposed, polished surface, the natural mineral cleavage of the mica leads to a pitted appearance. This can be seen on most other types of polished granite surfaces, but, because the mica flakes are not always orientated, the effect is usually less noticeable. The feldspars often show a swirling texture. This stone has been widely used from an early date. St Machar's Cathedral, Aberdeen, is generally credited with being the earliest, large scale use of granite for building. As with most other granites, it was used also on a large scale for civil engineering works including, Waterloo Bridge (in part 1817), Portsmouth Docks, and Bell Rock Lighthouse (or Inchape Rock), which is 131 feet (40 m) high and was designed by Robert Stevenson and Rennie in 1807. Many other quarries, such as Dancing Cairns, Sclattie and Persley, in the Aberdeen mass also supplied stone for building work generally, but, unless a record exists of the stone used, it is not possible by casual inspection to do more than determine that the granite is Aberdeen, or Rubislaw.

Granite from around Aberdeen used to be exported to many other countries. It is on record that dark grey, even-grained stone from Dyce Quarries, five miles north-west of Aberdeen, was used in the Bank of Australia, Melbourne (pre-1911). As a relief from the uniformly grey colour in Aberdeen, the pink and red of Corrennie and Peterhead granite may sometimes be seen. The outcrop of granite which makes up the Hill of Fare mass, 15 miles (24 km) inland from Aberdeen, is included in the Aberdeen granite. Two widely known stones were taken from it, Kemnay and Corrennie. Kemnay, pale silver-grey, with a yellowish tinge from the colour of the feldspar, is quartz-rich and contains both biotite, which is orientated, and muscovite mica. It was used for the granite houses of Kemnay and for Kemnay House itself (seventeenth century). More importantly, stone was quarried in large quantities and was used for several bridges spanning the River Thames. This stone forms the base of the Queen Victoria Monument outside Buckingham Palace, London. It is renowned for its use in the building claimed to be the second largest granite building in the world, Marischal College, Aberdeen, 'a poem in stone'. El Escorial, outside Madrid, Spain, is claimed to be the largest. The Kemnay Quarry, apart from being the first to use steam and electrical firing, is noted as the first to use Blondins, an aerial cableway used to bring blocks of stone to the surface from the bottom of deep quarries.

The Corrennie Quarries supplied, in contrast, a warm red-coloured stone, coarser-grained and quartz-rich, with bright, pink-red feldspars. In addition to its use for decorative shop fronts, for example, in Bond Street, London, it is best known for its use in the base and for the balustrade of the City Chambers, Glasgow (1887). In places, Corrennie stone has a streaked texture. Associated bodies of a more basic (lower SiO_2 content) nature occur in this rock and a quartz-diorite forms grey patches and bands throughout part of it. Blocks may even be half pink and half grey. An entirely grey stone was quarried from nearby Tillyfourie. Further to the west, Balmoral Castle is built of light grey 'local granite' and roofed with slates from nearby Foudland.

It was not unusual for granite to be used for the decorative effect given by the variety of colours displayed. This was a consideration with, for example, the Albert Memorial, Kensington Gardens, London. The wide range of colour shown by Aberdeen granites can be seen in the nineteen columns of the pulpit of Crathie church (1895), near Balmoral, which, it is recorded, was built at the desire of Queen Victoria.

Many of the smaller granite masses in the Grampian Highlands have been used mostly locally. Occasionally some have been more widely used, such as that at Ballachulish, a locality more commonly associated with slate. Ballachulish granite, notable for a frequent abundance of xenoliths, was used in part for the monument outside the Geology Building, Glasgow University. The stone was obtained from a demolished railway bridge.

Brief mention should be made also of Ailsa Craig, Firth of Clyde, Ayrshire, the remnant of a volcanic core. Most of the island is of a fine-grained microgranite, which contains the dark blue mineral riebeckite, instead of hornblende. Used on the island for building, it is much better known for its use as curling stones. It also supplied good quality setts.

In the Southern Uplands, an important, large intrusive granite mass and a very narrow vein were the sources for two well known, widely used stones. The first is the Criffel mass, Dumfries and Galloway. On its western edge are the quarries of Dalbeattie. The stone is pinkish-grey coloured, medium-grained, and contains oligoclase, plagioclase, biotite mica and hornblende, with many accessory minerals, particularly a clove-coloured sphene (a calcium titanium silicate ($CaTiSiO_5$) mineral), which is brown and greenish-yellow, grey, or black. It is widely found as an accessory mineral. The composition of the granite differs throughout the mass.

Because the quarries are near the sea, the stone was shipped far and wide, including to Ceylon. Examples in Great Britain, apart from the light grey town of Dalbeattie itself, include pillars at St Pancras Station, London; the lower Mosley Street side of the Midland Hotel, Manchester; part of the Albert Memorial, London; and the George V Bridge, Clyde, Glasgow. It is used as a facing stone for the Bank of Scotland, 30 Bishopsgate, London. Sweetheart Abbey, New Abbey, Dumfries and Galloway, uses 'Crifell Granite', which is not otherwise localized, as a contrast to the mass of the red sandstone building. Perhaps the best known use is for the lower part of the Pearl Life Assurance building, Holborn, London.

The silvery-grey coloured Creetown granite was quarried from an outcrop about 650 feet (200 m) wide and only about a mile (1.6 km) long. Because the quarries were also near the sea, the stone was shipped out widely. Records of its use, however, are scarce. Mersey Docks, part of the Thames Embankment, Aldermary House, Watling Street, London, and the Marks and Spencer store (1966), Argyle Street, Glasgow which also used Rubislaw granite, are some examples.

A number of famous quarries on the southern peninsula, or ross, of the Island of Mull, Inner Hebrides, supplied a red stone that became known generally as Ross of Mull granite. In fact, the mass, some twenty square miles (50 square km) in outcrop, ranges from a hornblende-biotite-diorite, to a muscovite-biotite granite and from a grey to a red colour. It is the red stone which has been widely used. It is pale to deep red-coloured, coarse-grained

Figure 3.11 The piers of Blackfriars bridge are models of the font of the former Blackfriars monastery. They were so designed at the wish of Queen Victoria who opened the bridge in 1869. The three drums of the columns are of solid Ross of Mull granite

Figure 3.12 The statue 'Asia' of the Albert Memorial, London, is of Sicilian Marble (see p 147) and has an inset slab of Ross of Mull granite. Much importance was given to the colours of the many granites used in the memorial. Ross of Mull granite was one of the earliest quarried in Scotland

stone, composed of pink to red orthoclase feldspar, brown biotite mica, and, in some places, white muscovite mica, which may be replaced by hornblende. The stone is noted for its flow-structure and for a blotchy appearance, caused by a rough clustering (clotting) of the feldspar. It is renowned for its widely spaced joints. Its earliest use was for Iona Abbey (seventh century), which is just across the Sound of Iona from the granite mass. Loose blocks, deposited by glacial action on the island, were incorporated into the structure. The joint system allowed large blocks to be won. The stone may be seen as pedestals on Holborn Viaduct, London; in the piers of Blackfriars Bridge, London (*Figure 3.11*); as columns in the Albert Memorial, London (*Figure 3.12*); and as pillars flanking the main south entrance of the University, Glasgow. In this city, Ross of Mull granite on the lower part of buildings was commonly combined with red sandstone above[10]. In the Northern Highlands, granite has only been used locally.

Irish granites

Important granite masses are found in Ireland, all of which have been worked at one time or another. The most important is probably the Wicklow-Leinster mass. The outcrop trends roughly south-west to north-east, and is 60 miles long by about 10 miles wide (100 by 16 km). In general, the stone is a grey-coloured, coarse-grained granite, with muscovite. A pink variety is known. Many quarries were opened in the rock and much grey Wicklow granite was used for buildings in Dublin. Blocks were also supplied to help build the Thames Embankment, London. Stone from Ballyknockon Quarries, County Wicklow, was used for the Wellington Monument, Phoenix Park, Dublin, for Trinity College (1832), Dublin; and for part of Dublin Station.

The Newry granite, stretching through County Armagh and into County Down, is best known for the Newry, Bessbrook and Castlewellan stones. The towns of Newry and Bessbrook were both built of local granite from an early date. The Newry granite is a complex of intrusions and the rock varies considerably. In general, the stone is a pale grey-coloured, fine-grained granodiorite, with biotite mica. However, there is a concentration of biotite in some areas and of hornblende in other places. As a consequence, the stone assumes a dark appearance as at Castlewellan, County Down. Stone from quarries in Northern Ireland was used in the base and pedestal and for some of the columns of the Albert Memorial, London. Newry granite road setts were once characteristic of Belfast streets and the stone has been used also for buildings, such as the Ulster Bank, Waring Street, Belfast. Stone from the Castlewellan Quarry, specifically, may be seen as columns on the Water Commissioners' Building, Donegall

Square, Belfast. Bessbrook granite has been used for the base of the pilasters of Abbey-Life House, 1–3 St Paul's Churchyard, London[11].

The nearby Mourne Mountains granite is a complex of five separate intrusions, which show only slight differences. In places, the edge of the mass is of a finer grain. This enabled good setts to be produced, which are said to have 'paved Lancashire'[12]. Mourne granite was used for the base of Telephone House, Belfast.

Masses in County Galway yielded a pink-coloured, fine-grained stone for the top, and a dark grey, medium-grained stone for the bottom, of the Parnall Monument, Dublin. Shantallow Quarry supplied many setts in Dublin. All the polished granite for the new Post Office for South Kensington, in Exhibition Road is reported to be of Galway granite and so is the base of the Fontenoy Memorial, Belgium. In the main, however, this mass was so intensively glacially rotted that it erodes easily. Stone taken from it should be selected with care.

Channel Islands granites

The Channel Isles, Jersey and Guernsey, have exported granite to the British mainland for a long time, mostly for kerbs, paving and setts. Jersey granite varies a good deal in character, from pale red to pink in colour and from fine- to coarse-grained. Stone from La Moie Quarries, near St Helier, was used for Chatham Docks. Guernsey supplied a stone known locally as Bird's Eye, which was exported to London as Blue Granite. It is a diorite type rock. Columns in Goodwood House, West Sussex, are recorded as being of Guernsey granite.

Imported granites

Granite may be found in many other countries, but it seems that it was not until the middle of the nineteenth century that foreign granite began to be imported into Britain on any scale. In 1864, granite from Sweden was imported in quantity, to help build the Thames Embankment, London, in which many other granites were also used. A variety with noticeably blue coloured quartz, quarried at Vanevik, Sweden, may be seen in the Coliseum Theatre, St Martin's Lane, London. There are few, if any verified references to the use of imported granite in ancient monuments and historic buildings. Since the 1860s, however, much has been imported and some varieties seem to have become fashionable for a period. Most of these varieties are not discussed in detail here. There are some, however, that deserve more than a brief mention.

Italy, not immediately brought to mind as a granite

supplier, has a number of granite quarries. Those at Baveno have acquired more than a local reputation. Pale rosy-pink in colour and fine-grained, this stone was used widely at least as far back as the sixteenth century. The Italian island of Sardinia supplies a lot of granite which is widely exported. Sardinian Grey and Sardinian Beige, Coral and Pink are the chief varieties. Sardinian Grey was used for the Ismaili Centre, South Kensington, London, with spectacular effect.

Egypt has supplied stone from Suwan, known as Syene by the Greeks and now as Aswan, since at least from 4000 BC. It is a hornblende granite, pink coloured, and composed of plagioclase and ortho-clase feldspar, quartz, a small amount of aggregated muscovite mica and hornblende, with magnetite as an accessory mineral. It is known world-wide as the stone of the twenty-two Cleopatra's Needles. One is

names; for example Balmoral Red, Royal Grey, Braemar Grey and Abergeldie Grey are from Finland. Grey Royal granite is from Norway and Imperial Red is from Sweden. The trade name of the stone cannot be taken as giving an indication of its provenance.

Two recently imported granites, currently being widely used for cladding demonstrate how a stone becomes available and then fashionable. The first, from Millbank, South Dakota, USA, called Imperial Mahogany in Great Britain, is a dull red-brown colour. It is coarse-grained, and shows a marked foliation and streaking out of the feldspars, which may be picked out by wisps of mica. It is one of the Older Granites, which have suffered later deforma-tion and mineral alteration. It may be seen as polished slabs cladding, for example, Blackfriars Station, London and Lloyds Bank, Victoria Street, London. The second example is from quarries in

Figure 3.14 Rapakivi structure is well seen in 'Baltic Brown' granite from Finland. The boundary between Finland and the USSR runs across this granite mass and similar stone may be seen used in Leningrad and other towns near the border

Figure 3.13 'An uncompleted Cleopatra's Needle'. A monolithic obelisk, abandoned by the early Egyptian quarriers, as yet not released from the granite bedrock at Aswan (Syene), Egypt. Blocks of this granite were used for the many 'Cleopatra's Needles' now scattered around the world. (Courtesy of Dr C. Welch)

in London, one in Central Park, New York, USA and another in the Place de la Concorde, Paris, France.

Norway has also exported much stone to Great Britain, particularly since the early 1900s. The Stock Exchange, Manchester, is an early example.

At one time, Aberdeen was a centre for granite processing of both British and imported stone. Many of the imported stones were given British-sounding

Finland, about 0.5 miles (0.8 km) from the border with Russia, on the Kotka to Leningrad road. Sold in Britain as Baltic Brown, it has large, flesh-coloured potassic feldspars, which form rounded crystals up to a few centimetres in diameter which are mantled with white sodic plagioclase, and, in some instances, rhythmically zoned with orthoclase. These feldspars are embedded in a matrix of normal texture, which consist chiefly of quartz and some coloured minerals. The stone exhibits Rapakivi texture (*Figure 3.14*). Polished slabs clad the main Lloyds Bank building, Leeds.

Intermediate plutonic igneous rocks

Syenite is not a common rock in Great Britain. The original type is comprised mostly of hornblende and orthoclase feldspar and comes from near Dresden, Germany. It is one of the quirks of geology that the rock at Syene in Egypt, from which the name was derived is actually a hornblende granite. Syenite, an intermediate plutonic igneous rock which is pale-coloured grey to reddish, occurs in relatively small masses. It may be thought of as a granite without quartz. Despite its relative rareness compared with granite *sensu strictu*, it is probably more noticeable in all the major cities of the world than any other rock, because of the popularity of one particular type, larvikite (from Larvik, Norway), which has been sold on the world market for many years as Pearl Granite, Imperial Pearl, Light Pearl, Dark Pearl, Royal Blue and several other varietal names. This rock contains large rhomb-shaped feldspars of different types intergrown with one another. Indeed, the rock may be made up almost entirely of feldspar. Because of the peculiar structure of the intergrown feldspars, light is reflected from different layers within the crystal which results in interference patterns and an iridescence, termed *schiller*. The bright play of colours is enhanced by polishing and the difference between an unpolished and polished surface is marked. The polished appearance, however, cannot be expected to appeal in every instance of its use. The stone has been widely used for shop fronts, and public house fascias. It may be

Figure 3.15 'Elephant and Calf' carved from a monolithic block of larvikite. Philadelphia Zoo. Pennsylvania, USA

seen used sculpturally for the monolithic 'Elephant and Calf', at the Philadelphia Zoo, Pennsylvania, USA (*Figure 3.15*).

Other instances of its use are: the Henry and Edsel Ford Memorial Auditorium, Detroit, USA, the new Mitsui Building, Tokyo, Japan, the entrance to the Mayfair Hotel, London, the Innocenti Building, Milan, Italy, the DGB Building, Dusseldorf, Germany, in the remarkable suspended staircase, of General Motors Research Staff Building, Detroit, USA, and for the

interesting modelling of a ship's prow on the new National Employers Federation Building, Bury Street, London. It has also been used with startling effect in the perfumery department of Harrods, London, where the ceiling is set with 250 lights directed to stimulate the schiller. The stone commonly is recorded as granite.

A visually attractive syenite containing the azure-blue mineral sodalite (a sodium aluminium silicate with chlorine) comes from Bahia Quarry, São Salvador, Brazil. Called Blue Bahia it is also known, inevitably it may be thought, as 'blue granite'. Sodalite-syenite adequately describes the stone, which, of course, can be given any name. It is currently being used with marked effect for the Ismaili Centre, South Kensington, London. An interesting stone in this family is a nephaline-syenite known geologically as foyaite because the original type described was from Mt. Foya, Portugal. It is worked in the Sierra de Monchique, Algarve in Portugal and shows radiating clusters of fine feldspar laths. It is sold as a syenite and is recorded as used in the Bank of Abu Dhabi, at the entrance to Stewart Wrightson's, Camomile Street, London[13].

Swedish Green 'Granite', a dark grey-coloured syenite has a greenish cast caused by the green coloured mineral epidote (a calcium aluminium iron silicate). It has been used decoratively.

Diorite is a fairly abundant intermediate plutonic rock but is of limited occurrence in Great Britain. Characteristically it is speckled black and white because the dark minerals are in clots. It is coarse-grained and composed mostly of plagioclose feldspar and hornblende. It may contain one of the pyroxenes (a group of complex silicate minerals). The stone may have a deep green cast from iron-silicate minerals which were altered very early on in the formation of the rock, and thus may be confused with Swedish Green 'Granite'. The mineral quartz may be present in diorite. In that instance the stone is termed a quartz-diorite and thus grades into grano-diorite. Diorite has been imported into Great Britain for decorative use. The best known is Ebony Black Granite from Sweden, which is even black in colour with shiny opaque metallic flecks. The lower façade of the Empire State Building, New York is clad with this stone, as is the Institut Français du Pétrole, Rueil Malmaison (Seine), France (1959). It has also been used by Milles for the sculpture of his eagle at Worcester, Massachusetts, USA; and it forms the base of the renowned US Marine Corps War Memorial in Washington, DC, USA. A similar stone, Black Swede H, is spectacularly used in the Imperial Theatre, Tokyo where it is teamed-up with Imperial Red Granite, also from Sweden.

Bon Accord Black 'Granite' from Sweden which is classified between diorite and gabbro is medium-grained and was, at one time, extensively worked in

Aberdeen. It has been used principally for shop fronts and for head stones. Black Diamond 'Granite' from South Africa is also used mainly for cladding. It is a syeno-gabbro and is uniformly black-coloured with shiny feldspar laths up to 1 cm long. It may be seen on the VIth Inn, Crown Square, Manchester. 'Andes Black' from South Africa, is a similar stone.

A geologically interesting rock named Kentallenite from the Scottish town of Kentallen, may be considered here amongst the Syeno-gabbro types. Coarse to medium-grained, it exhibits large shining plates of biotite mica. This 'handsome dark . . . ornamental stone' is recorded[14] as having been quarried as 'black granite' and sent to Aberdeen for processing, but no record of its use has been discovered.

Basic plutonic igneous rocks

Gabbro typically is a mottled dark-grey to black coloured, coarsely crystalline rock composed essentially of the minerals labradorite (a complex type of feldspar) and augite (a complex silicate of calcium, magnesium, iron and aluminium of variable composition). Iron-bearing minerals are common accessory minerals and because the rock is often rich in them it tends to weather more easily than some of the acid igneous rocks. The mineral olivine (a magnesium iron silicate, $(Mg, Fe)_2 SiO_4$) may be present to give the rock (an olivine-gabbro) a green cast. Olivine also weathers readily.

Gabbro is a rare rock in Great Britain. The Cuillins of Skye is the largest mass and it is not common elsewhere. The 'Black Granite' from Herrestad, Sweden is the best known example. The use of this stone in a highly polished state in the interior of the Ritz Hotel, London, is so often recorded that this appears to be its only use. It is usually mistaken for a marble. Recently, Indian Ebony Black, a related type of rock, has been imported into Great Britain and has been used for decorative cladding[10] and monumental work.

Ultrabasic igneous rocks

Serpentinite (or serpentine rock), a rock made up mostly of the mineral serpentine (hydrated silicate of magnesium and iron, $Mg_3Si_2O_5(OH)_4$), has resulted from the alteration of rocks such as peridotites and picrites which are rich in the mineral olivine. It is a secondary rock, formed by the *serpentinization* of other ultrabasic rocks. Therefore it is conveniently considered here.

Serpentinites are found in those areas of the crust which have been tectonically affected. The change probably occurred when the original rock within the Earth's lithosphere was forced upward, and became hydrated in the process. They are soft but variable ($H = 2\frac{1}{2}$ to 4), heavy, mottled, streaked and banded from virtually black, through red, green and grey to dirty white. The stone will take a good polish, but weathers readily to a poor-looking dingy grey when exposed. The name serpentine is from the supposed resemblance of the rock to the skin of a serpent. The best known mass in Great Britain is found in The Lizard, Cornwall where the rock was once extensively wrought. It was used on a massive scale for interior decoration, particularly in churches. St John's College Chapel, Cambridge has columns of serpentinite. It may also be seen in the floor at Peterborough Cathedral, in the pulpit and twelfth-century doorway of Landewednack Church on The Lizard[5], as blocks for steps and as columns in Truro Cathedral, and as innumerable, mostly Victorian, fonts in many churches. Because the stone weathers readily it is unsuitable for outside work. Nevertheless, interestingly, it has been used for columns on the shop front of (now) Mappin & Webb and of Loewe, Bond Street, London. The stone appears in many church monuments.

A narrow sill of serpentinite which outcrops on the shore and in the cliffs at Portsoy, Banffshire is the source of the so-called Portsoy 'Marble'. Predominantly darkish-green with lighter yellowish-green blobs and streaks, the stone now is worked, as is that at The Lizard, for small ornamental pieces and tourist knick-knacks. In the past it supplied the stone for a magnificent fireplace in nearby Cullen House[15]; and for fireplaces in the Palace of Versailles, France[16]. Other masses are found in Fetlar and in Unst, Shetlands. Stone from Unst was used locally and was also the source of soapstone and talc, minerals closely related to serpentinite.

Serpentinite is found also in Anglesey. The principle outcrop is near Rhoscolyn and it is a serpentinized gabbro, dark green, brecciated with some patches of the white-coloured mineral calcite ($CaCO_3$).

The stone was produced apparently in limited quantity, and was known as Anglesey Serpentine, Mona Marble, and Verde Antico. However, in this instance Verde Antico was used to indicate its appearance, not its provenance. It was used, as was most serpentinite from elsewhere, for 'marble-topped' tables, wash-hand stands, chests and so on. Many other stones were similarly used and the determination of the stone may occasionally help with the determination of the provenance and date of a piece of furniture. The best known use of 'Mona Marble' is in the chancels of Truro Cathedral. The shafts supporting the pulpit in the nave of Worcester Cathedral also are of this stone, and pieces of furniture in the Victoria and Albert Museum, London are topped with it. Llys Delas House, Anglesey has a fireplace made of 'Mona Marble'.

The areas of Piedmont, Italy and Thessaly, Greece are important sources of decorative serpentinite, not only in the past but also at the present. The stone is brecciated. This was caused, it seems, by big pods of the original rock being squeezed up into the cores of mountain belts. The stone is composed of small or large angular fragments, red, purple, green, grey and rarely black in colour, which are much veined, with the veins swelling and narrowing, some with contrasting white calcite. There is a profusion of names which depend on the quarry from which the stone is taken. Verde Antico (*Lapis Atracius* of the Romans) from near Larissa, Greece, is the classic and classical variety, noted for patches of calcite. *Rosso di Levanto*, from near Levanto, Italy, the other main type, is predominantly red to reddish purple in colour, with occasional white veins of soapstone (called sapone by the Italians).

The Greek and Italian serpentinites have been extensively used for ecclesiastical work, decoration, inlay and furniture. They may be found worldwide and are used decoratively for shop fronts and like purposes (*Figure 3.16*).

The island of Tinos, Greece is the source of a marble known as Tinos (Tenos, or Vert Tinos). It is a serpentinite with irregular whitish veins and it has been variously classified as a serpentinous marble or

Figure 3.16 A green serpentinite, *Verde* (or *Verte*) *Fraya*, used decoratively for a shop front in Regent Street, London

as ophicalcite. It was quarried in classical times by the ancient Greeks who used it extensively. It has been used for monolithic columns and for plinths, pavements and panels. It was used for sixteen columns in the semi-circular hall of the New Sessions House, London, built in 1907[6]. It is also used in the National Gallery, Trafalgar Square, London.

A serpentinized picrite, quarried at Polyphant (Polyfant, Pollaphant, in older spellings), Cornwall is a minor building stone in regional terms. Because it

is found in an area where other available stones such as granite or slate were either hard to work or not suitable, it became widely used and widely known, out of all proportion with the size of the outcrop. A very dark ultrabasic hypabyssal igneous rock, it probably resulted from the upward migration of peridotite. The stone is fine-grained and grey to dusky-green-blue with white specks and reddish to yellowish brown spots. As it may be easily worked it has been used for dressings, almost as a freestone. It is recorded that Saxon and Norman arches in Cornwall are made of the Polyphant stone[6]. It may also be seen as shafts of the columns in Truro Cathedral, where it is used to provide the colour contrast in the same way that Blue Lias and Purbeck Marble are used in other parts of the country. Additionally it was used for columns in the church at Pampisford and for the Celtic Cross (1914) at Bartlow, Cambridgeshire; as well as for some piers in Exeter Cathedral. A recent, spectacular use is for the new (1983) font, designed by John Skelton, in Chichester Cathedral. It is the stone used for the war memorial, a copy of an old Cornish cross, at Haverfordwest, Dyfed. Another fine example of its use is provided by Archbishop Temple's tomb in Canterbury Cathedral.

A similar stone, also a serpentinized picrite, was formerly quarried at Duporth (2 miles (3.2 km) east of St Austell, Cornwall), where two small intrusions which cannot be traced very far inland occur on the beach. Although it is now largely forgotten, this stone also was used in Truro Cathedral[17] for some of the vaulting shafts in the choir and transepts, in the baptistry, and in the shafting in the triforium. Duporth Stone, was used in the Cathedral '... with great effect ... and it might hold up its head and claim to be quite as handsome and suitable to the purpose as the Purbeck Marble that was found in churches in other parts of the country.' It is possible that some determination of Polyphant Stone should properly be of Duporth Stone.

Serpentinite may grade into a serpentinous marble depending on the quantities of the minerals present. Such a marble is known as an ophicalcite. Ophicalcites commonly result from the metamorphism of a limestone containing other mineral matter.

Asbestos

The substance commonly known as asbestos has been found in mortars used in countries around the Aegean Sea. It is known that the asbestos came from Cyprus. The name asbestos, however, is given today to a number of minerals which have different chemical compositions but which have one characteristic in common, they crystallize into long, thin fibres which can be fairly easily separated. Since these fibres are flexible, they may be woven into a fabric. Additionally the minerals are resistant to heat to different degrees.

The asbestos found in Cyprus is a fibrous form of serpentine which has been named crysotile (magnesium iron silicate, $(Mg,Fe)_3Si_2O_5(OH)_4$). This form provides about 90 per cent of the world's asbestos. In Cyprus it is found as veins intimately associated with ultrabasic rocks.

The perpetual lamp wicks of the Vestal Virgins were of amianthus, the name for asbestos used by the Greeks and by the Romans. It is derived from the Greek word for undefiled, a reference to the way in which it could be cleansed by fire. Interestingly, the quarries where the asbestos is extracted and the village nearby on Mount Troodos, Cyprus, are named Amiandus.

Rocks from minor intrusion

Among the smaller, finer-grained igneous intrusions the rocks named porphyry are of importance in relation to building and particularly to decorative stones.

The name porphyry is derived from the Greek word for purple. Pliny in his Natural History describes *Porphyrites leptopsephos* (white-spotted) from Egypt and it was this stone, Imperial Porphyry that was taken in quantiy to Imperial Rome as *Lapis porphyrites.*

A similar stone, but in this instance green, quarried in Greece during classical times was known at the time of Pliny as *Marmor Lacedaemonium Viride.*

Porphyry is an igneous rock of any composition that contains conspicuous, relatively large, crystals, known as phenocrysts, set in a fine-grained groundmass. The phenocrysts are normally of quartz (quartz porphyry) or feldspar (feldspar porphyry) or both (quartz-feldspar-porphyry).

The elvans

The granites of south-west England are intimately associated with a series of quartz-porphyry dykes called elvans. Elvan and grey elvan are names given by Cornish quarrymen and miners to dyke and sill rocks around the granite masses which are up to 150 feet (46 m) thick. These dykes are mostly of quartz-porphyry and it is to this rock that the name elvan should be restricted. Geologists continued the use of the stone workers' perfectly adequate classification and nomenclature. Later writers have tended to misuse the term. The term blue elvan was given to other rock types, principally to greenstone, which is now determined as dolerite (diabase), and to rocks such as serpentinized picrite. In the past many elvans were

Figure 3.17 A porphyritic granite, a microgranite and an elvan, all quarried locally, were used for the School of Mines, Camborne, Cornwall

quarried for local building, for example at Mayon and Douglas near St Austell; Helland, St Neot, Lanivet and Witheal near Bodmin; Trevailes and Roseorow near Penryn. In some instances elvans from several different localities were introduced into a building. One example is Truro Cathedral which used Pentewan, Wild Duck, Newnham and others.

(a)

(b)

Figure 3.18 (a) Blue-grey coloured elvan from Landrake was used by the Normans for the spectacular arch of St Germanus, Cornwall; (b) it was used also for the nearby much more recent entrance lodge to Port Eliot

Elvan from the Tarton Down Quarries, Landrake, Cornwall was used by the Normans for the magnificent west door entrance of the Church of St Germanus in St Germans, four miles away. All Norman stonework in this area is of this eye-catching blue-grey-green stone. It may be seen also in the nearby entrance lodge to Port Eliot, which is much more recent (*Figure 3.18*).

The most widely known elvan appears to be Pentewan Stone (Pentuan in earlier spelling), which certainly was used from an early date. A Roman inscribed stone built into the wall of Tregomy Church is a rough block of it. This stone is pale buff grey in colour. All elvans are more or less kaolinized and under the microscope the feldspar of Pentewan Stone is seen to be of minute scales of kaolinite with some quartz. These rather softer powdery masses commonly weather out from the stone to give it a characteristic pock-marked appearance. However, this is not detrimental. In fact it probably owes its good qualities as a weather resisting stone to the ground mass of quartz and white mica.

Pentewan Stone has a long history of use as a building stone. Clifton-Taylor[9] lists several houses built of it, for example a house at Travithen, Antony House, Torpoint, and Trevice House, near Newquay. The church at Fowey also is of Pentewan stone. In 1985 blocks of Pentewan stone were recovered from the beach near the original quarry and were used for repair and restoration work at St Austell Church, Cornwall. A warm yellow quartz-porphyry quarried near St Columb Minor was used for the local church and several houses around.

Greek and Egyptian porphyries

Of considerable importance, particularly in the archaeological context is the Green Porphyry of Greece and the Red Porphyry of Egypt. Both have been widely used as ornamental stones since at least the early days of the Roman Empire. The stone from the Marathonisi Quarries, Laconia, Greece, the *Marmor Lacedaemonium Viride* of Pliny was later known as *Porfido Serpentino*. This is unfortunate because the stone is not a serpentinite. Pausanias (second century AD) calls the stone Verde Antique and describes it as '... hard to work, but once worked (it)... might grace sanctuaries of the gods'. It was very popular in Rome and was also exported elsewhere. It was commonly known as *Porfido Verde Antico*. It was quarried at Demos Krokeae, in western Laconia and is renowned for the lighter green porphyritic labradorite feldspar crystals conspicuously set in a darker green fine-grained groundmass. It is sometimes found to have been used in Roman villas in Great Britain and in Ireland. As may be expected, it has been extensively used in Rome; for example in the church of St Giovanni in Fonte; St Maria Maggiore and St Pietro in Vincoli; St Vitali at Ravenna and for two columns in the Ava Coeli. Watson[18] also records an 'elaborately carved tombstone of white marble, erected in 1903, in the churchyard of Dullington, a village in Cambridgeshire, is inlaid with this rock'. Probably the most often visited example is the plinth of Napoleon Bonaparte's tomb in Les Invalides, Paris.

The Green Porphyry of Greece often is used with the famous Red Porphyry, the Imperial Porphyry or Porfido Rosso Antico, of Egypt. The Imperial Porphyry is as spectacular as the Green Porphyry. It differs in colour because it has a dark purplish-red groundmass caused by the presence of the mineral haematite in which are set pale-red, or pink to white laths of feldspar. The stone was first quarried from Lykabettus, north of the hill Gebel Abu Dakhan in the eastern desert of Egypt apparently by the Romans and not by the Egyptians. This is the only known locality where this rock occurs. Columns nearly 40 feet (12 m) high were sent from Rome for use in St Sophia, Constantinople. Other columns may be seen in Venice (*Figure 3.19*). A slab is used in the tomb of Henry III in Westminster Abbey and it was used for the cross behind the altar in the Chapel of St Andrew, Westminster Cathedral. One of the steps up to the Chancel in the spectacular Church of St Mary, Studley Royal, Yorkshire is made of sizeable blocks of this 'Stone of Rome'.

Figure 3.19 'The Tetrarchs', in Venice, Italy are carved in Imperial Porphyry from Egypt. Note the unfortunate repair of the right-hand side lower leg and foot in an obviously geologically inappropriate stone. (Photo: John Ashurst)

Dolerites

Dolerite is a common intrusive rock type in northeast England and in the Midland Valley of Scotland. Smaller sill and dyke masses are found elsewhere. The rock may also be called diabase, particularly outside Great Britain. It is a dark coloured rock consisting mostly of plagioclase feldspar and augite (calcium magnesium aluminosilicate, (Ca,Mg,Fe,Al) $(Al,Si)_2O_6$), a dark green to black pyroxene mineral. In many instances the markedly green mineral chlorite (one of a group of silicates which are related to the micas) may be present. Because of the presence of this mineral, field occurrences of dolerite were given the generic name of greenstone. This name, however, includes other rock types. Dolerite is medium-grained, dark, and heavy. The minerals can be distinguished normally with the unaided eye. Although dolerite has not been widely used in building it does provide striking examples of the local use of local material. Undoubtedly the biggest mass in Great Britain is the Great Whin Sill of northern England which may be traced from the Farne Islands, off the Northumberland coast at Bamburgh, across Northumberland through Teesdale to the western facing scarp of the Pennines. The Great Whin Sill is comprised mostly of quartz-dolerite. Much material has been taken from this sill and used as crushed rock and as setts. The names Whin and Trap have been used for the stone, but it should be noted that those names have been applied to other types of rock. The Romans built part of the renowned Hadrian's Wall along the sharp scarp crest of the Great Whin Sill and used stone from the sill itself as the building material. Blocks from the sill, used as part of the rubble filling the centre of the wall, are locally called Bluey. Not all of the Wall, however, is of quartz-dolerite from the Sill. Across the country the stone of which the Wall is built changes with the geology. The Romans used any suitable stone quarried close to the Wall.

A thick well-joined dyke of olivine-dolerite crops out at Carrickfergus, Co. Antrim, Ireland. It supplied the stone for the Castle which stands on it.

Thick sills of dolerite, up to 150 feet (46 m) thick cap Titterstone Clee Hill and Brown Clee Hill, northeast of Ludlow, Shropshire. They have been much quarried for roadstone, for setts which are used extensively in London and elsewhere, and may be found in local buildings. Large blocks are incorporated in the Iron Age camp on Titterstone Clee. The extraordinarily close jointing of a dolerite-type rock found at Corndon Hill, Shropshire, which allows it to be thinly laminated, enables it to be used as a tilestone; that is a stone, other than slate, which is used for roofing. It was used as far away as Llandrinio, Powys[19], at least as early as the mid-fifteenth century.

Around Exeter, Devon, a number of basic igneous rocks are known generally as the Exeter Traps or Exeter Volcanic Series. Some are of dolerite and closely related rock types. These have been extensively used in the city of Exeter for the City Wall, the mediaeval bridge, and the almshouses in Magdalen Street and in Gordon Road (*Figure 3.20*). The main quarries are at Pocombe and Thorveton. The Thorveton Quarry was worked by the Romans. A sill of somewhat serpentinized dolerite (greenstone)

Figure 3.20 A dolerite-type rock from the Exeter Volcanic series which crops out locally was used for the Almshouses, Magdalen Street, Exeter

Figure 3.21 Font of Clataclews stone. Church of St Petroc, Padstow

which runs through Rock, Padstow and which clips Cataclews (Catacleuse) Point, comes from a quarry at the Point. It is a fairly easily worked, dark greenish-blue-grey stone which was used locally for building. For example, it was used in the Norman parts of the church of St Petroc, Padstow (*Figure 3.21*) and for much of the mullions, tracery and font of the present-day church. Prior Vyvyan's Tomb in Bodmin Church provides a fine effigy. Clifton-Taylor[9] records that the effigies of Lord Marney and his son at Layer Massey, Essex are of this stone.

Confusingly, brown slatey-siltstones of Devonian age have also been quarried near Cataclews Point and they are sometimes referred to as Cataclews Stone in Church and other local guides.

Tuffs

Although it might be expected from a consideration of their genesis that volcanic igneous rocks would not provide stones suitable for building or for decoration, nevertheless, some have been used, particularly in those areas where other stones are not readily available. The glaringly white andesite tuff and lava known universally by the Peruvian name of Sillar, was used to build Arequipa, the 'White City' of Peru. Easy to work, the stone lends itself to elaborate carving as on the church of La Campagna in that city (*Figure 3.22*).

Tuff is the term used for consolidated fine-grained volcanic ash of whatever composition. The classification is on grain size, but it is possible to relate it to the original lava type, for example, andesitic tuff, or

Figure 3.22 Arequipa, the 'White City', Peru, is built substantially of a white andesite tuff, *sillar*. It may be easily carved as seen on the church of La Compagna. (Courtesy of Dr C. Welch)

(a)

(b)

Figure 3.23 (a) The eye-catching green-coloured altered volcanic ash from Hurdwick used for the Town Hall, Tavistock has, unusually, granite dressings (b)

Figure 3.24 Tuff is the material of the Etruscan necropolis of Cerveteri, near Rome. (Photo: John Ashurst)

hydraulic cement, which is a type of cement which sets quickly even under water and hence can be used for hydraulic works. It produces a compact and chemically resistant cement with a low setting temperature. Trass, because of its porous nature and light weight may be confused with pumice which was formed from a highly gaseous, rapidly cooled lava. Surprisingly sand suitable for building purposes is not readily available near Rome, Italy. Consequently a trachytic volcanic ash, was used. It is this material, named Pozzolana or Pozzuolana, which was crushed and mixed with lime to produce a hydraulic cement. When the cement is mixed with crushed tuff and travertine is added as aggregate, a cheap, strong and long lasting concrete was formed. The name Pozzolana is derived from the seaport Pozzuoli where a similar volcanic ash is also found (*Figure 3.25*). Compact varieties of the tuff were used as a

basaltic tuff. Commonly tuffs are layered and thus superficially may resemble sediments.

Tuffs have been rarely used in Great Britain. However, a tuff from Dennis Hill caps the buttress of the west Tower of St Petroc, Padstow. The best known example is the somewhat altered ash, green-coloured, and very free-working tuff from Hurdwick used to build much of Tavistock, Devon (*Figure 3.23*).

Tuffs occur on continental Europe, particularly in the Brohl valley and the Nette valley of the Eifel, Germany, and near Rome, Italy (*Figure 3.24*). That found in the Eifel is a grey to cream coloured, somewhat fragmented rock with much pumice-like dust of trachytic composition; that is, rich in silica and poor in dark minerals, with much feldspar. It is known locally as Trass and is of importance in that it is used as a building stone. It is also used, after being finely ground and added to lime, to give a

Figure 3.25 Layers of Pozzolana in cliffs near Tivoli, Rome may on casual inspection appear to be of sedimentary rocks because of an apparently bedded appearance. (Photo: John Ashurst)

Figure 3.26 A cut block of 'Peperino' at Marino, near Rome clearly shows dark coloured scoriae 'peppercorns', pieces of other pyroclastic material and markedly angular pieces of light coloured marble. (Photo: John Ashurst)

building stone in Rome. Another variety, Peperino, or Peparino Tufaceo is so named because it contains small dark pieces of pumice-like material (scoriae) fancifully thought to resemble peppercorns (*Figure 3.26*).

Many materials are pozzolanic. The term is used for any substance which although not itself cementitious, will combine with lime mortar to give hydraulic properties and strength. Little pozzolanic rock is found in Great Britain. Pozzalana recorded from France and from the Azores, Santorin Earth from Greece, and Tosca from Teneriffe, Canary Islands are a few other examples.

Volcanic glass

In certain conditions acid lavas which were poured out onto the Earth's surface cooled so rapidly that the lava did not crystallize. Instead it solidified to form a natural glass, obsidian. If it had cooled slowly at depth, a granite would have resulted. Very rarely is obsidian completely non-crystalline, very small incipient crystals are present. Volcanic glasses from past geological periods show devitrification, the very slow process of crystallization. The rock, when fresh, is shiny black, hard (H = 5-5½), brittle, with a marked conchoidal fracture giving extremely sharp edges. Although dark coloured, thin fragments are light and transparent. It was worked for use as an ornamental ('gem') stone by the ancient Greeks and the Romans. The stone is found in the Lipari Islands, Iceland, Central Anatolia, the USA and in great quantities in the Valley of Mexico. It appears not to have been used for building as flint was elsewhere but was prized as a material for arrowheads, sickle

blades, knives and so on. The Middle East imported the stone at least as early as 7000 BC from Central Anatolia. American Indians of every tribe worked spearheads and arrowheads from it. Small pieces shaped and worn for personal adornment are known as Apache Tears. Because of its glossy lustre it was fashioned into mirrors. Some examples up to 15 inches by 12 inches by 1 inch thick (38 cm × 31 cm × 2.5 cm) from the Valley of Mexico are in the Smithsonian (Natural History) Museum in Washington, DC, USA. Obsidian artifacts have been found in Great Britain and it would not be unexpected to discover the stone in an archaeological context.

Pumice is a highly vesicular, froth-like, volcanic glass, similar in composition to obsidian. In the Lipari Islands the bottom part of a lava flow may be of solid black obsidian passing up into white pumice in the upper part. Mostly the stone is ground to a fine powder for use as an abrasive, but it has also been used as a lightweight insulating material in building. Blocks have been found at archaeological sites in Great Britain.

Basalt

A prominent, and probably the commonest, rock in the world is basalt, a basic igneous volcanic rock, dark grey to black in colour. When fresh it weathers to a reddish colour. It is heavy, fine-grained, and composed mainly of plagioclase feldspar and usually augite. It often has grains of magnetite (metallic iron ore, Fe_3O_4). It may contain other minerals such as olivine and thus olivine-basalt. Normally fine-grained, the crystals cannot be distinguished by the unaided eye. It may be vesicular, and thus exhibit small vesicles where gas was trapped. It may also be scoriaceous or slaggy, and resemble clinker. Some exposures show vitreous basalt. Basalt occurs in flows of vast extent. The Deccan of India is a basalt plateau of over 500 000 square miles (1 300 000 square km). The Columbia Plateau, covering parts of Oregon, Washington State and Idaho, USA, covers some 200 000 square miles. The Antrim Plateau of Northern Ireland originally covered an area that stretched to Iceland and to Scotland (*Figure 3.27*).

Columnar jointing is a common feature in basalts. Because the columns could be easily taken apart, quarries between Bonn and Coblenz, Germany, were able to supply ready dressed columns that were merely put together again and extensively used for sea defence work notably in Holland. Watson[6] records that Blackpool, Clacton-on-Sea, Southend-on-Sea, Hartlepool and Hastings, all in Great Britain, used Renish basalt columns for a similar purpose. An undated advertisement issued by the London Basalt Stone Co. Ltd. states that Rhinish (*sic*) stone had been used in England since 1895.

Figure 3.27 Columnar jointing in basalt of the Giant's Causeway, Northern Ireland. The polygonal joint pattern is very marked when viewed from above. (Photo: John Ashurst)

Figure 3.29 The columnar structure of the basalt of the Giant's Causeway is neatly mimicked in its use for the public lavatories nearby. In 1986, these lavatories were under threat of demolition as being obtrusive in an environmentally sensitive area (courtesy of R.H. Roberts)

Figure 3.28 The sandstone (seen here) of Cologne Cathedral has weathered more than the basalt, the other main stone used in its construction. (Photo: John Ashurst)

Basalt from the Eifel area was also used to great effect, largely to build Cologne Cathedral (*Figure 3.28*). The Cathedral is built of many other types of stone including sandstones and limestones. The rock first used was a trachyte from Dranchenfels. It is the sandstone which is weathering badly and it is

planned to replace most of it with basalt which is still available and which is far more durable in today's polluted atmosphere[20].

The Mayen in the Eifel region is also the source of the widely known Niedermendig lava. It is markedly vesicular in texture and as a consequence it was much used, at least since about 1200 BC[21] for millstones, querns, and saddle-stones. The stone is frequently found not only in Great Britain but also across continental Europe on archaeological sites.

A dark, fine-grained basaltic rock from Mount Tmolus, Lydia is the original Touchstone. The earliest method of assaying gold was devised by the Lydians and known as trial by the Lydian Stone. Later other stones were used and they became known as Touch Stone or the Touch. The purity of the gold was judged by the colour of the streak left on the stone.

Recent research, however, indicates that the black pebbles known as 'Lydian Stone' from the River Tmolus are not a kind of black basalt. The River Tmolus was not known to ancient geographers. The river Pactolus which rises on Mt. Tmolus is believed to be in the Boz Dagh area of the Menderes massif, Turkey. There is no basalt in this massif. A full discussion is given in reference 22.

Although not widely used for building as its commonness would suggest, when used basalt has been used to great effect. The Giant's Causeway, Northern Ireland is renowned for the hexagonal pillars produced by the jointing system. This outstanding characteristic is neatly captured by the architecture of the public lavatories nearby which are built of basalt from the lava flow (*Figure 3.29*). Although this basalt flow covers a substantial area of Northern Ireland the rock has been little used. It is used locally for rubble-masonry and is seen occasionally roughly squared and dressed in Belfast. In the

Figure 3.30 Parliament Building, Reykjavik

Figure 3.31 The Cathedral, Funchal, Madeira, is of slightly differently coloured basalt blocks

Figure 3.32 Rough blocks of particularly scoriaceous basalt lava flow from nearby were used dramatically for the Holiday Inn, Grants, New Mexico. (Photos: John Ashurst)

Barm Valley to the west of the Antrim Plateau, however, it was used for houses which were commonly covered with stucco or colour washed. It was also well used in Gracehill.

Although Iceland, a country that developed architecturally from the turf-hut directly to reinforced concrete, is practically entirely of basalt and closely-related rocks, only one building is stone-built. This building illustrates the thesis that when man builds for status and to impress, he builds of stone, for it is the Parliament Building in Reykjavik (*Figure 3.30*).

The island of Madeira also illustrates this thesis. Most of the island is of basalt, which here and there yields blocks large enough for building. It may be seen used for the Cathedral, Funchal, for banks and public buildings, and occasionally for church statues. See *Figure 3.31*.

Basalt outcrops are found in the Galilee area of Israel and the stone has been used extensively in that area. The Church of the Primacy on the shore of the Sea of Galilee is mostly of basalt with light-coloured limestone dressings. The drab-grey dolomitic limestone of the Central Post Office, in Jerusalem, is heightened visually by the contrasting use of basalt.

Basalt covers extensive areas of the USA, and may be found used directly as a building stone as in the

Church at Flagstaff, Arizona; or in a modern manner as in the Holiday Inn Motel, Grants, New Mexico where a particularly scoriaceous vesicular stone from a basalt lava flow which forms much of the surrounding country has been used (*Figure 3.32*). The Devil's Post Pile, California shows a fine example of columnar jointing, comparable to the Giant's Causeway.

Igneous rocks were not always used in their natural state. An interestingly curious process used Rowley Rag, a doleritic rock capping Rowley Hill, Shropshire, England, which is similar to that of the Clee Hills. The stone was melted and then cast in moulds to produce steps, windowheads, slabs for tables and sideboards and mantlepieces. This reworked stone is believed to have been used in Handsworth and in Edgbaston. However, the process was not a financial success.

Classification

There are at least 400 named types of rock. Obviously it is not practical to place them all on the classification in *Table 2.1*. In any event a classification is an artificial construction in many respects. Rocks are placed into the classification on the basis

Figure 3.33 Basalt blocks with rusticated finish (with sandstone above) used for Parliament House, Melbourne, Australia. (Photo: John Ashurst)

Figure 3.34 Chamfered and rock faced rustication of basalt blocks is seen in the Treasury Building, Melbourne, Australia

of some characteristics which cannot be seen in a stone used in a building. It may not be possible, for instance, to determine some of the constituent minerals. For an accurate identification to be made it may be necessary for a specimen of the stone to be made into a thin section for microscopic examination. The descriptions in this and later sections should not be used as a basis for the determination of a stone in a building.

References

1. Hawkes, J.R. and Dangerfield, J. 'The Variscan Granites of south-west England: a progress report', *Proc. Ussher Soc.*, **4**, Pt. 2, 1978
2. Dangerfield, J. and Hawkes, J.R. 'The Variscan Granites of south-west England: additional information', *Proc. Ussher Soc.*, **5**, 116–120, 1981
3. Edmonds, E.A., McKeaven, M.C. and Williams, M. *British Regional Geology, South-West England.* 4th Edn., HMSO, London, 1975
4. Burton, M. (Ed.), 'Cornish Granite: traditional material for new contracts', *Stone Industries*, **14**, No. 10, 1979
5. Trinick, M., *Castle Drogo, Devon,* The National Trust, 1981
6. Watson, J., *British and Foreign Building Stones,* University Press, Cambridge, 1911
7. Elsden, J. and Howe, J.A., *The Stones of London,* Colliery Guardian Company Ltd., London, 1923
8. Ashurst, J. and Dimes, F.G., *Stone in Building,* The Architectural Press, London, 1977
9. Clifton-Taylor, A., *The Pattern of English Building.* Faber and Faber, London, 1972
10. Lawson, J., *Building Stones of Glasgow,* Geological Society of Glasgow, Glasgow, 1981
11. Robinson, E. and Bishop, C. 'Geological Walks around St Paul's', *Proc. Geol. Assoc.*, **91**, Pt 4, 1980
12. Whitlow, J.B., *Geology and Scenery in Ireland,* Penguin Books, Harmondsworth, 1974
13. Robinson, E. 'Geological walks around the City of London—Royal Exchange to Aldgate, *Proc. Geol. Assoc.*, **93**, Pt. 3, 1982
14. Anderson, J.G.C., 'The Granites of Scotland', *Special Reports on the Mineral Resources of Great Britain,* **32**, HMSO, Edinburgh, 1939
15. McLaren, M., *The Shell Guide to Scotland,* Ebury Press, London, 1967
16. Muir Wood, R. *On the Rocks: A Geology of Britain,* BBC, London 1978
17. Worth, R.N., *The Rocks and Minerals of Cornwall and Devon,* 54th Ann. Rep. R. Corn. Polytech. Soc., 1886
18. Watson, J., *British and Foreign Marbles and other Ornamental Stones,* University Press, Cambridge, 1906
19. North, F.J., *The Slates of Wales,* National Museum of Wales, Cardiff 1946
20. Seneviratne, G., 'Novel cement for Cologne Cathedral', *New Scientist*, 8 April 1976
21. Röder, (ed.), 'The Quern-quarries of Mayen in the Eifel', *Antiquity*, **29**, No. 114, 1955
22. Moore, D.T. and Oddy, W.A., 'Touchstones: Some aspects of their Nomenclature, Petrography and Provenance', *J. of Archaeological Science*, **12**, 59–80, 1985

4

Sedimentary rocks

Francis G. Dimes

Introduction

Igneous rocks, it has been estimated, form about 25 per cent of the exposed surface of the Earth's crust but occupy about 90 per cent of the volume. Sedimentary rocks, in contrast, form about 75 per cent of the surface, but only 5 to 10 per cent of its volume. Sedimentary rocks thus cover extensive tracts of the surface of the continents. Argillaceous rocks are by far the most abundant sedimentary rocks, occupying about 45 per cent of the area, with sandstones forming about 30 per cent and limestones about 28 per cent of the surface. It is not surprising, then, to find that sedimentary rocks have been widely used for building and decoration and that sandstones and limestones are the predominant rock types used.

Sandstone

A sandstone, by definition, is a rock in which the dominant mineral grain is quartz between 2 to 0.07 mm in diameter. It is formed by the lithification of a sand made up predominantly of rounded quartz grains. The word sand is commonly used to indicate a number of materials. The grains forming the beach at the sea, river or lake side are popularly referred to as sand regardless of their nature. However, a sand made up of the broken fragments of shells would be classified as a limestone if lithified. Sands made up of grains of the mineral zircon, volcanic ash or corundum are known. Coral sands are common in some parts of the world. Olivine sands are found in the Bay of Naples.

Commonly the grains have been naturally cemented, and the cementing material is deposited on the surface of the grains where it partially or completely fills the interstices between the grains. If

Figure 4.1 The large stone standing on the Hanger, Selborne, Hampshire is a quartzite. Such blocks, scattered across southern England are known as sarsens.

the cementing material is quartz and the original sand is thoroughly indurated with it, a hard, tough, resistant rock termed a *quartzite* is formed. The well-known sarsens of southern England provide an outstanding example of quartzite (*Figure 4.1*). There are quartzites which are igneous and metamorphic in origin (see *Tables 2.1, 2.2, 2.3*). The term quartzite describes the type of rock. It should not be used to imply a mode of origin.

Calcite is a common cementing material and may give a crystalline texture and appearance. If sufficient calcareous cement is present the rock is known as a *calcareous sandstone.* Many sandstones are cemented by one or more of the iron compounds, normally the red iron oxides or the brown iron hydrates, or both. They are known as *ferruginous sandstones.* Usually these are light red to deep

Figure 4.2 Strongly iron-cemented sandstone–carstone–resists weathering to form the Devil's Jumps, Surrey

Figure 4.3 A sandstone in which the grains are angular is known as a grit or gritstone. They may be massively bedded as in Bramley Fall Quarry near Leeds in the Millstone Grit

brown in colour. The colour is caused by the nature and amount of iron cement present. When iron minerals are present in substantial amount, the sandstone may be called *carstone* (*Figure 4.2*). The mineral gypsum is a less frequent cementing medium. The mineral dolomite is more commonly found as discrete grains and not as a cement. When it is present either as cement or as grains, the stone is termed a *dolomitic sandstone*. Mansfield Stone, of Permian age, from Mansfield, Nottinghamshire, provides a matchless example of a dolomitic sandstone.

Rarely are sandstones pure, that is made up solely of quartz grains with silica cement. Other mineral grains, as distinct from the mineral cementing medium, are present in greater or lesser amounts. Feldspar, commonly in a partially chemically decomposed state and derived from a disintegrated granite, may be present in considerable amounts. If it makes up a third or more of the rock the name *arkose* is used. Most arkoses are terrestrial deposits. Flakes of mica lead to a *micaceous sandstone*. Grains of the mineral glauconite (a complex potassium, iron silicate, $K(Fe, Mg, A1)_2(Si_4O_{10})(OH)_2$), present as small, rounded, green-coloured aggregates give the rock, particularly when wet, a green cast. The rock is termed a *greensand* when glauconite is present in any quantity. Other minerals such as gypsum and barytes may rarely be the cementing medium but may locally be present in noticeable amounts. Clayey material occurs in some sandstones and, if present in quantity, is not a desirable constituent because *argillaceous sandstones* are susceptible to frost action. All these cementing materials were carried into the original loose, incoherent sand by circulating waters. A sandstone is produced by deposition of material from solution to bind the sand grains together.

In some sandstones most of the individual grains are well sorted, that is they are all about the same size and are rounded. This is a reflection of the mechanical erosion which they have suffered. Larger pebbles may occur. If the grains are angular the rock is then termed a *grit* or *gritstone*, and it is normally, but not necessarily, coarse-grained (*Figure 4.3*).

The term *gritstone* has no unique definition. It is often used for a rock of any composition with grain size between 0.5 to 1.0 mm. The mica flakes in a micaceous sandstone are commonly concentrated along bedding planes with their long axes aligned parallel to the bedding. The rock is *fissile* and will readily split along these planes. If the bedding planes are closely spaced, splitting produces a *flagstone*. The name is believed to be derived from flaggstone, a name given by the Vikings to the flat stone which they found in Scotland. Some flagstones owe their fissility to thin layers of clay material. Commonly flagstones show ripple marks and suncracks. Sandstones may contain fossils.

Local concentrations of mineral matter, commonly but not always the same as the cementing material, may form around a centre or nucleus after the sediment was deposited. Such growths are known as concretions and result from the solution of material at one point and its redeposition elsewhere. In form concretions may be quite irregular but they are commonly found to be flattened ovals in section. They often lie along the direction of the bedding because water travels more easily along the bedding planes. If concretions are hollow, they may be internally lined with crystals. These types of concretions are called *geodes*. Concretions may also be called *doggers*. Frequently they contain fossils, which originally acted as the nucleus which triggered the deposition of mineral matter. They are a similar colour to the host rock but usually of a deeper shade. Local quarrymen's names have been given to these concretions. For example, ferruginous concretions in the Huddersfield White Rock, a sandstone of the

Millstone Grit Series, are known as Mare Balls. The name Galliard Balls is given to similar concretions found in the Woodkirk Quarry, from which a sandstone of Upper Carboniferous (Coal Measures) age is taken.

Examples and uses

Most sandstone nowadays is crushed for aggregate[1]. In the past it was widely used for building stone and pavements and is still used extensively today where it contributes greatly to the character of many buildings, particularly in the northern parts of Great Britain. Sandstones occur commonly throughout the geological column and most are used locally.

Precambrian to Silurian sandstones

The Precambrian age Torridonian Sandstone is an arkose in places and adds dramatically to the scenery of north-west Scotland. It has been used, for example, in the walls of Iona Abbey, Argyll. Until the middle of the nineteenth century, nearly all building in Scotland was of sandstone. Ordovician age sandstones were worked for flagstones near Pomeroy,

Figure 4.4 The fissile nature of the Hoar Edge Grit, Ordovician, enables it to be split into slabs for use as tile stones as on the remarkable roof of the Priors Lodge, Much Wenlock, Shropshire

Northern Ireland. Sandstones of Precambrian, Cambrian, Ordovician and Silurian age, however, have not been used generally outside the areas in which they occur. Even so, their use occasionally is eye-catching and thus more widely remarked. One example is the purple-coloured feldspathic Caerbwdi Sandstone of Cambrian age which gives the Cathedral of St Davids, Dyfed its most unusual purple appearance. The Ordovician age Hoar Edge Grit, named from Hoar Edge near Cardington, Shropshire, is somewhat coarse in grain, shelly and slightly calcareous. It was used not only as slabs (tilestones) on the Prior's Lodge, Much Wenlock (*see Figure 4.4*), but also as blocks for the Church at Church Stretton. It is one example of a sandstone that is suitable stone for both flagging and block stone.

Devonian sandstones

The Devonian is the oldest period to have yielded sandstones that were used on a large scale outside the areas where they crop out. The Old Red Sandstone is the name given to a series of rocks deposited mostly on the land surface; it is the continental facies of the Devonian. They consist of red, brown, chocolate and white sandstones, all with beds of coarse quartzitic conglomerates, thick beds of usually red-coloured marl and some impure limestones. They represent deposits laid down in a semi-arid climate in inter-montane environments and this led to distinctively different rocks in the areas where they crop out.

Over a large part of Hereford and Worcester, Gwent, Powys and Shropshire sandstones of Old Red Sandstone age are found. They have been extensively used. Because so much was used in and around the city of Hereford the general name Hereford Stone was given to them. Unfortunately that name gives no indication of closer provenance within this area. The massive tower (1300) and some of the remainder of Hereford Cathedral is of local Old Red Sandstone. However, the Cathedral was largely restored in Alton Mottled Stone, a sandstone from the New Red Sandstone, from Staffordshire in 1901–1905. The famous and magnificent Kilpeck Church, Hereford, with its spectacular south doorway is of Old Red Sandstone quarried from nearby (*Figure 4.5*).

Some beds of the series are a remarkable quartz conglomerate containing grey, yellow and red pebbles with pieces of decomposed igneous rock and jasper. They were the foundation of a massive millstone industry along the southern Welsh borders, and millstones of this type are of common occurrence at archaeological sites. In some areas beds of grey, green, yellow and reddish-brown micaceous flaggy sandstones, known geologically as The Tilestones, were once used for roofing in Gwent and in Hereford. They were normally laid, because of their weight, at a low pitch, sometimes down to 30°[2]. Red-brown and grey, compact, fine-grained stone, some of it flaggy and some thickly bedded, was at one time quarried near Hay-on-Wye, Powys. It was used for tilestones and buildings and was known as Racephas Stone. Red Wilderness Stone, which is a red-brown coloured, fine-grained and slightly micaceous sandstone from near Mitcheldean, in the Forest of Dean,

Figure 4.5 The Old Red Sandstone from nearby was used for Kilpeck Church, Hereford, with its spectacular south doorway renowned for the tympanum

Figure 4.6 Stone taken from many quarries in the Old Red Sandstone such as the Red Wilderness Quarry near Mitcheldean, Gloucestershire (seen here), was widely used in the Welsh Borderlands, and is commonly known as Hereford stone

Gloucestershire, was extensively quarried and used for many churches and houses in that area (*Figure 4.6*). Because of its reputation as a durable stone for sills, steps and flags it was used in the Cathedral in Liverpool (1908) and is recorded as used in Harrow School, Middlesex. Red sandstones of Old Red Sandstone age also have been quarried in Dyfed, Wales and near Edinburgh, Nairn and Elgin, Scotland. Near Edinburgh, the Old Red Sandstone was quarried for much useful building stone. The Craigmillar Quarries are the best known. The stone is purplish-white and cream in colour and is tough and markedly pebbly. It was used for Heriot Hospital (seventeenth century), Leith Docks (1876) and for kerbs. In many buildings in Edinburgh it has probably been confused with the much more widely used Carboniferous sandstones. Dull red, reddish-brown to bright red stone, with sporadic patches of feldspar grains and mica flakes occurs around Carmyllie, Angus. Flaggy sandstones and flagstones were once worked on a large scale. The flagstones are the source of the renowned Arbroath pavement. At one time, however, the most important stones were those taken from the Caithness Flagstone Series. Flagstone groups within this series provided pale greenish-white and pale ochre to blue, flaggy sandstones which were used in huge quantities for paving. The best flags were taken from finely fissile calcareous sandstone seams or beds, locally known as 'fouls', around Thurso. Caithness Flags were used extensively in London where some may still be seen. They were also used

...all over the world. Baron Liebig's great establishment on the River Plate, in South America, for the manufacture of his well-known meat extract, is floored throughout with Caithness flags.[3]

They are, in general, a compact, tough blue-grey stone. Large flags may still be seen vertically set into the ground as fences between fields in Caithness. The flags may contain fossil fish scales and fragments of fish.

Probably the most often seen, although certainly not the most widely recognized, piece of Old Red Sandstone is The Coronation Stone, the Stone of Destiny or Stone of Scone, in Westminster Abbey, London. This rectangular mass of coarse-grained, reddish-grey sandstone contains small pebbles of porphyrite or andesite about the size of a pea. There is little doubt geologically that the stone was quarried near the ancient seat of the Pictish monarchy at Scone, Perthshire. It was once thought that because the stone was once kept at Dunstaffnage Castle, Argyll, it was quarried near there. The rocks in that area, however, are quite dissimilar from that of the Stone. It is thought that the stone originally may have been a portable altar. The other Coronation Stone at Kingston-upon-Thames, Surrey is of sarsen (a quartzite).

The Eday Sandstone of the Orkney Islands, a thick sequence of yellow and of red sandstone was quarried at Fersness, Eday and used as building stone in Kirkwall and elsewhere on the Islands. It was used to build St Magnus Cathedral, which has a marked contrasting red-yellow look. The fine, yellow ('white') freestone was much prized.

Old Red Sandstone is also found in Ireland. The main outcrop is in the south-west of the island. Red-brown and yellow sandstones were used for much building and are probably seen to best effect in Tralee, Kerry.

Carboniferous sandstones

The Carboniferous System is one of the most important sources of sandstones in Great Britain. The system has been split geologically into three major divisions:

Coal Measures $\left.\right\}$ (Upper Carboniferous)
Millstone Grit
Carboniferous Limestone (Lower Carboniferous)

These major divisions are split into many subdivisions. The index of a recent geological map and recent literature shows a more complicated division. The divisions do not always refer to rocks laid down at the same time, but they are retained here for ease of explanation. It is possible to have many different types of rock laid down at the same *time* depending on geographical and environmental conditions. However, an apparently continuous bed of the same type of rock which extends across many square kilometres may have been deposited over a considerable period of time.

All the main divisions yield sandstones of major importance. The Carboniferous Limestone division, in southern England and the Midlands is predominantly a limestone. However, when traced northwards, into northern England and Scotland it is found to contain an increasing number of sandstone beds especially in its upper part. This has led to the apparent anomaly that an enquirer may be told that a piece of sandstone is from the Carboniferous Limestone.

Lower Carboniferous sandstones

Sandstone beds up to 50 feet (15 m) thick occur in Yorkshire (the Yoredale Series). They vary greatly from one place to another but have provided important building stones from many small quarries close to most villages in the northern Pennines. Locally, flagstones with surprisingly smooth surfaces were produced to provide tilestones.

Most building stones have been used near where they were quarried, as can easily be seen from the comparison of a geological map with a survey of the fabric of farms, field walls, and the older parts of villages and towns.[4]

In Northumberland sandstones of the Yoredale Series have a far wider significance and helped to make that county, perhaps more than any other, a county of sandstone buildings. The change in the proportion of limestone to mudstone and sandstone which begins in Yorkshire becomes more marked in Northumberland. In Northumberland there is considerably more sandstone present and the name Carboniferous Limestone is really a misnomer. A particularly important sandstone is the Fell Sandstone. It consists of pink-coloured, false-bedded and coarse-grained sandstones which are up to 1000 feet (300 m) thick. Another horizon in the upper part of the Carboniferous Limestone of Northumberland yielded flagstones, known as the Slate Sills, which were widely used as tilestones throughout the county.

Prudham Quarry at Fourstones, near Hexham, Northumberland, supplied a cream to brown, coarse-grained, slightly micaceous stone which is perhaps the best known of the Northumberland sandstones. The stone is famous because of its use for the Roman wall. In its heyday the quarry 'employed possibly 200 men'[5]. The stone was used extensively in Tyneside as well as in Newcastle-upon-Tyne, where it was used in the central railway station (1850) and the General Post Office (1870). The stone was even exported to London and to Edinburgh, a city with its own ample supply of fine sandstone. In Edinburgh it may be seen in houses in Craighall Gardens (1885–1890) and in Heriot Watt College (1886). It was used much more recently in the new office block above the bus station, St Andrews Square (*Figure 4.7*). The extensions to University College (1882–1883), London were also carried out in this stone.

Figure 4.7 Prudham stone, a sandstone from the Carboniferous Limestone series, was used for the Norwich Union Building, St Andrew Square, Edinburgh (courtesy of R.W. Gransbury)

Stone from Doddington Quarry, near Wooler, Northumberland, is no less well known. Fine-grained, and pink- to purple-grey, it is distinguished by being composed of up to 97 per cent quartz grains with the mineral haematite (iron oxide, Fe_2O_3) giving the gentle pink colour. When in green condition it is soft on extraction and easy to work (see also the account in reference 5).

Restoration of St Andrew's Church (1894), is in this stone. It was widely used elsewhere in Newcastle-upon-Tyne (*Figure 4.8*) and was also sent

Figure 4.8 Doddington Stone forms the wall in the school of Architecture, Newcastle University, Tyne and Weir. Note rising salt soiling. This wall was very poorly spun clean

to Edinburgh where it was used in St Giles Industrial Museum (1897) Observatory and the Wesleyan Hall, for example. It was also used for the Cathedral at Dunblane, Perthshire. It has been used recently (1984) for a building development in Lovett Lane, London. Buff-coloured Blaxter Stone from north-west of Newcastle-upon-Tyne is also used in this development. These stones make an interesting addition to the list of stones used in London, which otherwise has used little sandstone.

Dozens of quarries operated in the past and many are still working today[5]. Another local stone of interest is the Black Pasture Stone from quarries near Chollerford, Northumberland. Buff coloured with brown specks, this tough, fine-grained sandstone was used in the Roman Wall, for buildings in Newcastle-upon-Tyne and for some restorations at Durham Cathedral. It was also used for the Mitchell Library (1907) in Glasgow although Glasgow has an ample supply of local stone.

In the Midland Valley of Scotland the Carboniferous Limestone is divided into a Calciferous Sandstone Series overlain by a Carboniferous Limestone Series. Major sandstone horizons are found in each member and they are mostly light coloured and generally fine textured. Some have been extensively quarried and used.

If Aberdeen is the granite city then Edinburgh is the sandstone city, the 'Grey Metropolis of the North'. Undoubtedly the best known is Craigleith Stone from a quarry which, when originally opened, was outside Edinburgh but now is surrounded by the city. It was the stone used for nearly all building in Edinburgh. It is taken from the Calciferous Sandstone Series and is tough, tight and fine-grained. It is drab coloured, slightly calcareous and virtually unaffected by the weather. Because so much of Edinburgh was built of local sandstones the city has an entity not seen in most other cities. Craigleith Quarry is renowned for supplying large blocks.

In 1823, there was excavated a stone of such dimensions and weight as to be without parallel in ancient or modern times. In length it was upwards of 136 feet, averaging 20 feet in breadth and its computed weight was 1500 tons. It was longitudinal cut from a stratum of very fine rock. The greater part of it was conveyed to the Calton Hill, where it now forms the architrave of the National Monument, and the rest was sent by sea to Buckingham Palace.[6]

The Register House (1776–1826) in Edinburgh, together with St Andrews Church (1785) and the Old University (1789–1834) provide local examples of its use. The stone was also used for the floors and stairs of The British Museum, London (1828) and the old Bank of England, London (1770). Undoubtedly the most spectacularly visible use of Craigleith Stone is for the statue of Nelson on top of his column made of granite from Fogginator, Dartmoor which stands in the middle of Trafalgar Square, London (*Figure 4.9*). Some distance from Craigleith, a quarry at Barnton Park also supplied 'Craigleith Stone' which was used for the now demolished Imperial Institute, London (1880). However Barton Park Quarry was better known for a stone named Blue Liver Rock which is tough, dark blue-grey and medium-grained. Hailes Stone is also widely used in Edinburgh. Hailes Quarry supplied a white, a blue (blue grey, grey) and a red (pink) stone which were noted for their regular laminations caused by the amount of mica flakes the rock contains. Because of its strength the stone was highly regarded for foundations. It was used as a building stone for Dalry School (grey, 1876), Plew-lands Villa (blue, 1878), Red House, Cluny Gardens (red, 1880), Free Church Assembly Hall (blue, 1846), and the Royal Infirmary (pink, 1875), all in Edinburgh. It was recorded that 'Large quantities are now being exported to London'[7] but verified examples of its use there have not been found.

Glasgow is built on, and mostly surrounded by, the Upper Limestone Group of Upper Carboniferous age, which contains beds of sandstone. These provided much of the stone first used to build the city, although the sites from which the stone was taken

engineering works. It has been used from the earliest times; many castles, cathedrals, churches and houses were built of stone from this formation.

Geologically the Millstone Grit of northern England comprises a series of gritstones and sandstones interbedded with shales and mudstones. A number of grit groups are distinguished; the Silsden Moor Grit, the Kinderscout Grit, and the Rough Rock are important members. In the main the quartz grains comprising the grit groups are markedly angular in form. Because of this the stones were eminently suitable for use as millstones; hence the name for the formation. Millstone Edge is a well-known locality in south-west Yorkshire. In many places the Millstone

Figure 4.9 Craigleith stone, used here for the statue of Nelson, Trafalgar Square, is one of the few sandstones used in the capital. The stone has weathered very little. (Courtesy of Mrs C. Bennett)

Figure 4.10 A millstone made of stone from the Millstone Grit, used because of the angular grains of quartz, marks the boundary to the Peak National Park, Derbyshire

are now a matter of geological conjecture. Important quarries still remain in use. The best known is probably that supplying Newbigging Stone from Burnt Island. The stone is renowned for its use for Gothenberg Cathedral, Sweden. Hopetown in West Lothian is a currently active quarry in the Calciferous Sandstone Series. Important in historical context is Giffnock Stone (Giffneuk) from near Glasgow. This is a pale grey, fine-grained stone with a reputation of not weathering well in a smoky atmosphere. It was used widely in Glasgow. The stone was exported to Ireland and may be seen in the Customs House, the Assembly Buildings and elsewhere in Belfast.

Upper Carboniferous (Millstone Grit) sandstones

The Millstone Grit must be reckoned as possibly the most prolific source of sandstones in Great Britain, and architecturally, probably the most important. Sandstones from the division have an unparalleled reputation for durability and for use in large civil

Grit is remarkably fissile and was used, mostly locally, for flagstones and tilestones. Characteristically, the Millstone Grit is current-bedded. This is the result of the deposits being laid down under deltaic conditions. In some areas the stone contains a lot of feldspar and is lithologically an arkose.

All the grit groups have been used locally in buildings. Usually the fissile beds were used as tilestones, but some stones taken from the formation obtained a much wider repute. Darley Dale, sometimes known as Stancliffe Stone, which was taken from a number of quarries near Matlock, Derbyshire is generally regarded as the classic stone. Pale brown in colour, compact and close-grained, normally with darker brown ferruginous specks, feldspathic, with occasional flakes of mica, it was widely used because of its strength and toughness. The capitals of the columns of the canopy of the Albert Memorial are of the stone which was noted as 'perhaps the finest building stone in the kingdom'. King's College Hospital (in part), London is another example of its use. St George's Hall, Liverpool, was built from Stancliffe Stone which was taken from Stancliffe Quarries in the Dale. Darley Dale Stone was used by Henry Moore for his dramatic *Three Standing Figures* (1947) which stood in Battersea Park, London. Hall Dale Stone from the same area is a pink-coloured, fine-grained stone which was used for the Manchester Town Hall extension in 1938.

Whatstandwell Stone, used by George Stevenson for much of his railway construction, is another stone from the Dales. Coarser-grained than most and pinkish in colour, it was used for the original Euston Railway Station, London. It is intimately known by a certain proportion of the population because it was used for the prison at Leicester (1828) as well as the prison at Birmingham (1849).

Birchover Gritstone, quarried at Stanton Moor, Derbyshire, is also from the Dales. It is medium-grained and pink to yellowish-buff in colour. Its height-on-bed in the quarry may reach 9 feet (2.7 m). It has been extensively used, notably for public works in Lancashire, bridges over the Birmingham to Preston motorway, the Royal Insurance Building, Kircaldy, the Newport Civic Centre, and for many churches.

Bramley Fall Stone, the name of another of the classic stones, was used at one time as a general name for a number of stones wrought from an area north-west of Leeds, Yorkshire. The stone was taken from the Rough Rock Grit group, which is made up of the Rough Rock Flags, also known as Greetland Stone at Greetland, near Halifax, Yorkshire, overlain by the Rough Rock Grit. In general terms the Rough Rock Flags are a variable succession of generally fine-grained flagstone and sandstone beds with thin shale partings. The Rough Rock itself is mainly a massive, current-bedded gritstone which is often pebbly. The pebbles are chiefly quartz and are often of large size, up to 2 inches (0.8 cm) or more. Because of its great strength, its massive bedding and the large-sized blocks which could be obtained, it was used extensively for engineering works. Millwall Docks, London is one example. The Town Hall (1853–1858) and the Roman Catholic Cathedral (1904) Leeds, abutments of Southwark Bridge, London (Rennie, 1819), and the plinth course of the town bridge, Stamford, Lincolnshire, which has local limestone overlying, are other examples. Its best known use, however, must be for the Euston Arch, London, unpardonably now demolished.

Spinkwell Stone, from an horizon named the Gaisby Rock, is quarried near Bradford, Yorkshire and is nowadays known as Bolton Wood Stone. The Gaisby Rock provides excellent flagstones and building stone. Overall it is grey in colour. It is compact and fine-grained, with occasional flakes of white muscovite mica. It was used for the Town Hall, Manchester (1868–1876).

Huddersfield, Yorkshire, and the villages around are mostly of Crosland Hill Stone, a general name for stones taken from a number of quarries on Crosland Moor, above the town. The stone, taken from the Rough Rock member of the Millstone Grit, is brown-grey in colour, and fine-grained with occasional quartz pebbles, which may be of some size.

The stone was used for the majority of public buildings in the area around Huddersfield. It is stated to have weathered well except in Huddersfield Parish Church 'due to the frequent error of laying the stone oblique to the bedding planes'[8]. Known nowadays as Wellfield Stone or Johnsons Wellfield (*Figure 4.11*), recent use includes the University of

(a)

(b)

Figure 4.11 Massively bedded Rough Rock of the Millstone Grit taken from Johnsons Wellfield Quarry, Crosland Moor, near Huddersfield (a) is guillotined into regular sized blocks which may be easily laid for walls (b)

Edinburgh, Oldham Civic Centre, the restoration of entrance portico, Assize Court, York, the Free Trade Hall, Manchester, and the New Civic Buildings, Newcastle. This stone is now often used in Edinburgh for new works and as a replacement for Craigleith and Hailes Stones, which are no longer available. Waterholes Grit Stone, quarried a short distance from Wellfield Stone, is similar in character.

The Millstone Grit becomes less important for building stone when traced northwards. In central Scotland it contains very few beds of gritstone, but does produce important fireclays. In North Wales the Cefn-y-fedw sandstone of Millstone Grit age has been used locally for building. It was not more widely used because it was remote from transport. Stone quarried at Minera, west of Wrexham was used for the Bank of New Zealand, Queen Victoria Street, London (*Figure 4.12*). This is an interesting use in a city that has used little sandstone. Millstone Grit has been used locally in Ireland for flagstones.

Upper Carboniferous (Coal Measures) sandstones
Despite the name, only about five per cent of the thickness of the Coal Measures is coal, and it has

Figure 4.12 The Cefn-y-fedu sandstone of Millstone Grit age was uniquely used in London for the Bank of New Zealand, Queen Victoria Street. The pattern of dirt soiling is typical of coarse-grained sandstone

yielded some important sandstones. Many of the sandstones from the Coal Measures have layers of mica flakes and are so highly laminated that they may be split into slabs an inch (2.5 cm) or less thick. They occur particularly in the southern part of Yorkshire (the former West Riding) and the general name York Stone has been given to them. Unfortunately this name is also widely used for almost any sandstone coming from Yorkshire.

The Elland Flags undoubtedly were, and still are, the most important of the York Stones. The Flags form a well-marked, bold escarpment running from Mountain, through Pule Hill, Stump Cross, Bank Top near Halifax, Elland Edge itself, to Cowcliffe, Sheepridge and the Colne Valley. They have been extensively quarried and, where massive, were occasionally mined for building stone. Where the stone is flaggy it is used for paving and tilestones. The flagstone may be split into slabs from one to fifteen inches (2.5–38 cm) thick and many feet in length. The Elland Flags were wrought in the area around Northowram, Southowram, Hipperholme, and Brighouse. They are still worked extensively around Halifax, Huddersfield and Leeds. The Elland Flags are known by other names in other parts of the country; for example they are also called Brincliffe Edge Rock and Greenmore Rock. They are known as the Rockdale or Upholland Flags in Lancashire.

The flags have been extensively used for paving; at one time much of London's pavements were made of them. The City of London Corporation still makes extensive use of York Stone. It 'is considered to be the near ideal paving material as it is strong, colourful and remains non-slip throughout its long life'[9].

The paving of the floor of Westminster Hall and that outside the York City Art Gallery (*Figure 4.13*) are considered typical examples. York Stone was recently used for a paved floor at the mews conversion at the Royal Crescent Hotel, Bath (1983). The stone is also used for kerbs, as at Colchester, Essex. Although, as Clifton-Taylor[10] pointed out, the Elland Flags are not suitable for roofing because they hold so much moisture, they were used on the roof of the Gatehouse at Kirklees near Brighouse. The Elland Flags have also been used on a smaller scale for domestic building. For example, several houses in Ryder Gardens, Leeds, Yorkshire are partly built of the Elland Flags. The Grenoside Sandstone from the Sheffield area is probably the equivalent of the Elland Flags.

The importance of the York Stone flags should not overshadow the many dimension stones taken from the Coal Measures. Bolton Wood Stone was used for the Town Halls of Bradford and Leeds. Woodkirk Stone, from Morley near Leeds, Yorkshire supplies a fawn- to brown-coloured, massive, fine-grained sandstone which has been used for the Halifax Building Society's new headquarters building in Halifax,

(a)

(b)

Figure 4.13 York stone has been widely used for paving because of its durability and non-slip surface. In the forecourt of the City Art Gallery, York some slabs have been shot frame sawn, a process which it is claimed improves the non-slip quality

Yorkshire and for the Sheraton Inn, Stockton-on-Tees. The Royal Bank of Scotland, Falkirk and Beaver House, Manchester are two other examples of its recent use.

In the county of Durham, sandstones from the Coal Measures are of prime importance. They crop out over much of the county. Dunhouse Stone, quarried near Darlington is fine- to medium-grained and brown in colour. For many years it has been used for restorations to the magnificent Durham Cathedral (*Figure 4.14*). In the original cathedral building many other Coal Measure sandstones were used[11].

Figure 4.14 Most of the structure of Durham Cathedral is of Coal Measures sandstone from the Kepier Quarry but a couple of miles away to the north-east. Black Pasture sandstone (see p.66) and for the last fifty years Dunhouse Stone have been used for repairs and restoration.

Dunhouse Stone is renowned for supplying large blocks of stone and it was also used for Bowes Museum, Barnard Castle, and for the Town Hall, Middlesborough, Yorkshire. The Technical College, Sunderland, Durham is a more recent example of its use. It was also the stone chosen for restoration work at Castle Howard, Yorkshire, and for Birmingham Cathedral. Stainton Stone, from near Barnard Castle,

is fine- to medium-grained and creamy-brown in colour. It is eye-catching because of the localized large swirling streaks due to concentrations of iron-oxide minerals which are otherwise seen as specks generally spread across the surfaces. It was used for the extension to the Bank of England, Glasgow.

Auchinlea Stone, from Cleland, Lanarkshire is an example of a sandstone from the Coal Measures of Scotland. White-cream in colour, often with small, brown specks and medium- to coarse-grained, it was easily wrought but toughened considerably on exposure to the air. Its use is recorded in South Buchanan Street, Roseburn Terrace and Trinity in Edinburgh, as well as in Glasgow and in Carlisle.

The Pennant Sandstone is of Coal Measures age but has considerably different characteristics. It forms much of the South Wales coalfield and is also found in the Forest of Dean, Gloucestershire, and in Monmouth. It is dark-grey, blue-grey or pinkish-grey in colour and generally massively bedded, micaceous and feldspathic. The sandstone or grit grades in places to an arkose. Much of the series is false-bedded and in some areas it is conglomeratic.

Stone from the Pennant Sandstone or Grit is hard and durable. It has been extensively used for building. However, because the stone tends to weather to a rusty-brown colour it contributes, especially when used with dark-coloured slate roofs, to the drab and depressing look of the towns and villages in the South Wales valleys. The stone has been used on a large scale in Bristol, where it is commonly used as a plinth, with limestone above; Bristol Gaol may be cited as an example. Records indicate it was used in London[3,12], for example in the New Sessions House, Old Bailey. It was also used in Cardiff and South Wales generally. Because of its strength and durability Pennant Stone was widely

Figure 4.15 Bwlch-y-Maen farm, Craig-yr-Allt, Glamorgan, built of locally quarried Pennant Grit, is in part tallow white-washed

Figure 4.16 The gigantic sham of Castell Coch, Glamorgan, is built in Pennant Grit

used for civil engineering works such as the New Dock, Avonmouth (Forest of Dean), Cardiff New Pier (Forest of Dean), Bideford Bridge (Pennant), and the bridge at Littleton, Middlesex (Forest of Dean). The use of Pennant Stone for Caerphilly, the biggest castle of its type, and for the rebuilt Castell Coch, Glamorgan—that 'gigantic sham, a costly folly'— illustrate its use for monuments ancient and modern (*Figure 4.16*).

In North Wales, the Cefn Rock of Coal Measures age was the most important building stone in the area. It was extensively quarried, from its outcrop at Cefn-mawr and at Broughton, Clwyd since at least mediaeval times. The stone is also known as the Bryn-teg Freestone from the quarries of that name. Light-drab to buff-coloured, fine- to medium-grained with some interstitial decomposed feldspar, stone from the Cefn Rock is recorded as being used for the Parish Church, Wrexham, Ruabon Church (thirteenth century), the Free Library and Museum (1859), the Walker Gallery (1877), Liverpool, and for the 'new' University College, Bangor (1908).

Suitable sandstones of Coal Measure age were commonly used on a very restricted local scale. Stone taken from a bed known as the Big Flint Rock was used for railway bridges on the Wellington to Colebrookedale line, Shropshire. The stone is brown to greyish-white in colour and massive and false-bedded. This stone was used for the stone piers of Ironbridge.

Permian and Triassic sandstones

It may be argued that the Carboniferous System, and particularly the Millstone Grit and the Coal Measures, are the major sources of sandstone in Great Britain. This however, ignores the many famous sandstones from the next two younger Systems, the Permian and the Triassic. In their own areas and, indeed, outside, they have had just as marked and as dramatic an effect because they are mostly red in colour. Stones taken from the Permian and Triassic red sandstones have many points of similarity, as do the beds from which they are taken. Permian and Triassic sandstones may be found grouped together as the New Red Sandstone because the allocation of some of the beds to one System or to the other is the subject of geological discussion.

Collyhurst Stone, from Collyhurst a north-east Manchester suburb, is Permian in age and was the chief building stone of early Manchester[13]. In some places this sandstone is well known for its abrupt changes in thickness and reaches 800 feet (244 m) thick. It may be brecciated. It has well-rounded, not very well cemented quartz grains which have a distinctive purplish-red colour due to a coating of iron oxide. The stone shows marked dune-bedding. St Ann's Church, St Ann's Square, Manchester (1709) displays the character of the stone well. A great deal of other sandstone has been used for later restoration of this church and 'the mixture is unique and fascinating'[13].

Mansfield Stone, from Mansfield, Nottinghamshire, has been the source of confusion in nomenclature. It is a fine-grained dolomitic sandstone of Permian age consisting of angular and sub-angular quartz grains cemented by dolomite and, to a lesser extent,

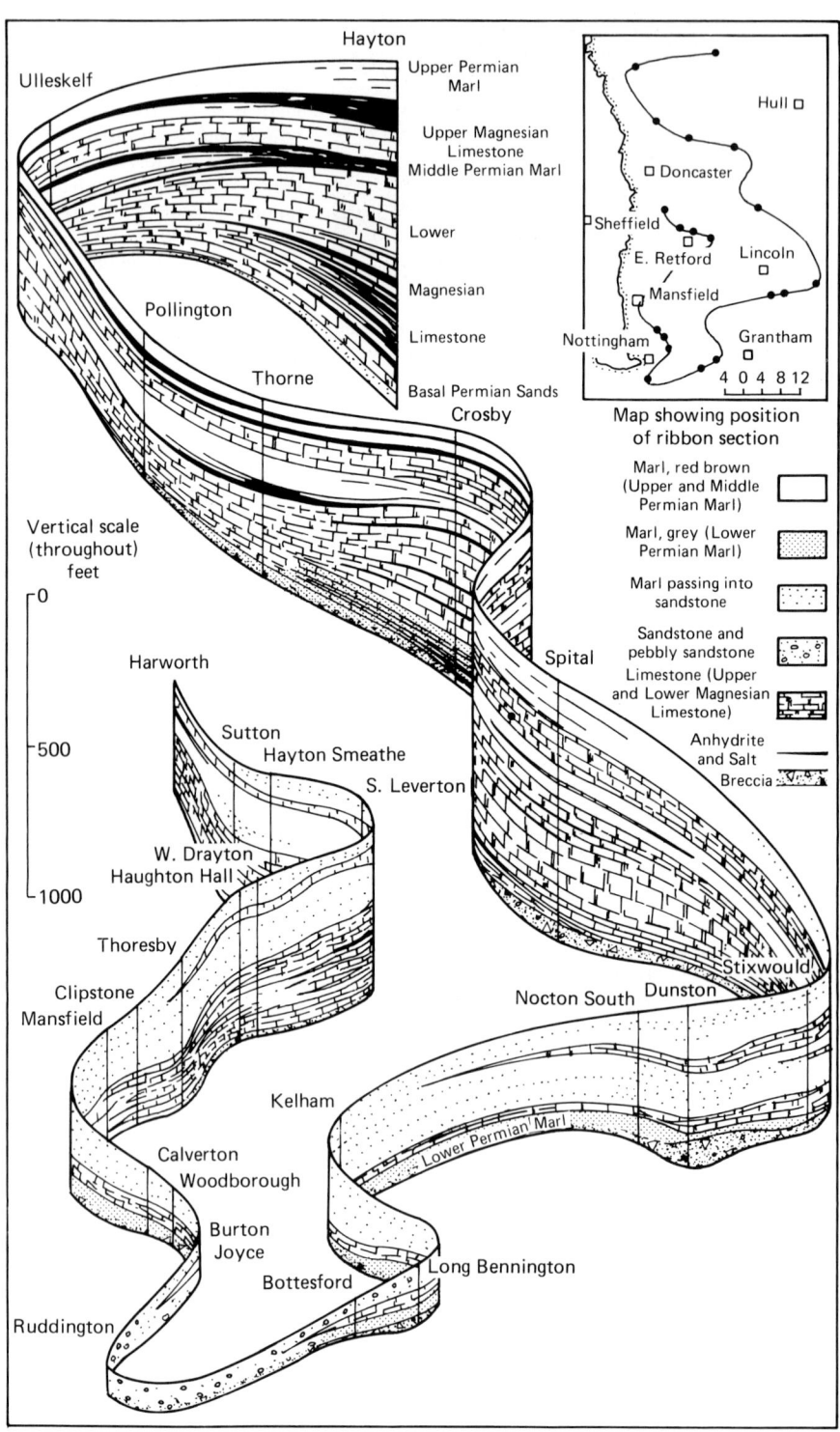

Hayton

Ulleskelf

Upper Permian Marl

Upper Magnesian Limestone
Middle Permian Marl

Lower

Pollington

Magnesian

Thorne

Limestone

Crosby

Basal Permian Sands

Map showing position
of ribbon section

Hull

Doncaster

Sheffield

E. Retford   Lincoln

Mansfield

Nottingham   Grantham

4 0 4 8 12

Marl, red brown
(Upper and Middle
Permian Marl)

Marl, grey (Lower
Permian Marl)

Marl passing into
sandstone

Sandstone and
pebbly sandstone

Limestone (Upper
and Lower Magnesian
Limestone)

Anhydrite
and Salt

Breccia

Vertical scale
(throughout)
feet

0

Harworth

Sutton
Hayton Smeathe

S. Leverton

Spital

500

W. Drayton
Haughton Hall

1000

Thoresby

Stixwould

Clipstone
Mansfield

Nocton South   Dunston

Kelham

Lower Permian Marl

Calverton
Woodborough

Burton
Joyce

Long Bennington

Bottesford

Ruddington

Figure 4.18 Dolomitic sandstone from Gregory's Quarry, Mansfield, Nottinghamshire is quarried from a formation, named the Magnesian Limestone, of Permian age. It was used in part for St Pancras Station, London and in restorations at Chichester Cathedral (1861)[3]

by calcium carbonate and silica. It is a true sandstone and should not be confused with Mansfield Wood-house Stone which is a dolomitic limestone. The sandstone was supplied as 'White' (or 'Yellow') and 'Red' Mansfield. The yellow variety is commonly yellowish-white when quarried but tends to weather white on exposure. The stone is fine- and even-grained, current bedded freestone (see p. 129). The two colours are used well outside its local area. Red Mansfield forms the capitals and piers alongside the Shap Granite columns at St Pancras Station, London (1873)[3]. It also forms part of the pavement of the Albert Memorial, London. Slabs of Red and White Mansfield Stone were originally used for paving in Trafalgar Square, London, but some of the white was replaced with Portland Stone. Both Red and White Mansfield Stone have also been used as block stone for construction. The Keep, or Little Castle (1612-1621) of that impressively-sited large house, Bolsover Castle, Derbyshire, provides an unrivalled example. The outstanding example of the use of

White Mansfield Stone is for Southwell Minster, Nottinghamshire, 10 miles (17 km) south-east of Mansfield. Watson[3], records its use for the Municipal Buildings (1852) in Windsor, Berkshire.

Penrith Stone is taken from sandstones of Permian age known as the Penrith Sandstone. The stone is bright red to pink and buff in colour and moderately coarse-grained. Many of the quartz grains are of the millet-seed type which indicates a desert sand origin. The stone is noteworthy because many of the grains have secondary outgrowths of quartz which are in optical continuity with the grains. Penrith Red is widely known and has been extensively used. Not unexpectedly, much of Penrith, Cumbria is built of it. Often the stone displays a sparkling surface. Lazonby Red (Plumton Red) from Lazonby, Cumbria is also from the Penrith Sandstone. It is red to pink in colour, with some buff (white Lazonby) beds, and medium- to fairly coarse-grained. Because of its gritty character it was sometimes known as the Lazonby Grit. St Adrian's Church, Carlisle (1900) is made of it.

(a)

(b)

Figure 4.19 Old barn (a) and recent house (b), both of Penrith sandstone from Strangeway's Quarry (seen in background in (a)), Halfway Wells, Great Salkeld, Cumbria

Figure 4.17 The ribbon diagram shows that considerable variation may be found both vertically and laterally in the lithology of a geologically named rock series. In the Permian rocks of Yorkshire and the East Midlands a local development in the Magnesian Limestone yields sandstones—Mansfield white (or yellow) and Mansfield Red (see p. 73). At Mansfield Woodhouse (about 3 km north of Mansfield) a fairly coarse, granular, somewhat crystalline limestone is found. This stone was used for part of the Palace of Westminster. (Diagram reproduced by courtesy of The Director, British Geological Survey. Crown Copyright reserved)

Permian sandstones form the country around Dumfries in Scotland and the stone taken from the quarries at Locharbriggs is renowned. It was used to build much of Dumfries, the 'Queen of the South'. Light-red in colour, medium-grained, it 'once provided about half the freestone used for building in Scotland'[14]. Much of the red city of Glasgow results from the use of the stone. The Kelvingrove Art Galleries in Glasgow is one example. Care must be taken, however, not to confuse the Locharbriggs Stone with Old Red Sandstone which is also used in Glasgow. It was exported to Canada and the USA. In Montreal, Canadian architects preferred 'the brighter New Red Sandstone from Great Britain'[3] to a local sandstone.

Lochabriggs Stone was used for the Museum for the Burrell collection, Glasgow (*Figure 4.20*), which won the Stone Federations' New Building Design Award for Natural Stone in 1983. There it was teamed up with Lazonby Stone which was used for paving. The stone was also used in Edinburgh.

The Mauchline Sandstone which tops the Ayrshire coalfield also provides an excellent building stone. The Ballochmyle Quarries produced a bright red-coloured, fine-grained stone with wind-rounded grains, similar to the sandstones of Dumfries and Galloway. Mauchline Sandstone was also used in St Vincent Place[15], Glasgow, and in Edinburgh[7]. Unless documentary evidence is available, it is extremely difficult to determine whether Lochabriggs Stone, Mauchline Stone from Ballochmyle or Penrith Stone has been used in a building. Appropriately The Burns Monument (1879), in Kilmarnock, is known to be of Mauchline Sandstone. The stone was also exported to North America.

The red sandstones in Dumfries and Galloway have been extensively used elsewhere in the west of Scotland. Remarkably soft when green, they are an example of a stone which is too weak for use as aggregate, but nevertheless provides an excellent and enduring building stone.

Around Hopeman, Grampian, an outcrop of pale-fawn coloured sandstone is considered to be Permo-Triassic but its geological horizon is uncertain. The stone is quarried under the names Greenbrae, Clashach and Hopeman Stone. Greenbrae Stone was used by the North of Scotland Hydro-Electric Board for many of its works and Board Houses. Clashach Stone may be seen in the Old Course Hotel, St Andrews. Permo-Triassic sandstones crop out in a broad sweep from around Annan, Dumfries and Galloway eastwards into the Vale of Eden, and around the northern edge of the Lake District. The Corsehill Quarry near Annan supplied a warm-red coloured, fine- and close-grained, slightly micaceous and finely laminated stone, taken from the Annanlea Sandstone which is certainly Triassic in age and is the equivalent of the St Bees Sandstone further south. Records reveal a surprisingly wide geographical range for its use including Liverpool Street Railway Station, London (1875), Cadogan Square Mansions, Chelsea, London, Jews' Synagogue, Great Portland Street, London[12], and 'there are several buildings in New York'[3]. Locally, large blocks have been used in building for houses and cottages. Its suitability for carving is illustrated by its use by Henry Moore for his *Figure* (1933-1934) and his *Reclining Figure* (1935).

The New Red Sandstone crops out in south-west England. Many quarries existed in the past including Broadclyst, Dainton, Exminster and Ugbrooke, in Devon. Many red sandstone churches may be seen, for example, in the lower Exe Valley. An important building stone is the Heavitree Conglomerate, found to the north around Exeter. It was used in Exeter with notable effect in the Cathedral Close (*Figure 4.21*). It was also used for Rougemont Castle in

Figure 4.20 Lochabriggs Sandstone with Lazonby stone paving was used for the Burrell Collection building, Glasgow. The wall incorporates a masonry doorway, part of the Burrell Collection

Figure 4.21 At first sight an unlikely stone for use in building, the Heavitree Conglomerate (Permian in age) is used with dramatic effect in the church of St. Pancras, Exeter

combination with local stone and in conjunction with other stones in the great red city wall which was begun about 200 AD by the Romans.

A remarkably coarse and bright red local conglomeratic sandstone, well exposed in the colourful cliffs, might, at first sight, be considered unsuitable for building, but was used for the charming late mediaeval Kirkham House, Paignton, Devon.

Red sandstones of Triassic age occur in Scotland, but are of more importance in England. The Spynie Sandstone is quarried near Hopeman under the names Spynie Stone and Rose Brae Stone. St Bees Stone, or Red St Bees, has been quarried near St Bees, Cumbria from early times. Carved Roman pieces of it have been found, and the Ancient Monument of Furness Abbey (1127 and later), Cumbria is an example of the use of the stone in extremely adverse climatic conditions. It is stated to have been used in Windsor Castle, Berkshire, but so is almost any other stone!

St Bees Stone is chocolatey-brown-red, fine-grained with slight laminations and is occasionally micaceous. Quarries on the northern edge of the Lake District at Aspatria, Cumbria supplied stone much like St Bees. It was used for the De Vere Hotel, Kensington, London and as dressings for St Polycarp's Church, Belfast. Another very similar stone taken from the St Bees Sandstone is known as 'Barbary Plane'. It was quarried near Langwathby, Penrith, Cumbria and used for the Library, Manchester.

The West Lancashire Plain and the Cheshire Plain are, to a great extent, underlain by rocks of Triassic age which include useful, important and widely used sandstones. Freestones in nature, most of them could be obtained in large blocks which can be seen in many local buildings. Stone from near Storeton, Wirral Peninsula, Cheshire was widely used, particularly in Liverpool, for many public buildings including the Customs House (1828), the Wellington Monument (1863), and the Lime Street Railway

Station (1871)[3]. Better known, however, are Woolten Stone and Rainhill Stone, which were quarried near Liverpool, Merseyside. Both are dull-red in colour and fine- to medium-grained. Woolton Stone was used for all the work of the external walls of the Liverpool Anglican Cathedral and Rainhill Stone was used for the internal walls. In a building where red sandstone is an integral part of the architecture, Red Wilderness Stone (Devonian) was used for pavements and steps and Penrith Stone (Permian) was used for some string courses[3].

Dull light-red coloured, medium-grained stone from Runcorn, Merseyside was of importance not only locally and in Liverpool, but also in Manchester where it was used in St Ann's Square for restoration of St Ann's Church and in the newer building of Chetham's Hospital School.

In the Yorton, Clive and Grinshill areas of Cheshire and particularly on Grinshill Hill many old quarries can be found. One of them, now Grinshill Stone

Figure 4.22 Highly false-bedded, brick-red mottled greenish, Red Grinshall stone of Triassic age used for the Castle, Shrewsbury. Weathering has accentuated the bedding planes

Quarries Ltd., is said to have been in unbroken production since Roman times. In the past, Triassic sandstone, named the Ruyton and Grinshill Sandstone, was extensively quarried and a 'Red Grinshill' and a 'White Grinshill' stone was produced. 'Red Grinshill' was used for many of the older buildings of nearby Shrewsbury, Shropshire, including the castle (*Figure 4.22*), the abbey and town walls. More recently the red stone has been replaced by 'White Grinshill' a whitish-grey coloured, brown-specked, fine-grained sandstone. It was used for St Mary's Church, with its magnificent spire, which is one of the three tallest in England. Perhaps the best known Triassic stone is Hollington Stone, quarried at Hollington, near Uttoxeter, Staffordshire. The stone is dull red, white, or mottled. The white stone is in fact yellow and the mottled stone was formerly said to be 'salmon' in colour. It is fine- to medium-grained and is remarkably easy to work when 'green' but toughens considerably on exposure. It was used for the incredible Alton Towers (1812 onwards) which is now a massive fun-fair. Hereford Cathedral was restored (1901–1905) with the stone which was supplied as Red Mottled or as Brown Alton Stone. Bracken House, Queen Victoria Street, London, until recently the headquarters of the *Financial Times* newspaper, which is printed on pink paper, is partly clad with Red Hollington Stone and some blocks show excellent cross-bedding. Without doubt the most spectacular example is the use of the stone for the new Coventry Cathedral (1954–1962), the same stone as was used for the old Cathedral, so fearfully destroyed in 1940 (*Figure 4.23*).

Banked up against the Carboniferous Limestone of the Mendips is a local deposit called the Dolomitic Conglomerate. It is extraordinarily variable in composition and ranges from a grey and red, coarse-grained sandstone to a massive rock made up of

Figure 4.23 Hollington stone is the common bond between the old Coventry Cathedral to the left and the new cathedral (right). The choice of the same stone by Sir Basil Spence, architect of the new cathedral, is a testament to a stone which at first sight might not be considered to be of use for building

boulders. Many of the boulders, which are of limestone and dolomite may weigh several tons. Many of them are markedly angular in form and set in a sandy matrix. The conglomerate could, with complete justification, be classified as a limestone.

The formation represents a thick scree which accumulated on and masked old mountain slopes. Although it is usually unsuitable as a building stone, the deposit has been worked at Draycott, near Wells, Somerset where it has a reddish tinge. Because it is possible to polish the stone it was sold as Draycott Marble or under the trade name of Bryscom. It was known locally as millstone or millgrit rock and was used for gateposts of farms and houses. It was notably used in Wells Cathedral for four tall pillars at the western end of the nave, and for the newer parts (1860) of Temple Meads station, Bristol. A table top made of the stone, 9 feet 2 inches by 4 feet 1 inch (2.8 × 1.2 m) is on view at Longleat House, Wiltshire. The inn at Rodney Stoke, Somerset deserves study if only for the fine use of the stone.

Triassic sandstone of variable colour and quality was worked in Northern Ireland, particularly at Scrabo Hill and at Dundonald. Reddish-brown in colour, well-jointed and cross-bedded stone from quarries on Scrabo Hill, known as Scrabo White, Scrabo Pink, Ballycullen and Glebe was widely used in Belfast. The Albert Memorial is of Scrabo Sandstone, as is St Enoch's Church. Cook's Centenary Church is built of sandstone from Glebe Quarry.

Jurassic sandstones

The Jurassic System has yielded a few sandstones, which in general, did not travel far. However, two must be especially noted. In the county of Northamptonshire, a division of the Jurassic known as the Inferior Oolite Series contains a member called the Northampton Ironstone or the Northampton Sand Ironstone (*see Figure 4.24*). It is mostly an oolitic ironstone deposit but in places is a ferruginous sand. It has a buff or brown colour derived from the contained iron minerals. North of Duston, on the outskirts of Northampton good building sandstone was obtained. Many quarries were opened around the town as well as in the neighbourhood of nearby Harlestone and of Moulton. It is stones from these or from other long-forgotten quarries in the same rocks, which are responsible for the warm russet-brown hues of Northampton itself and of many villages around. The Church of St Peter and St Paul, Moulton, serves as an example. Harlestone Stone was used for setts and for kerbs, and at Duston some beds are flaggy.

A pale-yellow, slightly calcareous, fine- to medium-grained sandstone from the district around Aislaby, near Whitby, North Yorkshire was used for Whitby Abbey (thirteenth century), the old Covent Garden, London, parts of University Library, Cambridge, and for 'the foundations of the old Waterloo Bridge and

Figure 4.24 The variability of the Northampton Sand Ironstone adds interest to buildings made of it, as at Ecton, Northamptonshire

Figure 4.25 In many buildings stone of local importance is used, illustrating the intimate relationship between geology and building. The charming Scarborough museum was built in 1829 to the design of William Smith (the 'father of English geology'). The side wings were added in 1861. The stone used was Hackness Stone (Jurassic), typically a calcareous sandstone, which came from the 'Great Quarry', west-north-west of Scarborough

London Bridge'[16]. Other similar sandstones of Jurassic age were worked and locally used in and around the Howardian Hills.

Cretaceous Sandstones

The Cretaceous System is commonly regarded as having no important building stone. To an extent that is true; but some Cretaceous stones are still available. Others must be noted because they are architecturally and historically important and were widely known, particularly across southern England, an area which, by-and-large, lacks good building stone.

The Wealden Series, the lowest part of the Cretaceous System, yielded slightly calcareous sandstones which were of importance in the Weald area which is otherwise mostly clay or chalk. Stone has been taken from the Ashdown Sand, the Tunbridge Wells Sand and the Lower Greensand. In the main, stone from the Ashdown Sand and the Tunbridge Wells Sand is usually buff- to brown-coloured, fine-grained, somewhat friable, and massively bedded with cross-bedding common. Scattered small pebbles may be locally present.

Where suitable stone was found many quarries were opened. Most are now long lost and impossible to trace. Many buildings throughout the Weald made use of the sandstone and it is not possible to suggest a provenance for the stone without supporting archival or documentary evidence. A fine-grained Wealden sandstone is commonly the best that can be suggested.

Sussex Sandstone and Wealden Sussex from near West Hoathley, Sussex are still available. They are fine-grained, and brown-yellow in colour. Stone from the Ashdown Sands quarried nearby was used for the small, but grand, Bodiam Castle, Sussex. A similar stone from near Hastings was used for restorations at Battle Abbey (pre-1911), Sussex.

In some areas, the Weald Clay, a formation within the Cretaceous contains calcareous sandstone beds which split readily. The best known and most important is a bed up to 30 feet (9 m) thick found near Horsham, Sussex. This stone was once extensively worked and was used for paving slabs and roofing under the name Horsham Stone. The sandstone was originally deposited in shallow waters and

(a)

(b)

Figure 4.26 Ripple-marked slabs of fissile Horsham Stone (a) were used not only for non-slip paving but also for tilestones on the church at Mickleham, Surrey (b)

many slabs have ripple markings. Such slabs were sometimes used for paving stables and stable yards, thus providing a non-slip surface for the horses. The nineteenth century Army Depot in Horsham was paved with these slabs. The Horsham Stone has been widely used as a tilestone and may be seen on many houses around the area (*Figure 4.26*). The roofs of the old Grammar School Building, Guildford, of the Church of St John, Wotton, and of St Katherine,

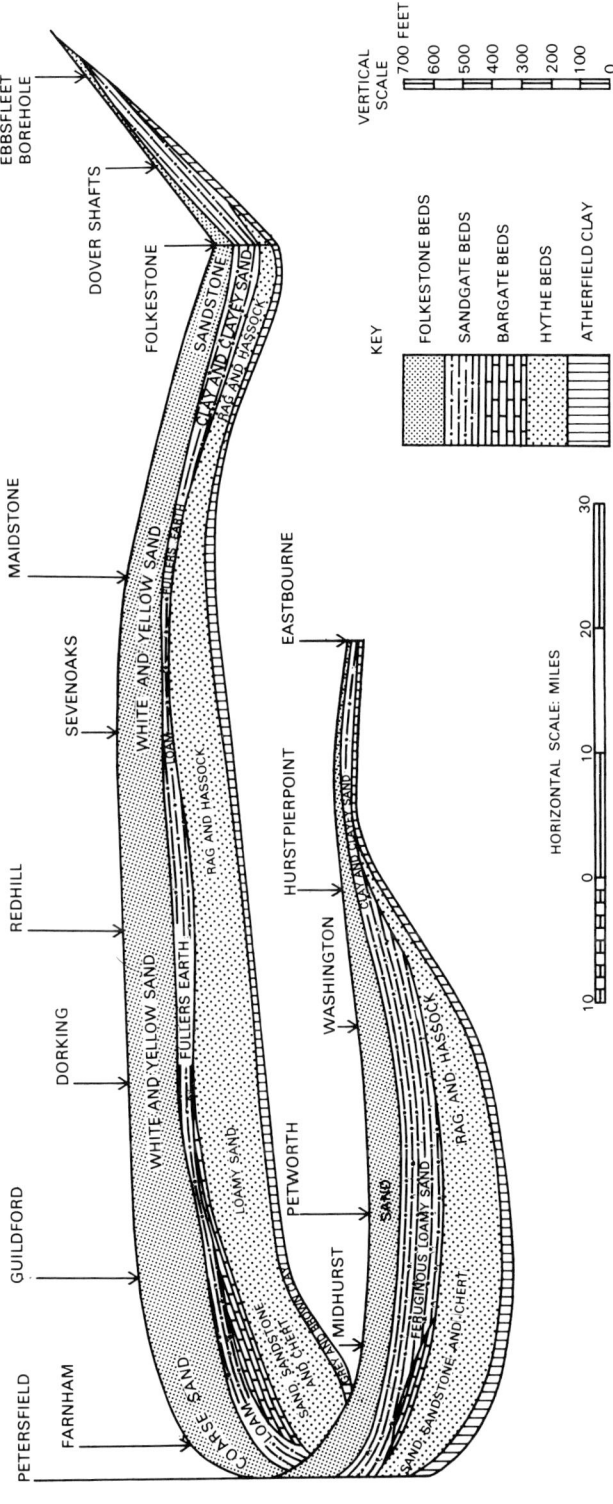

Figure 4.27 The major divisions of the Lower Greensand vary in thickness and lithology. In some areas they may yield stone useful for building which is not found elsewhere along the outcrops (see p.80). (Reproduced by courtesy of The Director, British Geological Survey. Crown copyright reserved)

(a)

Figure 4.28 (a) House near the Silent Pool, Albury, Surrey is of Bargate Stone (light coloured) and of irregular blocks of carstone from nearby Folkestone Sands (see page 81). (b) The house 'Tankards' in Eashing, Surrey, uses carstone as gallets ('nails') between blocks of Bargate Stone

(b)

Merstham, are three examples in Surrey. Locally known as healing stones, they were used at least as early as 1425 to roof the Draper's Guild Hall[17].

Stones from the Lower Greensand (Lower Cretaceous age) differ considerably one from the other, not only in thickness but also in geographical distribution (*Figure 4.27*). The Lower Greensand is divided into a number of formations, but is considered here as a unit and discussed on a geographical basis.

An outcrop which shows considerable lithological variation occurs west of Dorking, Surrey, over a large tract of country south-west of Guildford particularly around Godalming, and extends eastwards in a belt beyond Churt and into Sussex. It consists of a variable group of calcareous and glauconitic sands with discontinuous layers and lenses of cemented pebbly calcareous doggers which may be locally rich in comminuted shell debris. It also contains some cherty lenses. At one time many small quarries were opened to secure the pebbly doggers known as the Bargate Stone, and it was an important building stone in Surrey. The great tower of Guildford Castle (twelfth century) is mostly of Bargate Stone with flint and chalk courses. Bargate Stone is recorded as used for the Royal Grammar School, Guildford (Edward VI), and was used by P.C. Hardwick for Charterhouse School. It is renowned for its use by Sir Edwin Lutyens for Munstead Wood and Tigbourne Court, 'Lutyens' gayest and most elegant building'[18]. Easebourne Quarry, near Midhurst, Sussex was worked to supply stone to the surrounding Cowdray estate and for bridges in the area[19]. Querns found at Danebury Ring, Hampshire, have been petrologically traced back to the Lower Greensand at Midhurst where, in a long abandoned quarry, there is evidence of a type of production line for their manufacture.

Some beds of the Lower Greensand are locally rich in the green-coloured mineral glauconite. At Ightham, Kent, the Ightham Stone, a vividly green hard chert, with a glassy appearance, was occasionally used. In the early nineteenth century, it was used as road metal in London. Stone from another very restricted occurrence of a glauconite-rich sandstone was used with spectacular effect for the Church of St Mary at Husborne Crawley, Bedfordshire. Irregular seams of ferruginous sandstone in the form of sheets, tubular masses or box stones occur sometimes in some of the sands which are found in the Lower Greensand. The seams are commonly brown to red, friable or well-cemented, medium-grained sandstone. The sand grains are coated and cemented either lightly or heavily with ferruginous minerals. They are commonly known as carstone, or box stone, if box-shaped. Such rocks are not uncommon through the geological column, but they are found particularly in Mesozoic and Tertiary rocks. They are of common occurrence in the Folkestone Beds in Surrey and Kent, where they may exist as veins only an inch (2.5 cm) thick which run randomly across the bedding, or as veins a foot (0.3 m) or so thick with an interlaced 'wasp nest' structure. Blocks of over two feet (0.6 m) thick are known.

Unlikely though it looks, carstone has been extensively used for building; many cottages and houses at Wrotham, Kent (*Figure 4.29a*) and at Eashing and at

(a)

(b)

Figure 4.29 (a) Cottages of carstone, Wrotham Hill, Kent. (b) Brick dressings with carstone ('gingerbread stone') were used for HM The Queen's Stud, Sandringham, Norfolk

Albury, Surrey (*Figure 4.28*) are built of it. In Limpsfield and in Westerham, Kent, it has been used for paving with the stone set on end with the bedding planes vertical[20]. Along the Lower Greensand ridge from about Farnham, Surrey to around Wrotham, Kent, small pieces of carstone were, and still are, pushed into the mortar between the stones of the buildings. This technique is known variously as garnetting, galleting or nailing (*see Figure 4.30*). 'The nailed wall' was noted by Gilbert White[21] who wrote in Letter IV,

> From a notion of rendering their work the more elegant, and giving it a finish, masons chip this stone into small fragments about the size of the head of a large nail, and then stick the pieces into the wet mortar along the joints of their freestone walls; this embellishment carries an odd appearance, and has occasioned strangers sometimes to ask us pleasantly, whether we fastened our walls together with ten penny nails.

Other stones are similarly used; for example, Kentish Ragstone to the east of Sevenoaks, Kent, and flint,

which was used in the magnificent Goodwood House, Sussex. Small outcrops of the Lower Greensand occur around Ely, Cambridgeshire, and the Cathedral is built on one of them (*Figure 4.31*). Carstone also occurs and it has been used in the arcading of the cloister near the south transept door and in the outside wall of the south transept.

A distinctive ginger-brown coloured carstone is seen in the cliffs at Hunstanton, Norfolk. It has been found to be at least 58 feet (18 m) thick[22] in inland borings. It is conglomeratic, with quartz and chert pebbles and may be current-bedded. Finer grained and well-jointed carstone has been quarried over a long period of time near Snettisham, Norfolk. This is the 'gingerbread stone' which was used for the stables of Houghton Hall[10] and for many other buildings. An outstanding example is its use for HM The Queen's Stud, Sandringham, Norfolk. Cottages and walls in that area have been built using small slabs and large blocks.

Ferruginous sandstones other than those from the Lower Greensand may also be called carstone. Wimborne Minster, Dorset is often stated to be built of carstone and other stones. However, the stone is from an entirely different set of beds, the Agglestone Grit, in the upper part of the Bracklesham Group which are Eocene in age. Canford Magna Church, near Wimborne Minster, is made of blocks of grit collected from the heaths and from the Agglestone and the Puckstone. Local buildings, walls, barns and houses also used the stone.

The Upper Greensand (Lower Cretaceous) around Reigate, Merstham, Gatton and Godstone in Surrey contains beds of compact sandstones. Some of these rocks are known as firestone, malmstone, malm rock or Burrystone, others are called hearthstone. The Upper Greensand outcrop extends westwards through Surrey and into Hampshire. Throughout this area the rock is commonly referred to as malmstone. Hearthstone is a friable greenish-grey sandstone which was sold in blocks for household scouring purposes. Firestone, named from its property of resisting heat without decrepitating, occurs as massive, compact beds about two feet (0.6 m) thick. It is a calcareous, greenish-grey sandstone with muscovite mica and large amounts of glauconite. In places it becomes a siliceous limestone. Sponge spicules are abundant in the stone as fragments or as casts, which may be filled with glauconite or with silica in amorphous form. These stones were widely used and known under the general name of Reigate Stone or Merstham Stone. Merstham, Gatton and Godstone Stones are similar in nature. It is not possible to determine the provenance of a block used for building by visual inspection because the stone from these localities has no unique characteristics. Stone has been obtained from the north-east Surrey area possibly since Saxon times[23]. The stone was so

(a)

(b)

(c)

Figure 4.30 (a) Carstone 'nails' were used between blocks of Upper Greensand at Selbourne, Hampshire; (b) chips of flint have been pressed into the mortar between blocks of sarsen at Windsor Castle and flint has similarly been used on a massive scale between irregular blocks of flint for Goodwood House, Sussex (c)

important to Royal building programmes that during the reign of Edward III (1312–1327) the quarries of Reigate Stone were considered as valuable Crown property[12]. Despite its poor weathering properties it was extensively used in London because it was quarried nearby and could be easily carved (*Figure 4.32*). From the 'eleventh century to the sixteenth, large quantities were dragged by ox cart across the Home Counties'[10] Interestingly, the world's pioneer public horse-drawn and freight-only railways connected Wandsworth with Croydon, with a branch from Mitcham to Hackbridge. Its extension, the Croydon, Merstham and Godstone Railway (CMGR), which operated from 1805 to 1843, continued the line '...to a terminus at...underground firestone quarries at Merstham...'[24]. In 'Almost all old buildings [in London] we find occasionally introduced

Figure 4.31 Rough blocks of carstone from the Lower Greensand on which Ely Cathedral stands were incorporated into the exterior wall of the south transept

(a)

(b)

(c)

(d)

Figure 4.32 Reigate Stone was used extensively in the Tower of London, seen here in the arch of the entrance to the Bloody Tower with Kentish Ragstone forming much of the wall (a). It was also used for a delightful doorway arch in Deans' Yard, Westminster Abbey, (b). In each of these instances note obtrusive replacements with stones which are not geologically appropriate. (c) Beech house of Gatton Stone with brick dressings, Godstone, Surrey. (d) Side wall of White Hart Hotel, Godstone, also of Gatton Stone. This shows carstone galleting into poor and inappropriate re-mortaring which is leading to decay of the stone (see Volume 2).

large portions of stone from the vicinity of Rygate and Godstone'[25]. The Black Prince's Palace at Kennington (*c.* 1388), the vaulting of the crypt of Guildhall, the Tower of London and Henry VII's Chapel, Westminster, all bear witness to that statement. It was also used in Windsor Castle and Eton College (1443), Berkshire. Gatton House, supposedly built on the lines of the Corsini Chapel in Rome, and Gatton Church are local examples. In the 'Town Hall' nearby, there is an urn in memory of the deceased (and obviously a very rotten) borough.

The Malmstone outcrop to the west of Reigate has been quarried along its length for building stone. Examples may be seen in Farnham Church and the walls of Farnham Castle, Surrey. Much of Wiston

Figure 4.33 Eastbourne parish church, Sussex, built of Eastbourne Green Stone dug from reefs on the shore of the town

House, Susssex, is of malmstone, locally known also as malmrock. The Firestone was used extensively for fire places in, for example, the original house of Manresa, Roehampton, London and in Duntish Court, near Sherborne, Dorset.

Eastbourne Stone (Eastbourne Green) was taken from outcrops between tidemarks at Eastbourne, Sussex. A fairly tough, markedly green coloured sandstone, it was used for part of Pevensey Castle, Sussex. Perhaps it is to maintain the balance, that catapult balls found at Eastbourne are of the same stone.

The Upper Greensand of the Isle of Wight at one time yielded what was regarded as by far the best building stone on the Isle. It was quarried in many places, but principally in the neighbourhood of Ventnor and of Shanklin. The most important bed is a freestone three to five feet (0.9-1.5 m) thick, confined to the Southern Downs and seen in the cliff between Bonchurch and Black Gang. It is speckled pale-green to blue-grey in colour, and fine-grained with a varying amount of glauconite and of mica. The freestone was sawn into blocks as well as into lengths for mullions. It has a reputation for durability and it was used for ornamental and for structural work. On the Isle of Wight many houses in Ventnor, Bonchurch and Niton are built of it and it may be seen in Carisbrook Castle. An outstanding example of its use is for the detached bell tower of Chichester Cathedral in Hampshire. Winchester Cathedral was restored in part with the stone in 1825.

Tertiary sandstones

The Tertiary System has yielded few sandstones suitable for structural work. In general Tertiary sandstones are not consolidated enough for use in building. There are at least two exceptions, however, although they may be regarded as oddities. Sarsens, also known as grey-wethers, Druid stones or bridestones, are found as individual boulders which are often of considerable size, in an area south of a rough line from the Severn estuary stretching to Lowestoft, Suffolk. Two types may be distinguished; highly siliceous cemented sandstones (quartzites) and conglomerates of well cemented flint pebbles in a matrix of sarsen-like sandstone known as puddingstones. The sarsens of southern England, south of the River Thames are predominantly quartzites although some are markedly pebbly, with angular rather than round flint pebbles. They are far more widely distributed than is generally realized. The greatest concentration is in Wiltshire and Berkshire, where they often occur as 'valley trains'. They are also found in Dorset, Hampshire and Sussex. Generally they are white, fine-grained and well-cemented, sometimes with rootlet holes. They may have noticeably irregular surfaces.

They were much more naturally abundant in the past. They have been used for building from prehistoric times until recently for structures of all types. Stonehenge and Avebury Circle, for which over 600 sarsen stones were used, are the outstanding examples. The Megalithic monuments of White Horse Stone and Kit's Coty, Kent are also made of this stone. It was used too in Windsor Castle, Berkshire, where some walls are galleted with chips of flint. Some churches in Surrey made use of sarsen, and it has been used more mundanely for the wall alongside the car park of the public house at Avebury Village.

Properly, the name puddingstone should be applied to a conglomerate in which the contained pebbles and the cementing matrix are of equal hardness so that when broken, a smooth surface results. Most conglomerates break around the surface of the pebbles. Unfortunately the name puddingstone is commonly applied indiscriminately to all types of conglomerate. The Hertfordshire Puddingstone, of Tertiary age, is a classic example of a true puddingstone. It is composed of round flint pebbles up to two inches (5 cm) or so, set in a siliceous ground mass of sand grains and small flint fragments, all cemented by silica. Because of the shortage of stone suitable for building in Essex, puddingstone was widely incorporated in buildings and walls. It was also commonly used for millstones and for querns, one of which has been dated to 1500 BC[26]. Bradenham Puddingstone, locally known as pebble stone, is similar although less abundant. It has poorly-rounded irregular flints. It, too, was incorporated into local buildings, and was used 'in connection with rockeries, etc.' at Whipsnade Zoo[27].

Many local names, some restricted to a valley or two in Hertfordshire, have been used for Hertford-

(a)

(b)

(c)

Figure 4.34 (a) A 'valley train' of sarsens is spread along the valley bottom at Piggledean, near Avebury, Wiltshire. From sites such as these, stones were taken for the great monuments such as Avebury Circle, Wiltshire (b). (c) An inscribed sarsen, presented in 1967 to the City of Salisbury by the National Association of Master Masons. It stands near to the spot, indicated by an upturned cannon, from which the trigonometrical survey of Britain was begun

shire Puddingstone. Woe Stones, Hag Stones, Breedingstone, Growing Stone and Mother Stone are some examples[26].

Imported sandstones

Britain is plentifully endowed with sandstone and little is imported. The imported stone is mostly in the form of quartzite, which is of limited occurrence in Britain. However, one exception is a sandstone known as Grès de Vosges from the Department of Vosges, France. This fine- to medium-grained, yellowish to light olive grey (between 5Y 8/1 and 5Y 6/1), impure, slightly micaceous sandstone of Triassic age has been used, but as a colour match only, as a substitute for Kentish Ragstone.

Figure 4.35 In Hertfordshire, blocks of the locally occurring puddingstone may be found incorporated into walls and buildings. The stone has also been used ornamentally

Flint, chert and jasper

Although not always neatly placed into a classification, flint, chert and jasper may be conveniently considered here because they are composed mainly of silicon dioxide (SiO_2) the main substance of sandstones and closely allied stones.

Flint is found as nodules, layers of nodules and more rarely as bands in the top part of the middle and throughout the upper division of the Chalk formation. It is compact cryptocrystalline silica. All flint, whatever its immediate source, originated from the Chalk. This primary flint is black or dark blue-grey in colour and it breaks with a conchoidal fracture, a characteristic valued by early man because it provided a very sharp edge of use for cutting and scraping. It is possible also to split or 'knap' flints so that a moderately flat surface is obtained. Flint has long been used for building and many local names describe the immediate origin and form of use of it; for example field flint, squared flint, cobble, chequerwork and flushwork. Flint pebbles (cobbles, boulders, shingle, nodules, beach stones) and knapped flints have been, and are, still widely used for building. It is a difficult and intractable material which was used because no other suitable material was available in the areas where it is found rather than because of its intrinsic qualities. It is used for structural purposes and as a veneer.

Many examples of flint building may be seen in Kent, Surrey, Sussex, Suffolk and Norfolk. The Roman Wall of London incorporates much flint along with many other stones in an area where no building stone is found. Goodwood House (*c* 1790-1800 by James Wyatt) is an impressive example in West Sussex. It is 'one of his very few dull designs' according to Ian Nairn and Nikolaus Pevsner[28], but is nevertheless a magnificent use of what might be regarded as an unpromising material. Burpham Lodge, Arundel, West Sussex, which is much modernized is of large knapped flints. It is East Anglia that must take pride of place for the use of flint. Many churches in that area are entirely of flint. The Guildhall, Norwich, is an excellent example of the celebrated chequer work using flint and Caen Stone (*Figure 4.36*).

The name chert or hornstone is also applied to nodular silica which may be difficult to distinguish from flint. Generally the name is used for silica beds, layers and nodules which occur in limestones other than the Chalk. Any form of silica that can be used in the pottery industry is called flint in the Americas. The name flint is used outside the United Kingdom for silica deposits which would be called chert inside the UK.

Normally chert is thought of as being an impure flint, but the distinctive differences between flint and some chert are not immediately apparent. Generally chert has a hackly fracture compared with the markedly conchoidal fracture of flint. The name chert is often used for thick beds of massive chalcedony (SiO_2) which is a compact variety of silica made up of microscopic, or cryptocrystalline, quartz crystals with submicroscopic pores. Chert is prominent at some levels in the Carboniferous Limestone, the Jurassic Portland Beds and in the Lower Cretaceous Upper Greensand.

Chert has only been used locally and on a limited scale for building. The Old Grammar School, Chard, which is built of chert from the Upper Greensand, and the use of chert from the Carboniferous Limestone in walls and houses in Richmond, North Yorkshire are two examples[29]. Chert was mined until the end of 1968 by the Bakewell Chert Company, Derbyshire for use mainly in grinding mills in the Potteries.

Jasper, an opaque form of impure chalcedony even when very thin, is the name usually given to a red-coloured variety. Yellow, brown and green varieties are known. Lenticles of a dark-pink ('blood red') with large streaks and patches of darker red jasper occur in rocks of Precambrian age in Gwynedd, North Wales. At one time they were quarried two miles (3.2 km) north of Aberdaron. It was used for a Celtic cross nearby. Despite its hardness, toughness and the extreme difficulty of working it, an amazing use was made of jasper for the Norwich Union Insurance Group building on the corner of St James's Street and Piccadilly, London (*Figure 4.37*).

Limestone

Limestones consist chiefly of calcium carbonate ($CaCO_3$) in the form of the finely-divided mineral calcite which was originally a calcareous mud. Limestones were formed either directly or indirectly from mineral matter dissolved generally, but not always, in sea water and may be made up of as much as 99 per cent calcium carbonate. However, other mineral matter may be present in significant amounts. Limestones are very widespread and usually have a marked bedding. They are commonly richly fossiliferous.

Complicated classifications may be constructed, but for the purposes of discussion the classification used here is based on their mode of origin:

Chemical
Organic
Clastic or detrital

Chemical limestones are formed directly by precipitation of calcium carbonate from water. Calcium carbonate is only slightly soluble in water. However, most circulating ground waters contain carbon dioxide. Rain water, which is the source of most groundwater, also contains carbon dioxide. These

Plate 1 The clock tower, Palace of Westminster, London, popularly known as Big Ben, was originally built of Magnesian Limestone. Stone from Bolsover Moor quarry was used for the plinth with Anston Stone above. About 50 per cent of the stones above the plinth have now been replaced with Clipsham Stone

Plate 2 Serpentinite in outcrop at Kynance Cove, Lizard, Cornwall shows range of colour, veining and broken-up appearance

Plate 3 Serpentinite from the Lizard, Cornwall was used for the columns of these shops. Formerly the building was one shop. When the windows of Mappin and Webb were brought forward to the colonnade, *Rosso di Levanto*, a serpentinite from Italy, was used for the cills since serpentinite from the Lizard was not available. Its use was geologically appropriate and the result aesthetically pleasing. Recently it was replaced with a dark, fine-grained igneous rock that is visually unpleasant and geologically inappropriate

Plate 4 Columns of a 12th century doorway in St Wynwallow Church, Landewednacks, Lizard, Cornwall made from locally quarried serpentinite

Plate 5 A high concentration of the mineral glauconite is responsible for the green colour of the Church of St Mary, Husborne Crawley, Bedfordshire

Plate 6 Blue-hearted blocks of Clipsham Stone from Holywell Quarry, Clipsham, Lincolnshire were used by Donovan Purcell for replacement columns in the Galilee Porch of Ely Cathedral

Plate 7 Columns of Languedoc 'marble' contribute to the colourful Marble Trianon at Versailles

Plate 8 High decorative stone was used in many ladies' and mens' lavatories. The surround to the wash-hand basins in this men's lavatory in a stoneyard at Kennington Oval, London, is of Campan Vert

(a)

(b)

(c)

(d)

(e)

(f)

(g)

Figure 4.36 Some of the faces of flint. (a) Blocks of chalk containing nodules of flint were used, with blocks of basalt, for the harbour wall, Waterfoot, County Antrim; (b) split nodules of flint from the wall of St Peter's Church, Croydon; (c) nodules of flint, with dressings of Ham Hill stone, were used for Training College, Salisbury; (d) two adjoining cottages at Rustington, Sussex show contrasting styles of use of flint. That on the right uses split flint nodules, that on the left has round, evenly graded pebbles brought neatly into courses; (e and f) flints knapped to remove most of the cortex (the 'white skin') from some and to leave it on others, then grouped, lead to an interesting chequerboard pattern. This is seen on the church of St Thomas, Andover sub Foxcotte, Hampshire; (g) knapped flint with Caen stone produces the spectacular diaper flushwork on the Guildhall, Norwich

Figure 4.37 Jasper, which occurs as lenticles in rocks of Precambrian age around Aberdaron, North Wales, was used in 1905 for the Norwich Union building, Piccadilly. This building was one of the first in London to use Pentelikon marble from Greece

Figure 4.38 Ooliths result from the concentric deposition of calcium carbonate around a nucleus in highly carbonate-charged waters. The recent ooliths on the right were collected from the Great Salt Lake, Utah. The picture on the left shows an identical structure on the surface of Ketton Stone, from Ketton, Northamptonshire, an oolitic limestone about 175 million years old (Courtesy British Museum (Natural History))

waters convert calcium carbonate into calcium bicarbonate ($CaCO_3 + CO_2 + H_2O \rightarrow Ca(HCO_3)_2$) which has a much higher solubility and exists only in solution. When the charged ground waters reach the atmosphere at the surface the loss of carbon dioxide leads to the reprecipitation of calcium carbonate in the form of *tufa* or of *travertine*. The dividing line between these two is a matter of fine judgement. The name tufa is commonly used for a spongy, cellular, porous calcium carbonate deposit formed around seeps, springs and in streams flowing off limestone country. More compact, tougher forms, with a greater or lesser proportion of voids, generally regarded as having been deposited from hot springs[30] are named travertine. The name travertine is derived from Italian and is a corruption from the term *Tiburtinus*, the stone being found in great quantity at Tibur, near Rome, Italy and named by the Romans *Lapis Tiburtinus*.

Similar deposits may be formed by the dripping of water charged with calcium bicarbonate from the roofs of caverns in calcareous rocks. Layers of the mineral calcite are deposited one over another to build stalactites. The counterparts, rising from the floor, are stalagmites. In some instances layers of calcite encrust the walls or floors of caves. The encrustation is called *flow-stone, dripstone, cave onyx* or, more rarely, *waterstone* or *water marble*. As with stalactites, it is characteristically banded. *Onyx marble* is also a chemical precipitate. It is generally thought to be deposited from standing sheets of water and, in a sense, may be thought of as a horizontal stalagmite.

Chemically precipitated limestones were also formed in sea waters. In some areas, such as around

the Bahamas, around the Florida Keys, in the Persian Gulf and in the Great Salt Lake, Utah, USA, richly charged, warm, tide-swept and wave-agitated shallow sea water in tidal channels and in lagoons precipitates calcium carbonate in concentric layers, commonly round a fragment of shell or a grain of sand which acts as a nucleus. These small, mainly spherical carbonate grains are known as *ooliths* (*see Figure 4.38*). Some limestones are found to be composed nearly entirely of ooliths; they are called *oolitic limestones* or, *oolites*. Commonly the ooliths are about 1 mm, more rarely up to 2 mm (0.08 in) in diameter. In some rocks they are about the size of a pea; the name *pisolite* is then used.

Organic limestones consist largely or entirely of the fossilized shells of one or more organisms. The organisms removed calcium carbonate from the water in which they lived and used it for their shells or skeletons. Reef limestones, for example, are composed of a number of organic components; algal limestones originated from algae which secrete lime. Shelly limestones are made up dominantly of the fossil remains of shellfish. Coral limestones may contain complete coral colonies; crinoidal limestones are made up of fragments of crinoids (sea lilies), which are animals related to sea urchins and starfishes. The spaces between the fossilized organisms may be filled with broken shell matter or with calcareous mud. The fossils in a limestone may range from complete, unbroken shells to those that are completely broken up (comminuted). Many commercial 'marbles' are shelly limestones.

Clastic or detrital limestones result from the erosion of pre-existing limestones. The fragments range from fine-grained calcareous mud to pebbles of the original limestone, later consolidated and normally cemented with calcareous material into a new coherent rock.

The Lower Lias (Jurassic) Sutton Stone, from Glamorgan, South Wales was derived mainly from the Carboniferous Limestone, which it overlies in places. Draycott marble is a clastic limestone in some places. Many commercial 'marbles' which are called 'breche' are clastic limestones. Limestones may be *close* or *massively* bedded.

When pure, or nearly so, limestones are white in colour, as, for example, the upper part of the Cretaceous Chalk. Few limestones, however, are composed entirely of calcium carbonate. Most contain other mineral matter which will determine its overall colour. Clay is one of the commonest non-calcareous constituents of limestone. The lower the amount of contained clay the better the polish which can be given to a limestone. Limestone, probably more so than other rocks, shows gradations to all other sediments; a clayey limestone easily grades into a calcareous shale or calcareous clay, that is, a marl. Many other minerals may be present in limestones.

Dolomite, a calcium magnesium carbonate, ($CaMg(CO_3)_2$), may be present in considerable amounts. It may have originated as a chemical deposit, but more probably formed by the chemical alteration, termed dolomitization, of the original limestone by the replacement of calcium by magnesium. Pure dolomite rock is rare. The Carboniferous Limestone is dolomitized irregularly, sometimes on a considerable scale. Nearly all the limestones of Permian age in England contain dolomite. The Magnesian Limestone is a particularly well-known formation. The font at Coventry Cathedral is a boulder of dolomitized Chalk brought from Israel.

In general, dolomitic limestones are more resistant to weathering than pure limestones, but they are particularly vulnerable in heavily polluted atmospheres.

Quartz in the form of sand grains may also be present, either by itself or in association with other minerals. If there are large amounts of sand the limestone is called a sandy limestone. In some instances, complete removal of the calcium carbonate in a siliceous limestone leaves behind a 'skeleton' of silica. This is known as rottenstone and it has been used for polishing and as an abrasive. The dolomitized patches in the Carboniferous Limestone were also called rottenstone by men quarrying for limestone.

Rarely, a limestone may be rich in one of the iron minerals. Some oolitic limestones of Jurassic age in Lincolnshire and in Northamptonshire are rich in iron minerals, commonly *siderite* (chalybite, iron carbonate, $FeCO_3$) and *chamosite* (iron silicate, Mg, $Fe''_3Fe'''_3(AlSi_3)O_{10}(OH)_8$). If these minerals are present in sufficient concentration the rock is termed an oolitic ironstone and may be worked as an iron ore.

The complex iron-silicate, *glauconite* is an occasional constituent of limestones but it is not as widespread in limestone as in sandstones.

Pyrite (iron disulphide, FeS_2) may be present and in disseminated form contributes to the dark colour of some limestones and to the hydrogen sulphide smell which some of them emit when struck. Watson[3] records that stone from the Carboniferous Limestone of the Mendip Hills, Somerset is popularly known as Stink Stone because, when newly quarried, it emits a strong fetid odour. Manganese minerals, normally in the form of *manganite* (hydrated manganese oxide, $MnO(OH)$), may have a dramatic effect even when present in small quantities. It appears as attractive dendritic patterns on the joints or bedding-planes particularly of fine-grained limestones.

Although limestone is not quarried for dimension stone on the same huge scale that it is for crushed rock and for industrial use, it has, nevertheless, contributed greatly and sometimes dramatically to the appearance of many British buildings and towns.

Limestones are widely distributed geographically and, like sandstones, are of common occurrence throughout the geological column. They are less common in the older systems, but increase in prominence in younger rocks.

In the stone trade in Great Britain and in most other countries overseas it is usual to call any calcareous rock which can be cut and polished a 'marble'. This does not accord with the strict geological definition which is adhered to here.

Silurian and older Limestones

Geologically interesting limestones are found in the Precambrian, Cambrian, Ordovician and Silurian Systems. Although they were used locally for building they were not of commercial importance. The Wenlock Limestone, of Silurian age, became more widely known, not only for its fossils, including the 'Dudley locust', but also for polished slabs sold under the names of Fossil 'Marble', Ledbury 'Marble'[17] and Shropshire 'Marble'. The limestone was rarely used for building but it may be found in Dudley Castle, Worcestershire and in some churches around the area.

Devonian limestones

The Devonian System has yielded limestones which have had wide use. The principal beds occur in the Middle Devonian in a belt extending from Plymouth across to Torquay, Devon. Babbacombe, Petit Tor,

(a)

(b)

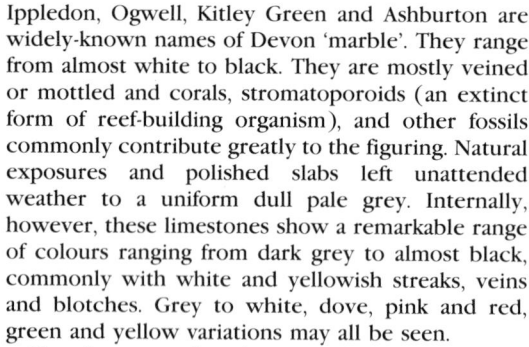

Figure 4.39 Unpolished blocks of Devonian Limestone used naturally for the Town Hall, Plymouth, with a south-west England granite plinth and serpentinite infill panels on entrance (a). Slabs of the limestone form an attractive pavement outside the town hall (b)

Ippledon, Ogwell, Kitley Green and Ashburton are widely-known names of Devon 'marble'. They range from almost white to black. They are mostly veined or mottled and corals, stromatoporoids (an extinct form of reef-building organism), and other fossils commonly contribute greatly to the figuring. Natural exposures and polished slabs left unattended weather to a uniform dull pale grey. Internally, however, these limestones show a remarkable range of colours ranging from dark grey to almost black, commonly with white and yellowish streaks, veins and blotches. Grey to white, dove, pink and red, green and yellow variations may all be seen.

The limestone has been used for building in Torquay. In Plymouth, where it was used for the post-war rebuilding, it may be seen beautifully applied for the Town Hall and for the matching surrounding paving (*Figure 4.39*).

It was more for its decorative effect, however, that vast amounts were quarried in the past. The last producing quarry at Ashburton, Devon recently ceased production of dimension stone. It yielded a dark-grey to black stone with white, yellow and red patches and veins. Ashburton 'Marble' was widely used as an internal and external decorative stone. It was exported to northern America where it is known as Renfrew 'Marble'. It was recently used for the Royal Bank of Canada, Port of Spain, Trinidad. It has also been widely used for internal ecclesiastical work, often as supporting pillars. For example, it is used purely for decorative effect for some pillars in Chichester Cathedral, Sussex. It may be seen on many shop fronts and was used for some steps and floors of the (now) British Telecom Tower, London. It is spectacularly used in the entrance of the Geological Museum, London, where the foyer, stairs and entrance arch exemplify the attractive use of British decorative 'marbles.' The wide range and variation of colour shown by the Devonian limestones makes it difficult to attribute any given example of its decorative use to a specific quarry because at one time several varieties may have been produced from any quarry. Commonly the best determination that can be given is Devonian limestone as in, for example, Salisbury Cathedral, Hampshire, where some original shafts presumed to have been of Purbeck 'Marble' were replaced by Devonian limestone shafts.

The limestones of Devonian age were noted not only for their beauty but also for their durability. As North[17] remarks '... greater used could be made of the ornamental varieties, because much of the domestic "marble" can withstand the British atmosphere better than many of the foreign crystalline marbles that are imported, into this country.' At one time Devon 'marbles' were widely exported to Europe as well as to Australia, America and South Africa.

Carboniferous limestones

The Carboniferous System is the first in the geological column in which limestones, named the Carboniferous Limestone, form a major constituent. The Carboniferous Limestone is responsible for many of the areas of outstanding natural beauty in Great Britain including the Mendips, the Peak District, and much of the Pennines. In these areas the limestones are extensively and attractively used both for building and for walling. It provides more limestone for industrial use in the chemical, pharmaceutical, cement, iron and steel and agricultural industries than any other geological formation. It also provides many building stones, which are usually cut and polished, then sold as marbles. However, the variety sold now is by no means as great as in the past.

Figure 4.40 Haddon Hall, Derbyshire is constructed of Carboniferous Limestone with dressings of Millstone Grit. Both stones were quarried from nearby the house

The overall appearance of the Carboniferous Limestone differs greatly from one locality to another. The differences are the result of the contained fossils and small amounts of other minerals disseminated through the stone. Much of the limestone is compact, tough, mainly massive, well-bedded grey-coloured rock with greater or lesser amounts of fossils, of relatively low porosity and very low permeability.

Porosity and permeability are important characteristics of building stones. Limestones are generally thought of as being porous, but they are not necessarily permeable. Permeability is the capacity of a rock to allow the passage of fluids such as water or oil through it. Permeability is measured by the rate of flow, that is, the amount of fluid passing through the rock in a given time. Porosity is the percentage of free space in a given volume of rock.

A porous rock is not necessarily permeable. Permeability depends on the size and arrangement of the pores. To be permeable a rock must have pores which form continuous through channels for the passage of fluid. For example, pumice is very porous, but not permeable. This can be demonstrated by the fact that it floats on water. If the pores were connected, the rock would fill with water and would sink.

Limestone can be virtually impermeable. A mock-up of a spandrel below a window sill to be used as part of a wall in Arundel Great Court, London, was constructed of six-inch (15 cm) thick Portland Stone. It was subjected to simulated driving rain for 24 hours. At the end of the test only small drops of moisture were found on the internal face (Personal communication by J.B. Forrest, lately of Frederick Gibberd Coombes and Partners.). Compact Carboniferous Limestone is sometimes used for water butts (*Figure 4.41*).

Compact, massive, grey-coloured Carboniferous Limestone has been widely used usually as block stone for structural building work in all the areas it is found. The many dry stone walls of the Pennines and elsewhere, testify to its robust durability. The delightful Haddon Hall, Derbyshire was built of blocks quarried from nearby, with dressings of Millstone Grit also quarried on the estate (*Figure 4.40*). The walls of Cardiff Castle, South Glamorgan, made of stone from nearby Wenvoe, provide another example. Carboniferous Limestone may be seen similarly used for many buildings in Ireland, notably in Galway City.[31] It is, however, the varieties of other colours and which contain fossil matter which have received more attention and which have been used for decorative effect. One of the classic Carboniferous Limestone stones is Frosterly 'Marble', which was

Figure 4.41 Contrary to widely held belief, many limestones, particularly the compact types, are virtually impermeable. The water butt at Lindale Trough, Cumbria (left) was carved from a solid block of Carboniferous Limestone. The butt at Whitehaven, north of Raw, Cumbria (right) is of slabs of Carboniferous Limestone with lead seals. (Courtesy of M. Mitchell)

formerly quarried at Frosterley on the banks of the River Wear, Durham. Dark grey to black in colour with eye-catching pale- to white-coloured sections of fossil corals, the stone was one of the first to be used in northern England for decorative effect. The fantastic columns in Durham Cathedral are an outstanding example of its use. A massive block was used for the tomb of Sir Thomas Gresham in the Church of St Helens the Great, London. Other blocks form the steps and the base of the alabaster font in St George's Chapel, Windsor Castle, Berkshire. Elsden and Howe[12] recorded that large slabs are used as radiator covers in the National Portrait Gallery, but apparently these covers have now been removed. The stone was also used for the step up to the High Altar in Peterborough Cathedral; and in Bristol Cathedral. It is recorded as having been exported for use in the base of the pulpit in the Cathedral at Bombay, India.[32] The stone was known also as Stanhope Black 'Marble'.[32] A tombstone slab by the south door of St Albans Cathedral, Hertfordshire has spectacular sections of corals (*Figure 4.42*).

(a)

(b)

Figure 4.42 An old tombstone slab, St Albans Cathedral, of Frosterly 'marble'. Fossil corals, white in colour, contrast vividly with the black of the limestone

Another classic and rarely seen stone is Duke's Red from Rowsley, Derbyshire. The stone is found on the estate of the Duke of Devonshire and the 7th Duke, fearful that the stone would be quickly exhausted, ordered that it should all be quarried and stored.[32] It is a deep red-coloured, fine-grained stone. It was given by the Duke of Devonshire and was used for the columns round the apse of St John's College Chapel, Cambridge. Not unexpectedly, it is used decoratively inside Chatsworth House, Derbyshire, the seat of the Dukes of Devonshire.

Derby Fossil, from Coalhill, and similar stones known as Derbydene or Derbydene Fossil or Monyash 'Marble' from around Wirksworth, Monyash and Cromford in Derbyshire are probably the most

(c)

Figure 4.43 Fossil crinoids in Carboniferous Limestone (seen here in Steeplehouse Quarry, Wirksworth, Derbyshire), are enhanced by cutting and polishing to contrast with the limestone in which they are embedded (a). The stone is used decoratively for (b) a plateau (standing on a table of onyx marble edged with serpentinite) in Chatsworth House, Derbyshire and (c) for flooring in the British Museum (Natural History) Geological Museum, London

widely used of the decorative Carboniferous Limestone stones. The stones are grey- to dark-fawn in colour and, when cut, sections of lighter coloured crinoids are prominent. Probably the most seen but least observed example is in the Royal Festival Hall, London where the entrance, stairways and foyers are clad with it. It has been widely used elsewhere, for example for the base of the columns in Chichley Hall, Buckinghamshire, inside 30 Gresham Street, London, in many London churches, in Westminster Cathedral and in the now sadly demolished Imperial Institute, South Kensington, London. It was used for the balastrade at the visitors entrance of Chatsworth House, Derbyshire (*Figure 4.43*). Many window sills are also made of it. A red-coloured variety is used for an eye-catching plateau in the Chapel corridor of Chatsworth House. Derbydene, specifically from Dene Quarry, Matlock, is recorded as used in Thorn House, St Martin's Lane, London. Matlock Fossil is a visually similar stone, quarried from near Matlock, Derbyshire. These crinoidal limestones occasionally are called screwstone.

Deepdale Fossil, from Deepdale, Yorkshire is light-brown to dark-grey in colour with many fossil markings. Swale Dale Fossil, from Barton, Yorkshire is pale brown in colour with many fossils. Orton Scar, from Orton Scar, Cumbria, is pale fawn with darker veins. Salterwath, from Crosby Ravensworth Fell, Cumbria, is dark brown with fainter markings. These stones demonstrate part of the range obtainable from the Carboniferous Limestone.

Hopton Wood Stone, a cream-coloured fine-grained crinoidal limestone, has been extensively used as a decorative and a building stone. It was beloved and extensively used by monumental masons and by artists. Barbara Hepworth's *Image* (1951-1952) is hewn from it as is Henry Moore's *Reclining Nude* (1937). A fine slab cross over five feet high (1.5 m) high and based on an early Celtic cross made of Hopton Wood Stone was erected at Heilbron, Orange River, South Africa. The stone has been used extensively in many public buildings including the Town Hall, Manchester, the Municipal Buildings, Leeds, St George's Hall, Liverpool and Chatsworth House, Derbyshire. It was also used for the paving of the river terrace of the Palace of Westminster, London and of the Bank of England in London. The fragments of crinoids appear as scattered darker spots within the compact fine-grained stone. This characteristic led to its use for headstones and this stone was one chosen by the War Graves Commission for military cemeteries of the First World War. In the past it was also used for kerbs and setts. Hadene Stone, quarried close to Hopton Wood is from the same geological formation and is visually indistinguishable.

Penmon Limestone from Penmon, Beaumaris, Anglesey is pale brown with darker veins and patches, blue-grey or grey-white in colour and is a close-grained, compact limestone. It is widely known as Penmon 'Marble'. It was used for Beaumaris Castle, and by the Mersey Dock and Harbour Board. It was also used for Edward I's spectacular Caernarfon Castle, Gwynedd, where it is banded with local Carboniferous brown sandstone to resemble the fifth-century walls of Constantinople.

In the past, many other stones were taken from the Carboniferous Limestone. Derby Black or Ashford Black warrants special mention. Near Ashford-in-the-Water, Derbyshire, beds of limestone never more than 2 feet thick (0.6 m) interspersed with shale partings outcrop over an area of about four square miles (10 square km). These limestone beds are very dark grey to black in colour, very fine-grained, somewhat muddy and, importantly, commonly unfossiliferous, although some beds are crowded with fossils. The stone will take a high polish. The stone was wrought mainly from underground and an industry which is now 'dead and almost forgotten'[33] was based on it. It provided stone used for 'chimney-pieces to table tops, from vases to jewellery, and from statuary to church flooring. At least one highly-polished slab was used as a mirror'.[33] The Derby Inlay Work (*see Figure 4.44*), or *pietra dura* was also based on it. The earliest recorded use is prehistoric; a skeleton was found with its skull adhering to a 2 foot long, 9 inches wide, 6 inches thick (0.6 × 0.2 × 0.15 m) dressed slab.[33] Hardwick Hall, Derbyshire has fireplaces of Derby Black; Chatsworth House, Derbyshire used much of the stone for decoration and structural work. In addition, quantities were

Figure 4.44 A magnificent example of the renowned Derby inlay work shows various coloured stones inlaid into a block of black Carboniferous Limestone (Derby Black 'marble'). (Courtesy of E.A. Jobbins)

'sold rough to other workers for finishing'.[33] Because of its uniform black colour, its fine-grain and its ability to take a high polish '... it is popular, preferred by many sculptors and marble workers to the Black Marbles of Ireland and Belgium'.[33] It is possible that this black 'marble' is more widespread than is commonly recognized. There were three black 'marble' producing areas: Ireland, Belgium and Derbyshire.

In Ireland the Carboniferous Limestone has an outcrop area about three times that of the United Kingdom and important black 'marbles' are taken from it, principally in Galway, Kildare, Kilkenny and Limerick. The local black Galway 'Marble' may be seen in the Cathedral of Galway and was 'used by Sir Christopher Wren in 1700 for the staircases of Kensington Palace'.[32] Kildare Black seems to have been used for little else than local walls and small buildings. Kilkenny's famous black and white 'marble' was used to face many buildings in Kilkenny. The white colour is due to veins of calcite and the sections of fossils. Kilkenny Black is well known from its use in 1872 to replace earlier Blue Lias columns on the west front of Wells Cathedral, Somerset. It has also been used for a fireplace in the White Swan Tavern, Chestertown, Maryland, USA, which was recently restored (1981) with the same stone. The walls of Limerick are 'of marble blocks...'.[34] In general all these varieties show white patches caused by fossil fragments or, occasionally, by larger, nearly complete fossils. Irish Black Marble appears to have been widely used during Victorian times.

Belgium has been and still is one of the world's leading producing countries of 'marble'. The industry dates back to the twelfth and thirteenth centuries. It should be remembered, however, that much stone was imported into Belgium, processed and then exported. Therefore, a reference to a stone being from Belgium may be misleading. Black coloured stone has been taken from the Carboniferous Limestone around Tournai since very early times. It has been imported into England since at least the twelfth century. Normally referred to as Tournai 'Marble', the stone is known to have been used for archaeologically and artistically significant fonts and for memorial slabs. Seven important Norman fonts of Tournai 'Marble' are known in Great Britain. They are at the Church of St Peter in St Mary Bourne, Hampshire, the Church of All Saints, East Meon, Hampshire, the Church of St Michael, Southampton, Hampshire, Winchester Cathedral, Hampshire, the Church of St Lawrence, Thornton Curtis, Humberside, Lincoln Cathedral and the Church of St Peter's, Ipswich, Suffolk. There seems little doubt that these fonts were fashioned in Belgium and imported into England in their finished state. To reach some of the churches the fonts must have been laboriously hauled overland for many miles. Undoubted mem-

Figure 4.45 Tournai Marble, a black stone from the Carboniferous Limestone of Belgium, acquired ecclesiastical significance in Britain. It was used for memorial slabs, such as that of Bishop Nigel, Ely Cathedral (a), and for fonts, such as that in the church of St Michael, Southampton (b)

orial slabs made of Tournai 'Marble' also are known; Bishop Nigel's tomb slab in Ely Cathedral, Cambridgeshire is one example (*Figure 4.45*).

There is, however, no unique test which will distinguish between the black limestones of Carboniferous Limestone age from Derby, Ireland and Belgium although the Irish Black commonly is speckled with fine white spots. It is possible that the study of the microfossils in a thin section may determine the provenance of a specimen, but any given section may not contain the microfossils on which a determination can be based. The study of a thin section implies that a sample must be removed from the object under investigation which may not be practicable. Purely visual inspection of black 'marble' does not enable the varieties to be distinguished. Carboniferous black 'marble' is sometimes confused with a black limestone of Devonian age. 'Plymouth Black marble forms the dark columns in the pulpit of St Paul's Cathedral, ...'[12], 'Derby Black ... probably occurs in many houses and churches'[12]; '... Thin black slab ... probably came from Tournai ...'[35] are extracts which point up the difficulty. The definite attribution of a black 'marble' is better based on archival or other written evidence. Black 'marble' was not commonly used by the Romans. Two Greek quarries were well known, one in Laconia and one on Lesbos. Other black stones were reported from Varro in Africa, Gaul (France) and Algeria. The Carboniferous Limestone of Ireland also yields other 'marbles.' The best known are Armagh Red and Cork Red (Victoria Red). They are partially recrystallized and red-stained, probably with hematite. Occasional crinoid ossicles may be present. Large quantities of both Armagh and Cork Red were used for mantelpieces and other decorative work. Armagh Red was used for the Armagh Catholic Cathedral (1873) and for some columns in St John's College Chapel, Cambridge (1869).[32] Cork Red may be found in the Exchange, Liverpool and the Exchange, Manchester. The red columns of the pulpit in St Paul's Cathedral, London (1861) were made of Cork Red.

Permian limestones

The Permian System includes marls, sandstones, conglomerates and limestones. One of the Permian limestones, the Magnesian Limestone, has been the source of many excellent and famous building stones and the cause of great controversy and of the appointment of a Committee of Parliament.

The story of the choice of Magnesian Limestone from the Bolsover Moor Quarry for the Palace of Westminster (the Houses of Parliament) in 1839, the substitution of indiscriminately selected Anston Stone and its subsequent deterioration is well known. (See for example, references 10 and 12.) The account given here is based mostly on Elsden and Howe[12]. Following the destruction of the Palace of Westminster by fire in 1834, a Commission of Parliament was set up to select a suitable building stone. The stone chosen was Magnesian Limestone from Bolsover Moor Quarry, Derbyshire. It was later discovered that the quarry could not supply blocks of stone of the size required. Another quarry, Mansfield Woodhouse Quarry, Nottinghamshire, also

in Magnesian Limestone was also unable to supply the stone in the sizes required. However Mansfield Woodhouse Quarry did supply 20 000 cubic foot which was used and 'has since been found to have worn well'. Anston Stone from Kiveton Quarries near Sheffield, Yorkshire, only eight miles from the Bolsover Moor Quarry, was substituted. 'The Anston quarries ... were worked indiscriminately from the surface to the bottom of the formation to a depth of 35 ft., the stone lying in 17 beds varying in thickness from 1 ft. to a few inches ... The whole of the beds were used, no particular beds were followed horizontally, no supervision at the quarries was provided for, and no seasoning of the stones took place ... The whole building, except the upper part of the towers and the front towards Abingdon street, was done with Anston stone. It cannot be denied that a great part of the Anston stone was of the first quality ... It is thus perfectly clear that the Commissioners' choice was not so much at fault as the supervision of the quarrying and the selection of the stone. The services of an expert were actually offered, for the modest salary of £150 per annum, to exercise supervision over the quarrying and delivery of the stone, but this offer came to nothing, because it could not be agreed who was to be responsible for the payment of this trifling amount ... the blocks used ... were selected by masons indiscriminately ... and no particular care was taken to mark the bedding, so that a great many stones were surbedded, an example of unpardonable slackness'.

In marked contrast, when the Museum of Practical Geology was built (1837–1848) in Jermyn Street, London, Sir Henry De la Beche, then Director of the Geological Survey and of the Museum, personally selected blocks of Anston Stone to be used in the building. When the Museum was demolished nearly one hundred years later in 1935, the stone was reckoned to be as good as new (*see Figure 4.46*). The Geological Museum has now been administratively transferred to the British Museum (Natural History) in Cromwell Road, South Kensington, London.

The Magnesian Limestone consists of upper and lower limestones separated by beds of marl. It crops out in a strip, rarely six miles (9.65 km) wide, from Nottingham, through Mansfield and Tadcaster to Darlington where it widens to the coast at Hartlepool, Sunderland and South Shields. The best building stones come from the lower limestones. They differ greatly from place to place.

Bolsover Moor Stone, from quarries on the moor, Derbyshire, a warm yellowish-brown, fine-grained dolomitic limestone was used for Southwell Cathedral, Lincoln Cathedral and Bolsover Castle, Derbyshire but not for the Palace of Westminster in London. Anston Stone, from Kiveton Quarries near Sheffield, Yorkshire, is pale brown to cream in colour, compact and fine-grained and was used to

(a)

(c)

(b)

(d)

Figure 4.46 Much Magnesian Limestone was used in York where it was known generally as Tadcaster Stone. It was used appropriately, for the City Gate, Tadcaster Road (a). (b) The Anston Stone entrance door of the Museum of Practical Geology (now the Geological Museum in South Kensington), opened in 1851 in Jermyn Street, was 'as good as new' when the building was demolished in 1935; (c) Bolsover Castle is of Bolsover Moor Stone, the stone originally chosen for the Palace of Westminster; (d) Roche Abbey is of stone taken from the Magnesian Limestone which crops out nearby. (Photo (b) courtesy British Museum (Natural History))

restore some flying buttresses of Westminster Abbey, London in 1847. The new (1851) Record Office, Fetter Lane also was built of this stone with limestone from Babbacombe, Devon and Kentish Ragstone. Anston Stone was used as recently as 1967 for repair work on the Palace of Westminster.

Mansfield Woodhouse Stone, Nottinghamshire is yellowish-brown in colour, somewhat crystalline and generally fairly coarse and granular in nature, although some of the stone is very fine-grained. It was used for paving in Westminster Hall, London and for the Martyrs' Memorial, Oxford.

Stone from Parliament Quarry on the west side of Common Lane, Mansfield Woodhouse is reputed to be that used for the Palace of Westminster. Huddleston Stone, from Yorkshire, is minutely cellular (micro-oolitic) or finely granular and pale grey to cream coloured. It was used widely and may be seen in York Minster, Selby Cathedral and Huddleston Hall. It was teamed with Red Mansfield Stone, a dolomitic sandstone, for the original Eleanor Cross, Charing Cross, London.

The famous Eleanor or Norman crosses were erected after 1290 by Edward I on his way to

Westminster with the body of his wife Eleanor of Castile. He erected a memorial cross at each place where his wife's body rested for a night. There were originally ten or more built. Those at Geddington (1291–1294) and Hardingstone, south of Northampton (*c.* 1295) are restored originals. They are made of Weldon Stone. Only a stump remains at Waltham, which was the last cross before London. The cross at Charing was destroyed in the seventeenth century. The present cross in the courtyard of Charing Cross railway station is a Victorian copy.

Roche Abbey Stone, from Roche Abbey, Yorkshire, which is white coloured, granular and sugary-looking, shows another variety of the Magnesian Limestone. Apart from Roche Abbey itself, the stone was used for Tickhill Castle, Yorkshire, which was licensed by Richard Lionheart and ruined by Cromwell, for Tickhill Church with its outstanding 124 foot (38 m) tower, and for many other churches in the area.

Tadcaster Stone was quarried to the west of Tadcaster, Yorkshire. It was used there for local building and transported to York to build the Minster. The well-known quarries of Jackdaw Crag and Lords and Smaws supplied stone for many important buildings including York Minster, Ripon Minster, Beverley Minster (Humberside) and many other churches.

It is a testimony to the Magnesian Limestone, which commonly has been noted to wear and weather well (although some did weather badly), that for the recent restoration of York Minster, Huddleston Quarry near Sherburn-in-Elmet, Yorkshire, which dates back to Roman times, was reopened.

The close correlation between building stone and geology may be especially observed from the use of the Magnesian Limestone. Many towns and most villages along and near the outcrop of the limestone are built of stone taken from it. The Romans and the Normans used it extensively.

Jurassic limestones

The Jurassic System has probably furnished more important, more enduring and more widely used limestones than any other system. Taken as a whole the Jurassic rocks are clays, shales, sands, sandstones with some ironstones and subordinate limestones (see *Figure 4.47*). Many of the limestones are markedly oolitic in character. As seen on p. 88, an oolite (properly an oolitic limestone) is a particular type of limestone. But the word is also used as part of the name of some specific formations, for example the Great Oolite, and the Inferior Oolite which have oolites as a major component. Many writers use the terms Lower, Middle and Upper Oolites as divisions of the Jurassic. This can cause confusion. Here the Jurassic section is divided simply into the Lias (lower Jurassic) and Oolites (middle and upper Jurassic).

Liassic limestones

The Lias formation consists mainly of clays with predominantly thin-bedded limestones in the lower part which provide hydraulic limestones in the south Midlands. There is a general tendency for the Lias to be more calcareous in the south of Britain and sandier in the north, where sandstones and oolitic ironstones may be found. The White Lias is a white to cream calcite-mudstone or rather impure limestone. It provides a dramatic example of a stone which although it has a very restricted outcrop, influences architecture both for style and appearance.

The allotment of the White Lias to the topmost beds of the Triassic System or to the bottommost of the Lias formation of the Jurassic is a matter of geological discussion. They are here assigned to the Lias, following the British Geological Survey usage.

Around Radstock, Somerset, the White Lias, a series of white, cream to pale-grey fine-grained limestones and calcite-mudstones, reaches 20 feet (6 m) in thickness. In that area it has been quarried for building stone on a large scale and its architectural effect is immediately obvious when entering Radstock (*Figure 4.48*). It has limited use elsewhere, for example as pinnacles between shafts of Blue Lias on tombs in the church at Curry Rivel, Somerset[35]; for small carvings in the voussoirs of the main West Door, Wells Cathedral[35] (*Figure 4.49*) and for rough building near Castle Cary, Somerset. The lowest part of the Lias, particularly in southern England, consists mainly of clays and marls with prominent thin-bedded limestones which are widely known as the Blue Lias. The limestones have been extensively used where they crop out for building and for ecclesiastical work, notably for instance, in some detached shafts, bases and capitals in Bristol Cathedral and for some shafts in the entrance porch of its near neighbour, the church of St Mary Radcliffe. Blue Lias was also used for shafts flanking the doorway at Wells Cathedral, and for shafts of the blank wall arcading in Exeter Cathedral[36], which is some way from its source. It has also been extensively used for paving slabs, kerbs and for tombs. The tomb in Wells Cathedral of Bishop Button II (died 1274), thought to be the earliest incised tomb in England, is a slab of Blue Lias. Blue Lias was also used for paving in both Wells Cathedral and in the Palace of Westminster. Kerbstones of the limestone may be seen at Chickerell and Lyme Regis, Dorset, and in many other towns and cities. As Donovan and Reid remarked[35] 'the stone commonly is misdescribed as Purbeck'.

Banked-up against the Carboniferous Limestone

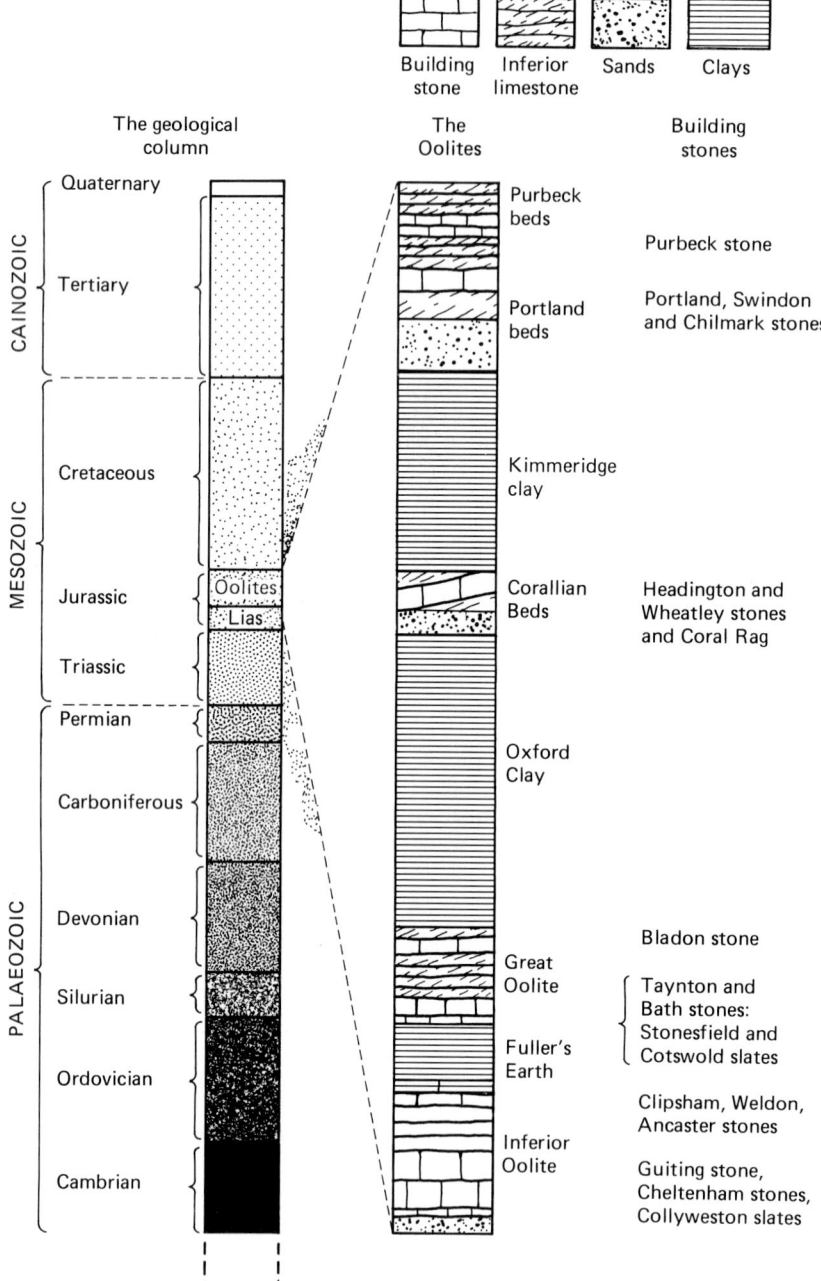

Figure 4.47 The generalized succession of the Jurassic rocks, together with the names of some of the building stones quarried from the major horizons. (After W.J. Arkell, *Oxford Stone*, Faber and Faber, London, 1947)

Figure 4.48 The direct relationship between geology and architectural appearance of buildings is demonstrated at Radstock, Somerset where the light coloured White Lias directly influences the street scene

Figure 4.50 Much Blue Lias was used for the chapter house of Llandaff Cathedral, near Cardiff. Sutton Stone, Dundry Stone, Coombe Down, Clipsham, Doulting, Beer, and Hornton Stone may also be found, with a roof of 'Westmorland Green' slate. Other stones have been used also and Caen Stone was used for some memorials and detailing. Few, if any, cathedrals are exclusively of one stone, the different stones commonly indicating building periods

Figure 4.49 White Lias was used for the small figures, mostly now decapitated, on the West Door of Wells Cathedral, Somerset

which makes up the Mendips, the Lower Lias appears as a pale cream-grey, coarse-grained limestone composed mainly of comminuted shell matter. At one time the Lias was quarried near Shepton Mallet, Somerset as Downside Stone. It was used for buildings in Shepton Mallet, in Wells Cathedral and for Nunney Castle, Somerset. A similar stone, also from the Lower Lias, was formerly quarried on the north side of the Mendips near Downside, south of

Bristol. It was known as Brockley Down Stone or Bastard Downside.

Sutton Stone, quarried near Bridgend, West Glamorgan is a massive whitish somewhat conglomeratic limestone which contains occasional large boulders of the underlying Carboniferous limestone. Like Downside Stone it is a littoral (near shore) deposit of the Lower Lias. It was used in Llandaff Cathedral.

An important limestone from the middle part of the Lias is Hornton Stone which was quarried at Edge Hill near Banbury, Oxfordshire. The colour may be blue-grey or brown with a greenish tint which is sometimes described as sage green. It crops out over the plateau area south of Edge Hill, capping the Burton Dassett or Little Bourton ridge. Lenticles of highly calcareous stone reach 1 to 2 feet (0.3-0.6 m) in thickness and may extend several yards. They commonly contain pockets or colonies of brachiopods. In the vicinity of Edge Hill the stone has been used for building and ornamental purposes (*Figure 4.51*). Further south, because of its ferruginous content, it has been exploited as a low grade

Figure 4.51 House of Hornton Stone (by Forsyth Lawson) with Painswick Stone dressings and Stonesfield slate roof. (Courtesy of J. Forsyth Lawson)

Figure 4.53 Unusually used in London, Ham Hill Stone from Somerset is found in Hampshire House, Bayswater Road

Figure 4.52 Memorial figure 1945–46 by Henry Moore, carved in Hornton Stone, Dartington Hall, Devon

calcareous iron ore. The best building stone is the least oxidized because it breaks into large blocks up to several tons in weight. The stone was often used by the sculptor Henry Moore, for example for the *Memorial Figure* at Dartington Hall, Devon. It was also used for his *Mother and Child* (1924), *Reclining Figure* (1947), *Square Form* (1936) and other pieces (*Figure 4.52*). Hornton Stone was used for the reredos of Ampleforth Abbey Church, Yorkshire, in the church at Harold Wood, Essex, the War Memorial, Staff College, Camberley, Surrey, the Moat House Hotel, Stratford-on-Avon, Warwickshire (where fine nests of Terebratulids can be seen in the stone), and elsewhere. This popular stone was used far more widely than is generally realized. The thirteenth century church at Hornton, Oxfordshire is a prime example of the use of the greenish brown variety.

Ham Hill Stone, from the upper part of the Lias, quarried at Hamdon Hill, near Norton-sub-Hamdon, Somerset, is a lenticular mass of detrital shelly limestone about 90 feet (27 m) thick although only about 50 feet (15 m) is worked for building stone. It has been worked at least since Roman times and some Roman coffins are made of it. A richly-toned brown in colour, it consists mostly of broken fossil shells with a ferruginous cement. Although the formation may be more or less sandy in places, the stone is correctly classified as a limestone, rather than a sandstone. Two beds were worked in particular. One was pale brown or buff in colour and known as the Yellow Bed. The second was darker in colour and known as the Grey Bed. It is a durable building stone which is most widely known for its use for the classic masterpiece, Montacute House, Somerset built in 1603. It was used also for Sherborne Abbey, Dorset. The window arches, quoins and coping stones of the west front, and the turrets of the tower, which are contrasted with a grey-coloured Devonian limestone, of Buckfast Abbey, Devon, are of Ham Hill Stone. Hampshire House, Bayswater Road, London (*Figure 4.53*) and the Ladbroke building, Piccadilly, London, are also of this stone. Its use was also extended to vernacular architecture, as seen unexpectedly in Hamstone House, Weybridge, Surrey. The outcrop of the stone extends southwards from Hamdon Hill to North Perrott, Dorset where it was wrought under the local name of North Perrott Stone.

Middle and Upper Jurassic limestones
Without doubt the limestones obtained from the series of Beds above the Lias (see *Figure 4.47*) have had a greater effect on the general appearance of towns, especially in southern England, than any other stones. Clay is the major constituent of the beds above the Lias and is of great importance for the production of bricks. However, the limestone members, primarily because of their ease of working and general consistency, have been extensively used

especially in southern England. One of these, the Portland Stone, has been used country-wide.

The limestones crop out over a large sweeping curve from the Dorset coast, through the Cotswolds where they form a prominent escarpment. The outcrop continues in a wide band through Oxfordshire and Northamptonshire, and forms a very narrow band north of the River Humber to sweep round to the coast near Redcar.

These Middle and Upper Jurassic limestones are generally oolitic in nature, but there are important exceptions. However, because the name 'oolite' is so familiar many of the important non-oolitic limestones are incorrectly referred to as oolites.

One of the important non-oolitic beds occurs at the bottom of the Lincolnshire Limestone, a unit within the Inferior Oolite. Inferior Oolite is the geological name for a formation which is found stratigraphically below the Great Oolite (*Figure 4.47*). It *does not* indicate that the stone is inferior in quality.

Around the village of Collyweston, Northamptonshire a sandy fissile limestone occurs at the base of the Lincolnshire Limestone. The fissile character is localized; in some directions the bed is found to become non-fissile. The bed varies in thickness. It is commonly 6 inches (15 cm) thick, but swells rarely to 3 or to 4 feet (0.8-1.2 m). The stone is wrought by removing sand (the Northamptonshire Sand) from beneath it and supporting the stone with wooden props. When the bed has been undercut, the props are knocked away and the limestone falls as large blocks known as 'logs'. From time to time the fall must be assisted by inserting wedges. The 'logs' are laid in the open with the bedding planes horizontal, and are kept liberally soaked with water, especially on the edges until frost is imminent. At that time the laid-out slabs are almost swamped with water. On freezing all of the 'logs' become a mass of ice. Under ideal conditions there should be a hard frost at night followed by a slow thaw during the day to 'move' the stone. Under those conditions water enters the bedding planes. When the next frost occurs further splitting takes place. After 'frosting' the stone may be 'clived' or split along the bedding planes. Once clived, the thin slabs are dressed for use and sold as Collyweston Slates, for use as tilestones (*Figure 4.54*).

(a)

(c)

(b)

Figure 4.54 When frost is forecast, horizontally laid 'logs' of Collyweston Slate are soaked with water (a). (b) After freezing the slabs may be split. This is known in Collyweston as 'cliving'. The split slabs are used as tilestones and may be seen extensively in Collyweston, where local oolitic limestone has been used for the houses (c). Note the obtrusive and unpleasant use of 'artificial stone' quoins seen behind an equally obtrusive electricity pole!

It is still widely believed that if the stone is not kept watered before frosting and is allowed to dry out it loses its fissile character. During mild winters the stone was sometimes taken back underground, covered with the dug-out sand, and the drift-mine sealed to prevent the 'logs' drying out. However, Honeyborne[37] demonstrated as long ago as 1975 that it was possible to get moisture back into a dried-out stone. If the moisture is re-introduced the 'logs' once again are susceptible to frost.

The stone commonly is bluish in colour but weathers to a familiar buff-colour. In the past the 'slates' were hung on wooden pegs; more recently nails were used. The size of the hole may be used as an indication of the age of use of the 'slate'.

Collyweston slates have been used since Roman times and are widely used for roofing in their own area. These tilestones may also be seen on Guildhall, London. They cover the roofs of a number of colleges at Cambridge including the First Court of Christ's College (1505–*c*.1511), and Caius Court of Gonville and Caius College (1565–1569). They were also used elsewhere[38], for example on Oakham Castle (1383) and on Phipps Mansion (1906), Westberry, Long Island, New York, USA. Over an acre of Collyweston slates cover the roof of the Haycock Hotel, Wansford-in-England, Peterborough.

Other historically important stones taken from the Inferior Oolites are also not markedly oolitic. Dundry Stone was worked from mines and quarries at Dundry Hill, south of Bristol, where traces of ancient workings may be seen. The old quarries were at the highest point of the hill just west of the village. The freestone is approximately 15 feet (4.6 m) thick, but the bed worked for building stone is only about six feet (1.8 m) thick. It overlies about 40 feet (12 m) of rag beds, which are stones which break with a ragged fracture and are not easily worked. The stone consists mostly of fragments of fossils. Fresh surfaces appear markedly granular and are commonly described as sugary. The stone was used for the great Gothic church of St Mary Redcliffe in Bristol, for St John's Church, Cardiff, in Llandaff Cathedral, and in several churches in the Republic of Ireland where its use may be traced along the waterways. An exceptional example of its use is in the Biconyll tomb (1448), Wells Cathedral. This is the only instance of its use in that Cathedral.

Doulting Stone, from Doulting near Shepton Mallet, Somerset is an exceptional pale-brown in colour and coarse-textured. It is described as a massive, granular, wedge-bedded bioclastic limestone in which fossils are uncommon.[39] Found on the south side of the Mendips, the building stone beds are about 45 feet thick (14 m) and only locally slightly oolitic. In places the character of the stone approaches that of the Lower Lias Downside Stone. Doulting Stone may have been formed, in part at least, by the erosion of the Downside Stone and other Lower Lias deposits.

In the past it was worked as two varieties; the Fine, Brown Bed or Brambleditch, and the Cheylinch (Chelynch), Grey or Weather Bed. The main example of the use of Doulting Stone is for Wells Cathedral (*Figure 4.55*). Elsewhere it has been used for restorations to Llandaff, Bristol and Exeter Cathedrals, for the interior nave and aisle of Guildford Cathedral, for the New (1898) Naval Barracks, Portsmouth, Hampshire, and as facings to some bridges on the M2 motorway.

Figure 4.55 The bulk of the fabric of Wells Cathedral, Somerset is of Doulting Stone, a granular limestone of Inferior Oolite age. Many of the Blue Lias limestone columns were replaced with Kilkenny Black 'marble' taken from the Carboniferous Limestone, near Kilkenny, Ireland

The Inferior Oolite at one time supplied such vast quantities of stone from quarries along the scarp of the Cotswold Hills at such places as Birdlip Hill and Cleeve Hill, near Cheltenham that the general name Cheltenham Stone was used.

Near Cheltenham and Gloucester a part of the Inferior Oolite is named the Lower Freestone. It is a pale-coloured oolitic limestone, commonly tough and compact and, on the whole, sufficiently free from fossils for it to be used readily for both building and carving. The Building Freestone reaches 130 feet (39 m) in thickness at Leckhampton Hill. Stone from Leckhampton Hill was used for Regency Cheltenham and for The Cross, Gloucester. Similar Cheltenham Stone was used for Tewkesbury Abbey, Gloucester.

Guiting Stone, from Guiting, Gloucestershire, warm-brown to yellow (Yellow Guiting) or white-cream (White Guiting) in colour is a coarse fossiliferous oolite which has been used in the north

Cotswolds since Norman times. It is taken from roughly the same geological horizon as Cheltenham Stone. Stanway House (*c.* 1630), Gloucestershire provides an outstanding example of its use. It may be seen also in Prinknash Abbey, Gloucestershire, the Royal Oxford Hotel, Oxford, and Abbey Bridge, Worcester.

Other Inferior Oolite stones, mostly named from where they are quarried, were also used outside their immediate area and thus achieved a wider renown. Painswick Stone, used for Gloucester Cathedral, is an example. Nailsworth Stone was widely used locally.

During Inferior Oolite times a basin of deposition ran northwards through Rutland, Lincolnshire and Northamptonshire, in which thick deposits were laid. Rocks deposited in this basin are known as the Lincolnshire Limestone. They crop out at Kettering and thicken rapidly northwards to reach a maximum of about 130 feet (39 m) at Sleaford. From here the deposit thins towards Market Weighton, and is recognizable north of the River Humber as the Cave Oolite which is 38 feet (12 m) thick.

The Lincolnshire Limestone is divided into two parts, with the upper beds resting on an eroded and channelled surface of the lower beds. These features strongly resemble modern carbonate deposits in shallow seas and the channels were probably formed under water by currents on the shoals of ooliths.

The Lincolnshire Limestone is not a homogeneous deposit, either vertically or laterally. The building stone is wrought mainly from the Upper Lincolnshire Limestone. Because the section exposed in any one quarry may vary considerably both laterally and vertically stone from one quarry may often resemble stone from another. The practised eye, however, may be able to distinguish the stone taken from the different quarries.

Without doubt, Barnack Stone, no longer obtainable, from Barnack, near Stamford, Lincolnshire, is the classic stone taken from the Lincolnshire Limestone. Coarse-textured and shelly, this stone was so highly regarded that the Abbots of Peterborough maintained quarrying rights on it. It was one of the earliest of the stones worked from this formation, which was known to have been quarried from at least the Roman period until the fifteenth century, when it seems to have been worked out.

Barnack Stone was used for Peterborough Cathedral and is particularly known for its use for Ely Cathedral (*Figure 4.56*). It was identified as the stone of the Losinga statue in Norwich Cathedral and the Romans re-used large blocks of it for the recently discovered (1976) river wall along the Thames. Burghley House, Cambridgeshire (formerly Huntingdonshire) is built of it.

Ancaster Stone from near Grantham, Lincolnshire varies within the quarry, as do most stones. Two main varieties may be distinguished; a cream-buff

Figure 4.56 The magnificent Prior's Door, Ely Cathedral is a magnificent testament to the enduring qualities of Barnack Stone

coloured oolite, usually fine grained, but with some slightly coarser beds with broken fossil matter; and a coarse shelly variety with a large amount of crystalline calcite, known as the Ancaster Rag. Ancaster Stone may be locally rich in small, rolled gastropods and may be pisolitic.

Ancaster Stone was used for part of Lincoln Cathedral, for numerous mansions and churches in Lincolnshire, and in the Town Hall, Holborn, London. It was also used for some Cambridge colleges including the Chapel, St John's; Tree Court, Gonville and Caius; and Trinity Hall.

Casterton Stone, also called Stamford Stone, from near Stamford, Lincolnshire, is beige-coloured and somewhat coarser grained than others in this group. It was used for many buildings in Stamford, notably for its Town Hall. It was reputedly used for Pembroke and for Trinity College, Cambridge. Elsewhere it was used in Truro Cathedral, Cornwall, Oundle School, Northamptonshire, and the Post Office, Cambridge. At one time the stone was sold as

Stamford Grit. A compact, usually blue-hearted, sparsely oolitic variety, was smoothed, rather than polished, and sold as Stamford Marble.

Ketton Stone from Ketton, near Stamford, Lincolnshire is generally very pale cream to yellow-buff in colour, with some blocks a distinct pink. In some beds it is beautifully regular medium-grained oolite. Other beds, called Ketton Rag, are more heavily cemented with crystalline calcite and the ooliths are more variable. The Ketton oolite and Casterton Stone may be difficult to distinguish. A characteristic feature of Ketton Stone is the absence of crystalline calcite as a matrix. This is in marked contrast with other oolites from the Lincolnshire Limestone.

The fine Ketton oolite has been used in Downing College, Cambridge, where pink-coloured blocks are prominent (*Figures 4.57 and 4.58*), for repairs to the Palace of Westminster, in the City Hall, Norwich, for Cotterbrook Hall, Northamptonshire, and for Martins Bank, Coventry.

Clipsham Stone, from Clipsham, near Oakham, Leicestershire is a buff- to cream-coloured, medium-grained oolite with shell fragments. It is possibly the most widely known of the Lincolnshire Limestones because it was used in the past by the Romans. More recently it was used for restoration work on the Palace of Westminster and for the Berkeley Hotel, London. The London Stone, which, until 1960 was incorporated in the south wall of St Swithin's Church, Cannon Street, London is of Clipsham Stone. The London Stone is now set in a niche in the wall of the Bank of China on Cannon Street. The Stone has been in existence since at least 1198 when it was known as the Lonnenstane.

Many blocks of limestone, notably some blocks of Clipsham stone and other Jurassic limestones, are found to be blue-hearted. This means that the centre

Figure 4.58 Ketton Stone, including some pink coloured blocks, used for the north (or 'Wrens') door during the rebuilding of the north-east corner of the north transept of Ely Cathedral in 1699, provides a strong and unpleasant contrast with the Barnack Stone used for much of the fabric. Although both stones are taken from the Lincolnshire Limestone, due regard must be paid to the colour and structure of the stone when restorations are carried out

Figure 4.57 The remarkably fine oolitic limestone from Ketton, Northamptonshire was used for Downing College, Cambridge. Blocks of pink stone are noticeable

of the block is blue-grey in contrast to the buff-brown colour of the surrounding stone. Normally any iron minerals in sediments are oxidized and a brownish colour is seen in the subsequent rock. However, iron minerals in the reduced condition, which have been deposited in an oxygen-free environment, have a blue-grey colour. These blocks are commonly rejected as flawed, although they are thought by many masons to be more durable than the cream-coloured stone[40].

Blocks of blue-hearted limestone are often not used because they are not homogeneous. However, Donovan Purcell deliberately used blue-hearted Clipsham Stone for replacement columns in the Galilee Porch of Ely Cathedral to provide a contrast and to avoid a dull uniform appearance.

Blue-hearted blocks of limestones, like all limestones, eventually weather to a grey-coloured surface.

Weldon Stone, from near Corby, Northamptonshire, is thought to have been used for the old, pre-Fire St Paul's Cathedral, London, although some authorities think that the imported Caen Stone was used. It is a pale-brown to buff-coloured, fine even-grained oolite with variable amounts of shell matter and an open texture. There are at least three varieties: Fine Bed, Coarse Bed, which is generally shelly and has voids, and Hard Rag, which occurs intermittently through the beds. The stone is said to be particularly resistant to frost. Blocks re-used in Roman times were found in the river wall, London. Kirby Hall, Northamptonshire provides an outstanding example of its use and many Cambridge colleges including Kings College Chapel, Cauis, Jesus, Clare Hall, and Sidney Sussex used the stone. Boughton House, Northamptonshire, and Rushton Hall, Northamptonshire testify to its popularity, as does the new building in the Market Place, Northampton.

The Cave Oolite is a well-cemented, compact oolitic limestone within the Lincolnshire Limestone. It has a considerable number of patches of a crystalline calcite, much of it in optical continuity, which cements ooliths of varying size. It crops out

(a)

(b)

(c)

(d)

Figure 4.59 (a) Weldon Stone from a quarry immediately behind was used for this delightful Quarry Master's House, near Corby, Lincolnshire; (b and c) Edge bedded Weldon Stone (pp.104, 120) has weathered badly at Kirby Hall, Northamptonshire; (d) The Eleanor Cross (p. 97), mostly of Weldon Stone, at Geddington, Northamptonshire, although much restored through the years is one of the two crosses which now remain substantially complete

from the River Humber through South Cave and Newbald. There it occurs as a considerable spread and was quarried on a large scale west of the village. It was used in Beverley Minster, Humberside where it was called Newbald Stone and Cave Marble. It was also used for interior work around Brough, for Holderness Monastery and for Hull Docks, all in Humberside.

Higher up in the Jurassic, the Great Oolite Series contains many well-known and widely used oolitic limestones. At the base of the Great Oolite Series is a thin-bedded fissile sandy limestone, remarkably similar in appearance to the Collyweston Slates at the base of the Inferior Oolite. These are the famous tilestones known as the Stonesfield Slates.

The Stonesfield Slates are light brown in colour and were formerly mined near Stonesfield, Oxfordshire. They were frosted in a similar manner to those from Collyweston. They appear to have been used

(a)

(b)

Figure 4.60 The Stonesfield slate, geologically similar to Collyweston slate, was used widely around the village of Stonesfield, seen in (a) on Home Close, High Street; (b) a cottage outhouse roof of Stonesfield slate in Filkins, Oxfordshire is reputed to be 300 years old

since Roman times, but some authorities, for example Arkell in his book *Oxford Stone*[41] doubts whether the Romans discovered the 'frosting' process. Stonesfield Slates were once widely used in the Cotswolds. They are now unobtainable and old buildings are bought just to obtain the 'Slates' for re-use on new buildings. They are renowned for their use for the roofs of many of the colleges in Oxford. It is doubtful if many people could distinguish between a Stonesfield and a Collyweston Roof from ground level.

The name Stonesfield Slate should properly be restricted to the stone taken from the Stonesfield Slate horizon. These beds are thin and are restricted to a small area around the village of Stonesfield. Further afield similar stone of about the same horizon may be found along a line which extends roughly from Andoversford through Naunton to Stow-in-the-Wold. These 'Slates' are better known as Cotswold Slates and probably many identifications of Stonesfield Slate should be Cotswold Slate.

From place to place, naturally laminated beds occur in thicknesses which make them suitable for use as tilestones. They are commonly known as Presents.

Bath Stone

Bath Stone, the most famous of the stones wrought from the Great Oolite Series, was at one time quarried and mined on a large scale around Bath, Avon. The stone was named from the localities where it was quarried; for example, Stoke Ground, Winsley Ground, Westwood Ground, Box Ground (or St. Adhelm Stone) and Bradford Stone.

There is no unique characteristic which distinguishes one variety from another. It is possible, however, to group them into three distinct horizons (see *Figure 4.61* and *Table 4.1*). Coombe Down Stone has fine veins of crystalline calcite running through it, as does the equivalent stone to the east, Box Ground. The veins are a very good indicator, but not an absolutely unique characteristic of these varieties. Allen Howe[42] states that ' ... Coombe Down Stone ... is liable to contain thin veins of calcite and small iron-stains ...', while Arkell[41] maintains 'the test for Bath Stone in a building is the presence of fine vertical calcite veins. These are infallibly present in Box Ground Stone and are called "watermarks" by the Oxford masons ... They never run parallel to the bedding, and when they appear to do so in a building it is a sign that some of the blocks have been joint-bedded'.

Bath Stone has been used since Roman times; some Roman buildings, now nearly 2000 years old, are still in use. A fine example of the use of Bath Stone, and certainly the most easily seen, is Apsley House (The Wellington Museum) at Hyde Park Corner, London (*Figure 4.62*). It was originally built of brick and was

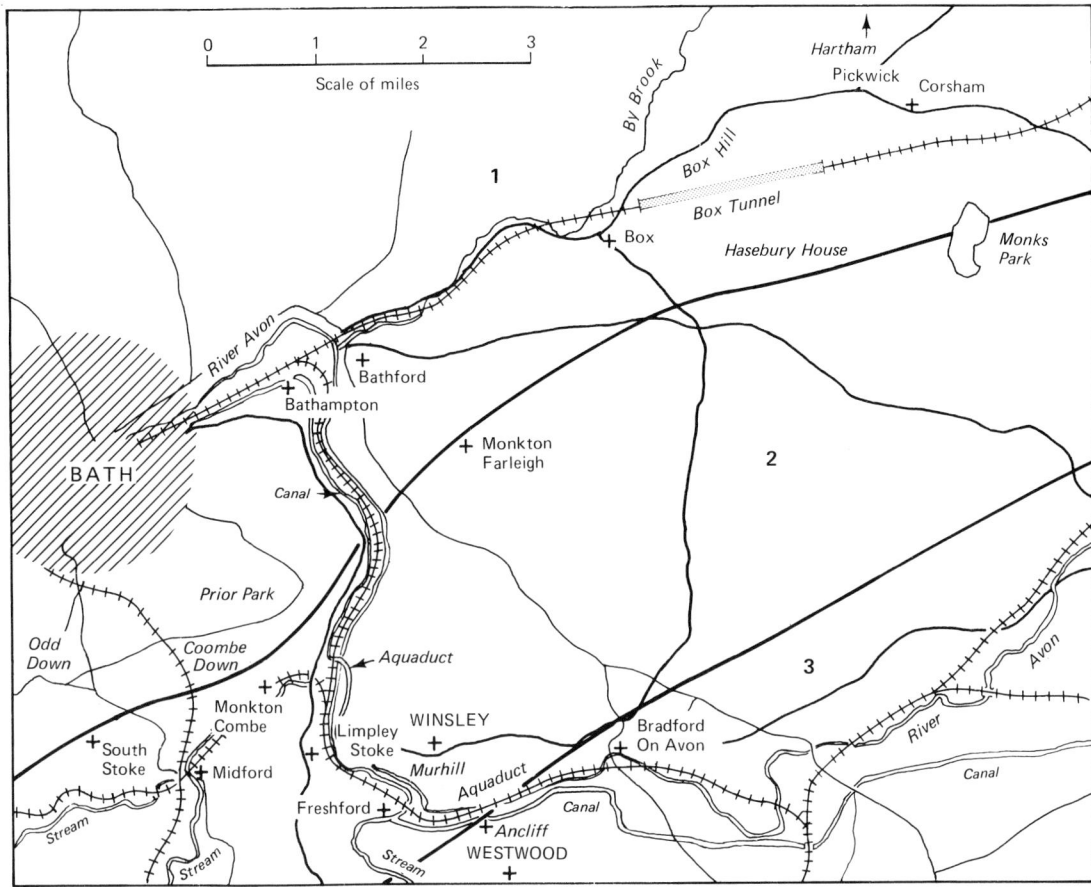

Figure 4.61 The lines on the map showing the principal
Bath Stone Quarry locations separate the groupings shown
in Table 4.1. (After W.J. Arkell, *Oxford Stone*, Faber and
Faber, London, 1947)

Table 4.1 Characteristics of Bath Stone

Stratigraphic position	Name of variety*	Characteristics
3: Higher than 2 stratigraphically	Bradford Stone	Characteristically of poor quality, very shelly with shells in well marked layers. markedly current bedded.
2: Upper	Farleigh Down Bathampton Down Winsley Ground Freshford Ground Stoke Ground Westwood Ground	Characteristically soft, not shelly (but there are rare large shells) and usually rather finely and evenly graded. Farleigh Down is typically brown, the others are paler.
Straddles levels 1 and 2	Monk's Park	Cement characteristically crystalline, paler and finer in grain than others.
1: Lower	Coombe Down Odd Down Box Ground (in Corsham-Box area)	Characteristically shelly/fragmental and medium grained.

*Many other local names have been used for different varieties of Bath Stone. It appears that the varieties Monk's Park, Ridge Down and Corsham Down were not widely used until the Box Railway Tunnel, near Bath, was built[4,5].

(a)

(b)

(c)

Figure 4.62 (a) Perhaps the most seen example, Apsley House ('No 1, Piccadilly') is clad, over brick, with Box Ground Stone variety of Bath Stone; (b) the minarets of the Royal Pavilion, Brighton. Originally of Bath Stone these were replaced with glass reinforced fibre, and are now being replaced again with Bath Stone; (c) Bradford Stone, a coarse, shelly variety of Bath Stone quarried at Bradford-on-Avon, Wiltshire, was used for the walls of this cottage in Bradford-on-Avon; finer grained Bath Stones form the quoins with Ham Hill Stone dressings

covered in 1828 with Box Ground Stone, shortly after it was presented by the grateful nation to the Duke of Wellington. An interesting contrast is seen between the Box Ground Stone of the house and the Portland Stone pillars supporting the railings. Monk's Park Stone was used for Salisbury House, London, the Polytechnic, Battersea, London, the Town Hall, Capetown, South Africa, and more recently for the Sun Alliance House, Bristol. Coombe Down Stone was used in the northern and western faces of Buckingham Palace, London and for restoration of Henry VII's Chapel, Westminster Abbey in about 1923.

Many other buildings in other cities are recorded as being built of one or another variety of Bath Stone, but it is difficult to distinguish the varieties when they are in a building. As Arkell wrote in *Oxford Stone*,[41] 'There are many varieties of Bath Stone and not even the experts can tell them apart'. Bath Stone (as a generic term) was used widely for dressings for churches. Many housing estates of the Victorians and later, employed the stone for window-sills and for copings to walls. For example, ' . . . it has been used with excellent effect as dressings in red-brick residences on the Westbury Estate, Putney (London)'[12].

Cotswold Stone

Other oolitic limestones of Great Oolite age were formerly available on a wide scale from so many quarries in the Cotswolds that the general name Cotswold Stone was given to them. Care must be taken to distinguish them from the geologically older Cheltenham Stone of Inferior Oolite age.

Taynton Stone, quarried at Taynton, Oxfordshire, is one of the best known and earliest used of the Great Oolite stones. Brown in colour with paler brown streaks, it is coarse in texture and shelly. It is renowned for its use for the Wren church of St Stephen Walbrook in the City of London, and for the interior of St Paul's Cathedral, London. Stone for both of these buildings was supplied by Thomas Strong who had ' . . . a reputation . . . for being a progressive craftsman, expert to a degree rare among country-bred masons . . . up-to-date in his methods capable of executing designs . . . with intelligence and fidelity'[44]. The stone was also used for some early Oxford Colleges, including Magdalen, Merton and St John's, and for Eton College (1448–1450). It was also spectacularly used for most of Blenheim Palace in Oxfordshire. A similar type of stone was quarried at Minchinhampton, Gloucestershire.

Although unrecognized for many years, Alwalton 'marble' has now been identified as the stone of the columns in the entrance porch of Peterborough Cathedral. It was also used for some of the columns in the Galilee Porch of Ely Cathedral and in the lowest storey of St Hugh's Choir, Lincoln Cathedral.[38]

The stone is an extremely oyster-rich limestone from the Great Oolite. It crops out as a tough blue-grey bed along the Alwalton Lynch on the banks of the River Nene at Alwalton near Peterborough, Northamptonshire. The 'marble' polishes to an interesting, attractive and distinctive surface which is commonly recorded as Purbeck 'marble', although it is, in fact, quite different. The 'marble' was certainly known to and used by the Romans at nearby Castor. The Abbey of Peterborough held the workings.

The recumbent effigy of Abbot Benedict (1177–1193) in Peterborough Cathedral is made of Alwalton 'marble'. The twelfth century font is also a fine specimen. The font is supported on pillars and a base made of Purbeck 'marble', and the difference

Figure 4.63 New Purbeck 'marble' columns (front) with drums placed 'in bed', with original Alwalton 'marble' columns (rear) in Galilee Porch, Ely Cathedral

Figure 4.64 Alwalton 'marble' was wrought from a thin bed exposed in the banks of the River Nene, at Alwalton Lynch, Northamptonshire, where fallen blocks may still be found

(a)

(c)

(e)

(b)

(d)

(f)

(g)

Figure 4.65 (a) The thick bedding and widely spaced joints of Portland Stone are seen in the cliffs at Portland Bill, Dorset; (b) Portland Roach clads the Economist Building, St James's Street, London. It may contain masses of the fossilized alga *Solenopora* (c); (d) Portland Stone slabs are used to remarkable effect on the domes of the Victoria and Albert Museum, South Kensington, London; (e) the characteristic black and white weathering found on Portland Stone, particularly in polluted atmosphere, may lead to distressing patterns. Architectural detailing should ensure that rain water does not flow across surfaces; (f) the copy of The Magna Carta, presented by Great Britain to the United States of America on its Bicentennial, rests on a slab of gneiss from Ardivachar Point, North Uist (the oldest rock in Great Britain), which in turn rests on a slab of Portland Stone; (g) the colour difference, accentuated by weathering, is displayed in Lloyds Bank, Stamford, Lincolnshire which used Portland Stone, bottom storey, Bath Stone above and Portland Stone, uppermost storey

between the two stones may be easily seen. Similar stones have been worked as Raunds Marble north-east of Northampton and as Stanwick Ragstone near Higham Ferrers near Raunds.

Portland stone

Towards the top of the Jurassic another important oolitic limestone, the Portland Stone, is found. The Portland Beds, from which stone is taken for building, form the tilted tableland of the Isle of Portland, the two arms of Lulworth Cove, Dorset and the cliffs of the Isle of Purbeck. The Portland Stone beds are remarkably well jointed.

The stone is a fine- and even-grained oolite and may be so fine-grained that it is sometimes difficult to see that the stone is oolitic in structure. A very pure limestone, it is about 95 per cent calcium carbonate. When first quarried the stone is warm cream in colour. However, particularly when used in smoke-polluted atmospheres, it weathers to a characteristic black and white colour. The sheltered side is blackened and a skin of calcium sulphate develops underneath.

The various beds of the Portland Stone series differ in character and in thickness. The building and quarry trade names of Base Bed or Best Bed, Whitbed and Roach are generally applicable to types of stone rather than to precise geological horizons.

A typical generalized section through the Portland Stone series is:

Strati-graphic level	Bed name	Thickness
Top	Roach	3 feet (0.9 m) or more
	Whit Bed	7 to 15 Feet (2–4.6 m)
	Flinty Bed	2 feet (0.6 m)
	Curf	0 to 4 feet (0–1.2 m)
	Little Roach or Base Bed Roach	0 to 3 feet (0–0.9 m), notably impersistent
	Base Bed or Best Bed	5 to 10 feet (1.5–3 m)
Base	Chert Beds	60 to 70 feet (18–21 m)

Not all of the beds are necessarily present in any one quarry and the beds may vary greatly within limited areas.[45] If the Flinty Bed and Curf are present, the Whit Bed and Base Bed may easily be differentiated. If they are absent it may not be possible to distinguish between the two. Base Bed Roach may be replaced by fine oolite. Veins of calcite, called Snailcreep, may be found running through the stone. Snailcreep is similar to the watermarks seen in Bath Stone.

Roach is normally found at the top of the Portland Stone series. It is a cream-coloured oolitic limestone, honeycombed by mostly empty moulds of fossils. In some of these moulds the internal casts of shells may remain. In particular, internal casts of lamellibranchs (*Trigonia*) are known locally as 'orses 'eads. Internal casts of gastropods (*Aptyxiella*) are known as Portland Screws. The term roach has been applied to a number of different rocks in various parts of the country. It has been used for a conglomerate and the Old Red Sandstone in the Lake District, for rock in the Coal Measures of Staffordshire and for other rocks elsewhere. To be unambiguous the particular roach should be specified, for example Portland Roach.

The Portland Roach, not widely used before 1939, has, since the end of the 1939 to 1945 war, been increasingly used for its decorative appearance. It has been used to great effect in The Economist Building, St James's Street, London, for the Commercial Union House, Birmingham; and recently (1982) for Finwell House, Finsbury Square, London. The French Lieutenant met his woman on blocks of Portland Roach making up The Cobb at Lyme Regis, Dorset.

The Canadian Pacific building, in Finsbury Square and St Paul's Cathedral Choir School are other examples. The Assize Courts, Cumberland House, Crown Square, Manchester is a fine example, faced with an unusual type of Portland Roach containing masses of algal origin (*Solenopora*).[46]

'The earliest known users of Portland Stone were the Romans in about 55 BC',[47] and columns of Portland Stone were found at Dorchester, Dorset. The oldest known building of Portland Stone (undifferentiated) is Rufus Castle, on the Isle of Portland itself, which is generally dated at 1080 AD. The stone was sent to Exeter and to London in the fourteenth century[48] where it was used in the Tower of London (1349) and in London Bridge (1350). Following its use, first by Inigo Jones for Banqueting Hall, Whitehall, London (1610) and secondly by Christopher Wren for the re-building of St Paul's Cathedral London after the Great Fire of 1666, Portland Stone became generally popular.

Its use is more widespread throughout the British Isles than any other Jurassic oolitic limestone. It has also been used on a large scale elsewhere around the world. It '. . . is the only limestone found in the city of Newcastle'.[49] It was used for the Metropolitan Cathedral of Christ the King, Liverpool, for the engraved plaque commemorating Eric Gill at Hopkin's Crank, Ditchling Common, Sussex and, unusually, as tilestones covering the domes of the Victoria and Albert Museum, London. It was also used for building in Colonial Williamsburg, Virginia, USA.

Although the Portland Beds are named from the Isle of Portland, they are thicker, better exposed and geologically more interesting in the Isle of Purbeck where the Portland Stone reaches 115 feet (35 m) in thickness. The stone was quarried on the Isle of Purbeck from early times and is known as Purbeck-Portland. Two freestones, called the Pond and the Under Freestone were worked. Stone from quarries at Seacombe, near Swanage, Dorset was used for paving, kerbs and steps. The staircase of the Sedgwick Museum, Cambridge is made of it[3]. Portland-Purbeck is recorded for use for the lighthouse at Margate, for part of Dover Pier[3] as well as for local churches.

Stones of the same age as Portland Stone but of totally different character are quarried in the Vale of Wardour, Wiltshire, under the names Chilmark Stone, Tisbury Stone and Vale of Wardour Stone. The fact that these stones are of Portlandian age has led to a number of misconceptions that the stone is similar to that found on the Isle of Portland itself. Although some sandy oolitic beds of Portlandian age are recorded in the Vale of Wardour, the Chilmark, Tisbury or Wardour stones are sandy, glauconitic limestones. They were quarried and mined near Tisbury, Chilmark, Chicksgrove, Wockley and at Lower Lawn, Wiltshire. The most extensive galleries were those at Chilmark. Many individual beds were named including the Trough, Hard or White Bed, the Green Bed and the Fretting Bed. However, after exposure, when stone from these beds is dry, it does not seem possible to recognize any differences between them.

The Vale of Wardour stones have been recorded as used in many important buildings (*Figure 4.66*). Salisbury Cathedral (thirteenth century) is built of

Figure 4.66 Grains of the mineral glauconite in Chilmark stone, a sandy limestone, are responsible for the green cast seen in Salisbury Cathedral

Chilmark Stone. This stone specifically was also used for Hampshire County Council Offices (1910) and extensions (1932), the West Gate, City of Winchester, restorations by His Majesty's Office of Works (1932), and by Sir Gilbert Scott for restorations to St Albans Abbey, Hertfordshire. Chilmark Stone was used for the remarkable 125 feet (38 m) high church spire at Teffont, Wiltshire. The south front of Wilton House, Wiltshire is of stone from the Chilmark Quarries. It may be directly compared with stone from the nearer Upper Greensand used for the east front. The Chilmark Trough Bed was recorded as having been used for the renovation (1867) of the Chapter House, Westminster Abbey, London.

The stone of Blandford Forum church, Dorset, is said to be from the Tisbury Quarry but has been called incorrectly Wiltshire Greensand. Tisbury Stone, specifically, was used for Winchester College, Hampshire.

Purbeck 'Marble'

The Purbeck Beds of the Isle of Purbeck, the Isle of Portland, the Vale of Wardour and elsewhere, which overlie the Portland Stone beds, consist of a varied series of limestones, shales, shellbeds and mudstones. The famous Purbeck 'Marble' is part of this series. More than twenty beds of limestone were recognized and named individually by quarrymen including Laning, Red Rag, Shingle, Spangle and Upper Tombstone Bed. Each bed is said to have its own particular uses, for example, tombstones, kerbstones, many of which can still be identified in use, flooring, setts and steps. Some of the limestones can be easily split into thin slabs which were used as tilestones.

There are many fossils in the Purbeck Beds. Certain fresh-water snails (*Viviparus*) occasionally built laterally extensive, but not very thick beds, of limestone which now constitute the Purbeck 'Marble'. The 'marble' occurs as two thin beds near the top of the Upper Purbeck. Each bed never exceeds four feet (1.2 m) and seldom is more than one foot (0.3 m). The 'marble' was used by the Romans, but after that period, there appears to have been little demand for it until the twelfth century. The quarry at Worth Matravers, Dorset, is mentioned in about 1190 and after that the fashion for the stone seems to have caught on.

The notable examples of its use include parts of Salisbury Cathedral, Wiltshire (*Figure 4.67*), and the beautiful choir columns of Ely Cathedral, Cambridgeshire, where the stone is seen properly in bed (*Figure 4.68*).

Purbeck 'Marble' has been used for many of the columns of the choir of Exeter Cathedral. They have recently been cleaned and, oddly, left unpolished to reveal a dull-grey surface. This does not show to best advantage the surface pattern for which the marble

Figure 4.67 Small figures at the base of the central column of the Chapter House, Salisbury Cathedral, show the typical surface pattern of Purbeck 'marble' caused by countless small fossilized gastropods ('snails')

Figure 4.68 The variation in Purbeck 'marble' is seen in the columns in the south choir aisle, Ely Cathedral, which are constructed of drums laid, properly, in bed

is best known or display a contrast with the main stone of the fabric. It seems to negate the purpose for which the stone was originally chosen.

Exeter Cathedral is possibly one of the best recorded examples for the use of stone. The use of Beer, Ketton, Doulting, Bath, Salcombe, Caen, Ham Hill and Portland are all well documented (see, for example, reference 40).

The 'Marble' was used as far north as Durham for some shafts in the Galilee Chapel of the Cathedral and is recorded in Normandy, France. Apart from its use as a structural element, the 'Marble' has been used extensively for effigies, coffins, incised slabs and other ecclesiastical adornments. They are extensively monographed by Rosemary Leach[51].

Cretaceous limestones

The Cretaceous system has yielded some limestones which, while not widely used, have attained a degree of importance particularly in southern England.

Lower Cretaceous limestones

The Weald Clay near the base of the Cretaceous contains subordinate beds of shelly limestone and beds of slightly calcareous sandstone. Two main varieties of limestone are found known as Small-'Paludina' and Large-'Paludina' limestone. They are composed of either small or large species of the freshwater mollusc *Viviparus*. Small-'Paludina' limestone contains the small species, *Viviparus elongatus* and the Large-'Paludina' limestone contains *V. sussexiensis*. These beds of Wealden Marble are rarely one foot (0.3 m) thick. In many areas they are a maximum of about six inches (15 cm), but commonly are only two or three inches (5–8 cm)

Figure 4.69 Cross sections of the large species of the gastropod *Viviparus*, of which the Large-'Paludina' 'marble' is mostly composed, distinguish Wealden from Purbeck 'marble'

thick. They have been quarried for a long time and have been used both as a structural and an ornamental stone. They are usually known by the name from where they were wrought. The Large-'Paludina' limestones include Bethersden 'Marble' (Kent), Petworth 'Marble' (Sussex), Sussex 'Marble' and Laughton Stone (Sussex). The Small-'Paludina' Marble was quarried at Charlwood, Surrey.

Large-'Paludina' occurs only in the Weald Clay and does not occur in the Purbeck. Therefore, the presence of Large-'Paludina' is diagnostic of a Wealden Marble even if it is not possible to suggest a provenance. Small-'Paludina' limestone from the Weald Clay and Purbeck Marble may easily be confused, especially when seen isolated as slabs or columns in buildings. Other limestone beds within the Weald Clay may contain the fossils *Margaritifera (Pseudunio)*, (the 'Unio' Marble') or *Filosina (Cyrena)*. Slabs of these beds are often seen in paving and sometimes as columns and steps. They were no doubt passed off originally as one of the Wealden 'Marbles'.

The Wealden 'Marbles' do not appear to have been used extensively for building. It is generally recorded that some thin shafts and the old steps to the altar in Canterbury Cathedral are of Bethersden 'Marble'. However, at least some of the blocks which make up the steps are of 'Unio' Marble'. Bethersden 'Marble' may also be seen in Bethersden Church, Kent and in the fifteenth century tower arch of Biddenham Church, Kent. Wealden Marble (Large-'Paludina' limestone known locally as winkle stone)[52] was used for Petworth House. Presumably this is Petworth Marble dug from nearby.

All Saints' Church, Staplehurst illustrates well the use of locally quarried Small-'Paludina' limestone which is only one to two inches (5 cm) thick by the Normans as well as its use through Early English times. Large-'Paludina' 'Marble' was used in the church during the Perpendicular period[53]. In this church these Wealden limestones may be directly compared with Purbeck 'Marble' used for some Early English moulded bases and little bell capitals.

Otherwise unspecified Wealden 'Marble' of the Large-'Paludina' type was used as slabs in the floor of the Painted Hall, Naval College, Greenwich, London where it is referred to as Purbeck (*Figure 4.70*). Chest tombs of Wealden 'Marble' may be seen in the churchyard of St Mary, Reigate, Surrey.

Kentish Ragstone, taken from the Hythe Beds of the Lower Cretaceous Lower Greensand Formation is an important building stone especially in southeast England. The main quarries were around Maidstone, Kent and are still in use today (*Figure 4.71*). The stone occurs in beds up to two feet (0.6 m) thick, which alternate with sands known as hassock. Kentish Ragstone is a sandy glauconitic limestone which is dark-blue to green-grey in colour. The

Figure 4.70 Although stated to be of Purbeck 'marble', the floor of the Painted Hall at the Royal Naval College, Greenwich, also contains many slabs of Wealdon 'marble'. This is distinguished by the appearance of Large-*'Paludina'* (see p. 114)

Figure 4.72 Kentish Ragstone was used in large quantities by the Victorians, particularly for ecclesiastical building in London. Commonly, Bath Stone was used for the dressings because of the intractable nature of the ragstone, as seen in the church of St Mary, Fulham. No entirely satisfactory substitute stone has been found for restorations to buildings of Kentish Ragstone

Figure 4.71 Resistant beds of Kentish Ragstone stand out from the friable, more easily eroded 'Hassock' in Furfield Quarry, Kent

lithology is essentially limestone containing up to 90 per cent or more of calcium carbonate with 5 per cent or more silica and glauconite grains. The proportions of these minerals may differ considerably and the lithology varies considerably along its outcrop. In some instances the proportion of silica is substantial and the stone may be called a chert.

Kentish Ragstone was widely used in London in Roman and in mediaeval times. Most of it probably came from the Maidstone area and was carried by boat down the River Medway and then up the River Thames. The Roman ship discovered at Blackfriars, London[54] was carrying a cargo of Kentish Ragstone which was almost certainly from the Maidstone area.

Tough and intractable, it is not freely worked, but nevertheless has been used effectively for countless churches in London, (*Figure 4.72*) and earlier for the walls of Londinium. It was also used for the Tower of London, and for the New City Prison, Holloway (1849-1852), but it had the uncomfortable reputation of sweating when used on interior walls. No better example of its use exists than the great house of Knole in Kent[10].

Kentish Ragstone and Hassock grade into each other. In general terms Hassock is more friable, and is normally classified as a sandstone because it is loosely-cemented, calcareous, argillaceous, glauconitic and sandy. Occasionally it is sufficiently cohesive to allow it to be used as a freestone, and not uncommonly ragstone walls were lined with Hassock. It is said that fireplaces were made of the stone.

Upper Cretaceous limestones
The Cretaceous System takes its name from the major formation within it, the Chalk (*Creta*), a limestone that may be up to 98 per cent pure calcium carbonate. It is white to pale-grey in colour and very fine-grained. The Chalk is uncemented and soft in southern England, cemented and tough in northern England and exceptionally tough and impervious with recrystallized calcite within the pore spaces in Northern Ireland. Although the Chalk in Northern Ireland, known as the White Limestone, proved unsuitable for building, Chalk has been used elsewhere on a considerable scale for building.

Boynton Stone, from near Bridlington, Yorkshire was used in that area[17]; Amberley Quarry, Sussex,

(a)

(b)

(c)

(d)

(e)

Figure 4.73 Although Chalk is not noted for weathering resistance, it has been widely used, particularly where no other suitable stone was available. It needed however, to have its 'feet dry and head covered'. Not unusually walls were thatched as at Hendon, Wiltshire (a); (b) the Chalk walls of a cottage at Lenham, Kent stand on an impervious flint plinth. Undoubtedly the cottage was thatched originally; (c) built of Totternhoe Stone, Woburn Abbey was quite inappropriately patched with Bath Stone, leading to a disastrous appearance; (d) beautifully proportioned Ashdown House, Berkshire, has walls of locally dug Chalk; (e) offering little resistance to the mason's chisel, Chalk is easily worked, leading to a riot of carving as seen in the arcading in the Lady Chapel, Ely Cathedral

yielded large blocks of easily worked soft Chalk which was used for vaulted ceilings in Arundel Castle, Sussex, in Chichester Cathedral, for some groined ceilings in St Saviour's Church (now Southwark Cathedral) London, and in the new (1907) Catholic Church, Norwich, Norfolk. Chalk from around the Grays, Essex, area was brought into London, with Kentish Ragstone, from early times.

Chalk with no certain provenance but probably from Beer, Devon is noted for its use in St Stephens' Chapel, Westminster, London and in the crypt of Lambeth Palace, London.

Many cottages, barns, houses and walls built of Chalk may be found along its outcrop. These buildings and walls were commonly thatched and had deep eaves so that water was thrown clear of the wall to prevent excessive weathering. The delightful Ashdown House, Berkshire is an example of the use of Chalk on a larger, grander scale.

In detailed lithology the Chalk differs considerably in its characteristics both laterally along its outcrop and vertically. Certain types were recognized from an early date as of particular use for building. These types became used through a wider area than was locally dug Chalk.

Beer Stone, taken from near the base of the Middle Chalk is probably the best known of the Chalk building stones. It is a creamy grey-coloured, highly calcareous variety made up of minute, irregular, apparently corroded fragments of shells cemented by a calcareous matrix which appears largely crystalline in form. Occasional larger pieces of fossil matter are seen, and grains of glauconite with a lesser amount of quartz grains are scattered throughout the rock. The stone has been worked at Beer, Devon, apparently since Roman times; a 'Roman quarry' existed in 1932. It was also quarried in Hooken Cliffe, west of Beer Head. It was worked from open quarries until the overburden of other Chalk beds became too great. Tunnels were then made to extract the stone. The Beer freestone bed is up to thirteen feet (4 m) thick. It hardens considerably on exposure 'and is altogether much stronger than Bath Stone and very much superior to Caen Stone which was once so much used in England'[55].

Beer Stone has been widely used. It may be seen in St Ann's Cathedral, Belfast, Northern Ireland and in the altar and reredos of Christ Church Cathedral, St Louis, Missouri, USA.

In Britain its use dates back to Norman times when it was used for the doorway of Axminster Church, Devon. It was used more recently for Peak House, Sidmouth, Devon, which is entirely of Beer Stone. The Grandison tombs at Ottery St Mary, Devon, dated at 1360 testify to its durability. Perhaps its best known use is for Exeter Cathedral, Devon which dates back to Norman times.

Totternhoe Stone, from near Dunstable, Bedfordshire is also widely known. Greenish-grey in colour, it contains an abnormal amount of small fragments of the fossil bivalve *Inoceramus*. This results in it having a gritty feel, which has led to the stone being described incorrectly as sandy. The stone is taken from a well marked bed within the Lower Chalk. It appears to set in as a thin bed in Berkshire, continues through Oxfordshire and Buckinghamshire, reaches 15 to about 25 feet (4.6–7.6 m) thickness through Bedfordshire, Hertfordshire and Cambridge, and thins through Suffolk and Norfolk to only 2 feet (0.6 m). Its texture is compact and fine-grained and it is worked as a freestone.

Totternhoe Stone is renowned for its use in the twelfth century Woburn Abbey, Bedfordshire, for the organ screen in Peterborough Cathedral, for St Albans Abbey, and for the parish church, Luton and the Priory Church, Dunstable.

Burwell Stone (or Rock) of Cambridgeshire, is the same geological horizon as Totternhoe Stone. At Burwell the stone was dug from pits and it had long been worked for building material. The uppermost bed was called the bond or bondstone and said to be the best stone. Burwell Stone was quarried near the village of Burwell, Cherryhinton (formerly Hinton), Eversden and elsewhere around Cambridge. Many early buildings of Cambridge University used the stone, including the unparalleled King Edward's Gateway (1426).[38] The Lady Chapel of Ely Cathedral is a *tour de force* of carving in a stone which provided no obstacle for the mason's chisel.

Chalk is commonly called clunch by the mason and others. This term should be restricted to the types of Chalk found in East Anglia. The origin of the term is obscure and the word is often applied to other types of rock.

Tertiary limestones

Limestones are poorly represented in rocks of Tertiary age and in Britain only one is of any importance architecturally.

Quarr Stone, from the eastern end of Quarr Wood, near Quarr Abbey, Isle of Wight was quarried from the Bembridge Formation which comprises the Bembridge Limestone, overlain by the Bembridge Marls. The limestone is freshwater in origin and up to 26 feet (8 m) thick. It is pale grey but with a green cast and massively bedded. It is made up of molluscs, which normally are represented by casts or moulds. The shells are replaced by calcite in some instances. A most unlikely looking stone for building purposes,

Figure 4.74 Most of the stone quarried at Quarr, Isle of Wight, was used on the mainland for many churches, notably for the interior of Winchester Cathedral, and for Beaulieu Abbey. On the Isle it was used for the small but delightful Quarr Abbey

it was extensively worked and used during the Middle Ages. It was highly esteemed and was used in many churches in Sussex, in Winchester Cathedral, for the Priory at Lewes and in Chichester Cathedral. It has also been identified as one of the many stones used in Westminster Hall, Palace of Westminster, London. More compact and less carious limestone from the Bembridge Limestone, which characteristically contains the nucules, variously ornamented small globular bodies about the size of a large pinhead, of the lime-secreting freshwater alga *Chara*, also has been quarried in the past on a fairly large scale, principally at Binstead, near Ryde, Isle of Wight. Quarr Stone passes laterally into Binstead Stone. Binstead Stone has been used locally on the Isle of Wight. On the mainland it may be found in Winchester Cathedral and in many Sussex churches. It was also used for the external walls of the imposing Beaulieu Abbey, Hampshire, which at the Dissolution, was used as a quarry to supply stone to build some nearby houses.

Septarian nodules

Septarian nodules (concretions or septaria) are brownish- to greyish-coloured, calcareous nodules ranging in size from a few centimetres to a metre or more in diameter. They occur particularly in clays and are notably common at some horizons within the London Clay. They are usually more-or-less bun-shaped and are frequently found to have a flat bottom with a convex upper surface. Their characteristic feature is an internal arrangement of cracks which are arranged concentrically and radially to form the boundaries of roughly polygonal masses which were supposed to be seven sided. It is said that this is the origin of the name septaria.

The cracks are filled with distinctive yellowish-brown calcite but some may be found to be open. In some instances the nodules are found to have no cracks. The cracks arise from shrinkage of the nodules which are then infilled by the deposition of calcite by percolating water to fill or partially fill the cracks. Commonly on weathering the calcareous clayey matter of the nodule is worn away more quickly than the calcite veins, which then stand out as ribs in a distinctive honeycomb pattern. The septaria may be richly fossiliferous. Septaria have also been called beetle stones, turtle stones and cement stones.

At one time septarian nodules from the London Clay were collected together to make cement (Roman Cement or Parker's Cement) because the proportions of calcareous and argillaceous matter were about right for the process. Polished slices were used as tops of ornamental tables[17]. They were used for building in parts of East Anglia where no other suitable building stone exists. The church at Wrabness, Essex, on the banks of the River Stour, the

Figure 4.75 In an area devoid of other building stone, septarian nodules from the London Clay were used for Orford Castle, Suffolk

church at Chelmondiston, Suffolk, just off the banks of the River Orwell, the church at Frinton-on-Sea, Essex, and the Norman church at Clacton-on-Sea, Essex are built substantially of septaria. One of the best examples of septaria masonry work is stated to be Orford Castle, Suffolk (*Figure 4.75*). Colchester Castle Museum is another excellent example. The septaria were taken from pits dug in the London Clay or from nearby river or sea beaches where they had been washed out from the clay. The river beach at Wrabness is a well-known locality for the concretions.

Tufa

Tufa, which is principally calcite, and contains iron oxides responsible for yellow and red colours, is a spongy, porous rock which forms from carbonate charged waters, around springs and seeps and in streams. Commonly it will contain leaves, stems, gastropods and other organisms, or their remains.

Local deposits of tufa are well known in Great Britain and it is still being deposited. The carbonate is commonly deposited on plants, and on other objects, hence the petrifying springs such as those at Matlock, Derbyshire. Tufa is the term restricted mainly to the recent deposits of spongy nature.

Streams from springs issuing from the Hythe Beds, the Chalk in Kent, the Lincolnshire Limestone, and elsewhere are still depositing tufa. There are many occurrences in Kent. For example, at Wateringbury at least eight feet of tufa fills a channel in a small valley. At East Barming a tufa deposit 14 feet 9 inches (4.5 m) thick has been measured.

Tufa was known to the Romans when they came to Britain, since there are extensive deposits in Italy. It is frequently found in the remains of Roman buildings where it has been used as a light-weight, insulating material. Some buildings seem to have been constructed largely of tufa. However, because of its lightness, it was used mainly to fill the webs of high ribbed vaults, for example.

The vaulting above the high choir in Gloucester Cathedral is of tufa from deposits at nearby Dursley. The vaulting of the nave and choir roofs of Sherborne Abbey, Dorset used tufa, known locally as French Pummy[56]. It was also commonly used in Norman buildings. Leeds Church Tower, Kent (twelfth century) is of tufa as are mediaeval buildings in East Malling. Tufa was also used in Cliveden House, Buckinghamshire.

Travertine

Travertine is the name normally given to the more compact form of tufa. Like tufa it is characterized by the presence of many irregular cavities. It is usually opaque in thin slabs and may be banded. It is being deposited at the present day from hot springs in places such as in Yellowstone Park, USA. Deposits of travertine are quite common and occur in a number of countries. Travertine as known in the stone trade ranges from very pale cream, through yellow to dark brown and is banded and compact with some cavities.

The Cannstatt Travertine from near Stuttgart, Germany has a limited outcrop but has been widely used worldwide. It was used for façades of buildings in Berlin, in Buenos Aires, in the Hague, as well as for internal work including the Hotel Winthrop, New York, USA. It has also been used for monumental works such as the William III monument at Breda, Holland and the mausoleum of August Thyssen, Mülheim, Ruhr, Germany.

Large deposits of travertine are found in the Sienna and Tivoli districts of Italy and important deposits exist near Rome, Naples and Florence. It was the

(a)

(b)

Figure 4.76 (a) Travertine, of different colours, set with bedding planes vertical, used as cladding for flats in Turin; (b) statue by Henry Moore, outside the UNESCO building, Paris, of traventine with horizontal bedding

Figure 4.77 Travertine used structurally, was the stone chosen by the Romans for the Colosseum. (Photo: John Ashurst)

(a)

material used by the Romans for the Colosseum in Rome (*Figure 4.77*) and for many other buildings.

Travertine has been imported into Great Britain and many other countries in vast quantities for flooring, walling and cladding. Most comes from the renowned quarries at Tivoli and Sabino near Rome. It is particularly recommended for paving and treads because it is claimed that it is non-slip and has a non-fatiguing effect upon pedestrians. These qualities are attributed to the voids in the stone. The voids are frequently filled or 'stopped', in the modern use of the stone, which is often for cladding without regard to the bedding.

Travertine is said to resist abrasion remarkably well. This is borne out by its use at St James's Park Underground Station, London. The stone was used for the Cloaca Maxima, Rome. Tivoli travertine was recently used in a private hospital in St John's Wood, London. Roman travertine was used by Henry Moore for *Reclining Figure* (1957–1958) seen outside the UNESCO Building in Paris.

Onyx and onyx-marble

Despite many papers and articles,[30] considerable confusion exists in the use of the names onyx and onyx-marble. The two substances are different in appearance and different in chemical composition.

Onyx is a cryptocrystalline variety of quartz (SiO_2) and is the name given only to a banded black and white form, which has probably been produced by artificial colouring.[30] Onyx cannot be scratched with a penknife blade because its hardness is about $H=6.5$.

Onyx-marble is an exceptionally fine-grained, generally translucent variety of calcite ($CaCO_3$). It is normally banded and it ranges in colour from nearly

(b)

Figure 4.78 (a) Onyx-marble used for decorative external cladding on a bank front, Charing Cross Road; (b) Vase of onyx-marble, Chatsworth House, Derbyshire

white, through ivory, yellow, green, reddish, red-brown to brown. It can be scratched with a penknife because its hardness is approximately $H=3$. It has been highly prized since early times, not only for its translucent property, but also as a luxury material for 'marble' bathrooms.

Onyx-marble now is produced in many countries including Italy, Argentina, Algeria (possibly the largest producer), Turkey, Iran and Pakistan. Mexican onyx-marble, used by the Aztecs, is highly prized and was used in the entrance hall of the Trocadero Restaurant, London, now sadly demolished. Onyx-marble from Argentina is usually sold as Brazilian Onyx. This illustrates the point made by P.A. Males[57] that 'One should always be suspicious of the accuracy of names that include a locality. Although not always the case, a large number of such names do prove to be mineralogically incorrect'.

Watson[32] records the use of Algerian Onyx-Marble in the Grand Opera House in Paris and in the Credit Lyonnais building, Rue du 4 Septembre. Onyx-marble is often used for small ornaments such as table lamp stands, clock cases, ash-trays, statuettes and particularly eggs, apparently from a very free-laying bird. Decorative table tops, both ancient and modern, are commonly partly or wholly of onyx-marble. A fantastic use of onyx-marble from Turkey may be seen in Barclays Bank, Piccadilly Circus, London. Gibraltar Stone or Gibraltar Onyx, which, in the past, was mostly used for small tourist knick-knacks, is from stalagmitic deposits in the limestone caves of Gibraltar.

Imported limestones

There is a wealth of limestone to be found in Great Britain and its suitability as a building and as a decorative stone was recognized at an early date. It seems surprising, therefore, that much limestone is imported. Most is cut and polished and sold by the stone trade as decorative 'marble'. Colour is normally the principal factor controlling its choice.

French limestones

The earliest known imported limestone, Caen Stone, was used structurally. It is probably the best known of the French limestones in Great Britain.

Traditionally the stone has been imported since Norman times and it is recorded as being used by Paul of Caen, Abbot of St Albans, in 1077. The stone was quarried at Caen, Calvados, Normandy from underground galleries where it is 90 to 100 feet (27–30 m) thick. The quarries are of great antiquity; Merovingian coffins made of the stone have been found around Caen. It is also amusing to read that protests at its import 'not withstanding almightie God hath so blessed our realms in a most plentiful manner [with limestone]' were made as early as 1577 by William Harrison in *Description of England*[17].

Caen stone is often described as an oolitic limestone which resembles Bath Stone, Painswick Stone or other stones. In fact, it has no direct equivalent in Britain. M. Dunham and K.C. (now Sir Kingsley) Dunham[58] wrote that the stone consists 'of pellet limestone, having rounded and ovoid pellets of cloudy calcite mud up to 0.15 mm diameter set in a matrix of clear calcite crystals of rhombic habit, averaging about 0.1 mm but in places ranging up to 0.6 mm in breadth. The remains of a small, multi-chambered foraminifera constitute a microfauna in the rock'.

In hand specimen Caen Stone is a fine-grained limestone, yellowish to yellow-white or quite white in colour. It was used extensively in ecclesiastical and royal works. Canterbury Cathedral, Kent is a good example of its use. It is recorded that it has also been used in Salisbury Cathedral, Winchester Cathedral, Chichester Cathedral, Worcester Cathedral, Norwich Cathedral, Rochester Cathedral, Durham Cathedral (The Neville Screen), the altar of St Mary's Roman Catholic Church, Belfast, the font of St Peter's Church, Antrim Road, Belfast and the Church of St Margaret, Walmgate York. It is teamed with knapped flint in the Guildhall, Norwich (see *Figure 4.36g*). It has been used, in part at least, for Windsor Castle, Hampton Court, Buckingham Palace (particularly the east façade), and the interior of Beaulieu Abbey, Hampshire. At one time it was used in London for building monumental structures to the exclusion of all other material. Its uses included such buildings as the Junior Athenaeum Club at 116 Piccadilly (1849), the Carlton Club, Pall Mall, and the columns supporting the main floor of the Museum of Practical Geology (now demolished), Jermyn Street, London. Caen Stone was used by the Normans for the central White Tower of the Tower of London, finished in 1097.

When seen in a building where the light may be poor and the surface dirty and rubbed it may not be possible to differentiate between the Upper Cretaceous Beer Stone, fine-grained Upper Jurassic Portland Stone and Caen Stone. Care must be taken in determination and a freshly broken surface is preferred for study.

Caen Stone is no longer available and as there is a requirement for repair and other building work on existing structures of Caen Stone, a number of French limestones are imported. They are sometimes offered as a matching stone but none of them is. There is also a tendency to call them all oolitic but only a few are. They are imported under many names, for example St Maximin (Oise), Moulin à

Vent (Meuse), Richemont (Charentes-Maritimes) and Lepine (Vienne). In general they are Jurassic in age and are mostly pale-buff in colour and fine-grained. Longchant Stone which is pale-buff and fine-grained is markedly oolitic. Euville Stone (Meuse), a pink-beige coloured, medium-grained, bioclastic limestone was once used extensively in Paris, although St Vaast Stone, from near the city itself, is commonly said to be the 'stone that built Paris'. Tuffeau Stone from south-west Paris was used for the Palace of Versailles (Seine-et-Oise). The Catacombs of Paris are exhausted limestone quarries.

France produces both true marbles (marbres) and limestones (pierres marbrières). The limestones are mainly pale-coloured. Many of those produced in the Ardennes, near the Belgian frontier, are virtually identical with the Belgian stones.

Over 200 French 'marbles' are known. A comprehensive survey of French masonry limestones together with an assessment of their possible behaviour was undertaken by Honeyborne in 1978[59]. In the past, French limestones were imported into Great Britain. Their use is not always recognized. For example, Birmingham Council House used a variety known as Gris d'Alesia, from near Dijon, which is of similar appearance to Carboniferous Hopton Wood Stone. Similarly Forêt des Brousses, Burgundy, was polished like marble and used for the interior decoration of the New York Central Railway Station in 1917. The more compact limestones are worked primarily for decorative purposes. In the Boulonnais, Napoleon Stone and the closely allied Lunel, Notre-Dame A and B and Rubane Stones, which are virtually indistinguishable, have been exported widely. They were used mostly for decorative cladding of shop fronts.

The Campan group of 'marbles' are principally quarried from the Espiadet quarries, Campan Valley, Hautes Pyrénées, France. In the past this Department was an important centre for French 'marble' and it was largely developed during the reign of Louis XIV. The stone from the quarries has nodules of limestone which have been drawn out and later cemented with a mainly greenish chloritic matrix. Pink, brownish and red coloration is also found.

The colour determines the name given to the stone. Campan Vert is one of the best known. The dominating colours are light and dark green with irregularly shaped white markings. Campan Rouge is similar but red in colour. Campan Mélange is a mixture of the two colours.

The Trianon in Versaille, France is thought to have been called the Marble Trianon because of its external decor of Languedoc marble pilasters. However, some of them are of Campan Rouge and Campan Vert, which are known to have been extensively used by Louis XIV at Versailles. Campan Marble may also be seen in Westminster Cathedral,

London and it 'is popular for making the tops of the tables that may be seen in the numerous restaurants and cafés in Paris'.[32] It has also been used as a decorative stone in Roman baths in London. It is also used in the entablature of the Chapel of the Sacred Heart, Brompton Oratory, London and was used in pavements in Peterborough and Bristol Cathedral.

Belgian limestones

Belgian 'marbles' are limestones of Carboniferous age. Belgium is one of the world's leading 'marble'-producing countries. A large amount of limestone is quarried, but large amounts of stone are also imported. The imported stone is processed and may then be exported as 'Belgian marble'.

Some of the well known Belgian stones include Rouge Royal, Rouge Griotte, St Anne, Bleu Belge and Petit Granit. In spite of its name, Petit Granit is a limestone which is sold as a 'marble'. In the past a marble effect was achieved on porcelain by dabbling the glaze with sponges which may have been wrapped in linen. This porcelain was known as Rouge Royal and it was commonly used in Victorian lavatories. The Rouge Royal 'marble' had a similar use and the distinction between the two is sometimes not obvious.

Italian stones

Italy is renowned for marble, especially Carrara Marble. It also produces much limestone. The five major regions which produce marbles and limestones are:

1. The area around Carrara, Tuscany, which produces true white marbles and 'blue' marbles such as Bardiglio, Italian Dove and Bleu Turquin;
2. The area around Sienna, Tuscany, which produces yellow limestones (known as Sienna 'marbles') and travertine;
3. The area around Veneto and Lombardy which produces limestones of Jurassic age including Red and Yellow Verona;
4. Piedmont which produces many of the modern 'green-marbles' which are serpentinite;
5. The area around Istria (now partly in Yugoslavia) which produces limestones of Cretaceous and Tertiary age.

There is production elsewhere, but normally not on a large scale. Some areas have a substantial output of a particular stone, for example, travertine from near Rome.

Although Italy is thought of as a marble-producing country, much of the output is not marble. This is now recognized in recent Italian literature[60] which classifies output as:

1.1   True marbles (recrystallized calcareous rocks);
1.2   Polishable calcareous rocks;
1.3   Polishable calcareous breccias;
1.4   Serpentines and ophicalcites;
2.1   True granites and other igneous rocks;
2.2   Gneissic metamorphic rocks;
3   Travertines;
4   Stones.

Many references in literature, building records and archives to marble from Italy should be treated with considerable reserve. Many of the stones are not marbles in strict geological definition. In addition, Italy has a long tradition of importing stone, processing it and then exporting it around the world. Many Italian limestones are colourful and have been used for decorative panels as well as wine coolers, vases, table tops and other items of furniture. Italian marble was used decoratively for the famous sixty-six columns of 'Yellow Marble of Sienna' for the Throne Room of HM the King of Siam in Bangkok, Thailand.

Many of the Cretaceous limestones from the Istria peninsula are known in Britain as Roman Stone. In general the limestone is a cream-grey colour with greater or lesser amounts of broken fossils which gives it a spotted appearance. Where there is a considerable amount of fossil matter the stone has a marked brownish spotted appearance. The limestone is also known by its Italian name Bianco del Mare. Aurisina is a well known type of Istrian limestone and Nabresina is a variety of it. The name Veseljie Stone has also been used. An attempt was made to launch the stone under the name Jubilee Stone at the time of HM Queen Elizabeth II's Jubilee in 1977.

Superficially the stone resembles the Carboniferous Hopton Wood Stone and Hadene Stone and was accepted as a substitute for them. Istrian stone has been quarried since at least the time of Imperial Rome. It has been widely used and is recorded[33] as being freely used in England for ornamental work. It is seen in Vienna and extensively in Venice.

The Cretaceous rocks of the Trieste area also provide a series of decorative limestones under the name Repen. For example Repen Zola and Repen Classico. Some of these stones may be confused with some of the Aurisina series and, in fact, they are all from the same series of beds. Repen Zola was used for internal decorative work in St George's Hall, Liverpool, Merseyside (1848), for the ballustrades of the main staircase in the Law Courts, Hull, Humberside (1908) and was freely exported to the USA.[32]

Swedish limestones

An interesting Swedish limestone was used on the half pace of the west end steps of St Paul's Cathedral, London. There are two varieties; one is a fine-grained reddish muddy limestone and the other is a fine-grained greenish-grey muddy calcareous siltstone.

Both contain the distinctive fossil cephalopod *Orthoceras*, which is seen in section in the paving. Detailed study of the fossils in the stone indicate that it is of Ordovician age, with a strong possibility that it came from Sweden.

Swedish literature records that dressed building stone was exported from Gotland and Øland to Germany, Denmark and England during the fifteenth, sixteenth and seventeenth centuries.[61] Documents dealing with building work by Christopher Wren record that he used 'Swedish' or 'Swedes' stone and 'Denmark' stone or 'Red Denmark'.[62] There is now little doubt that these references are to red and grey *Orthoceras* Limestone of Ordovician age from the Island of Øland, Sweden.

The stone was widely used in Scandinavia, Germany and Holland. There does not seem to be much recorded information about its use in England, but the cloisters at Hampton Court Palace and the paving at Somerset House, London are made of it.[62] 'Swedish Marble' is recorded as being used for the floor of St George's Hall in Windsor Castle.

Similar rocks of the same geological age crop out in several other places in Sweden. Quarries at Brunflo, Järntland produced large amounts of stone since the end of the nineteenth century. This stone is still available today, but the limestone from Øland is now quarried on a more modest scale.

The slabs on the half pace of the steps of St Paul's Cathedral are made of stone from the Brunflo quarries (*Figure 4.79*). The same stone was also used to replace some paving at Hampton Court Palace, at Somerset House and at the Royal Hospital, Chelsea. An eye-catching modern use of the Øland limestone is on the shop Henning Glahn in Sloane Street, London.

Figure 4.79 Transverse and longitudinal cross sections of *Orthoceras* provide distinctive white markings in the Swedish Limestone used on the half landing of the west end steps, St Paul's Cathedral

Records of Swedish Stone, Denmark Stone or Orthoceras limestone suggest that the stone was quarried in Sweden. However, to determine the exact provenance of a stone detailed petrological and palaeontological study is necessary.

Spanish limestones

Spain has a massive output of 'marbles', many of which are limestones which have been used since Roman times. One, Brocatella, is a classic decorative stone. It is red and yellow mottled with small white patches which are made up of the broken up remains of fossils. It has been used for ecclesiastical work and may be seen among the many decorative stones used in Westminster Cathedral, London.

A very unusual Cretaceous limestone from Arteaga, Spain contains rudists (a highly aberrant type of lamellibranch which mimics a form of coral). One variety, which appears to have yellow nodules on a reddish ground, is used for infill panels beneath the ground floor windows of the Norwich Union building, St James's Street, London. It was also used as flooring in the entrance to Fluor House, Euston Station, London. The same stone forms the floor of the Louvre in Paris. Red and Grey varieties were used for the map of the world on the Embankment of the River Tagus, Lisbon, Portugal, near the monument of Henry the Navigator.

Portuguese stones

Portugal has lately been developing its decorative stone production. The stones have been classified, scientifically by the Direcção-Geral de Geologia e Minas.[63] Limestones of Jurassic age are worked. A good example is Emperor's Red (Encarnado), which has been used in Britain for ecclesiastical decorative work.[32]

Israeli limestones

Perhaps the most widely known and certainly the best recorded 'marbles' are those used by Herod Antipas, Herod the Great and Pontius Pilate. The use of 'marble' in Palestine is recorded in the Bible and 'marble' has been used through the centuries. Israel has lately increased its quarrying capacity and has been actively exporting stone, particularly to Belgium and Great Britain. The limestones are nearly all of Cretaceous age, roughly equivalent to Lower and Middle Chalk of Great Britain. The font of Coventry Cathedral is a three tonne boulder of dolomitized Chalk brought from the Valley of Barakat, near Bethlehem[64]. Unfortunately this font, 'more ancient

than the Christian Faith itself', is recorded as sandstone in the early edition of a glossy guide to the Cathedral[64]. 'Marble' of Eocene age is also known.

Stylolites are a common feature in some limestones from Israel. They appear as darker, wavy sutured lines, roughly parallel with the bedding and consist of a minute column-like development roughly at right angles to the bedding. Stylolites are believed to have formed due to solution and pressure acting together along original bedding-plane surfaces within the rock. As a result the insoluble material in the limestone was concentrated along bedding planes. An interlocking suture may be seen on polished slabs and although if hammered the stone probably would break along that line, it will not fall apart as is sometimes feared by those unfamiliar with the feature. In fact, Perlato de Sicilia (Sicilian Pearl) from near Trapani, Isle of Sicily, which is currently fashionable in Great Britain is noted for its stylolites, and this is one of the characters for which it is chosen.

Many Biblical buildings of Israel remain as enduring evidence of the durability of the stones used, especially in that climate. Little is recorded of the origin of the stone of the First or Second Temple, but Herod used blue-green veined stones of the Cretaceous Hatrurian Formation for the House. The Western, or 'Wailing' Wall, is of huge blocks of Cenomanian dolomitic limestone. Ninety per cent of the present-day output of all building stone is used in Jerusalem[65].

Stone from Israel is decoratively used on the fronts of some shops of the Marks and Spencer chain of stores. It was used also on the Banco di Roma, Brussels.

'Marbles' from other countries

Apart from the countries and examples described here, most countries in the world produce 'marbles' and many of them are now major producers. Many of them appear on the British market from time to time. However, in dealing with ancient monuments and historic buildings due regard must be paid to history because at any time only certain stones were available. Nevertheless, unusual decorative stones, normally in small quantities, were occasionally brought in by the dilettante completing his 'grand tour'.

Evaporitic rocks

A number of rocks, widely dissimilar in chemical composition, are grouped together and treated as sedimentary rocks because they have one thing in common: they were precipitated from ancient seas and lakes due to evaporation in arid climates. These rocks are known collectively as evaporites. Rock salt (or halite), potash, anhydrite and gypsum are included in this group. The precipitation of these minerals implies concentrations of elements far greater than normally found in sea water. Modern theories suggest that their formation is due to a recycling action whereby the evaporating waters are continually replaced rather than simple evaporation. Some uncommon elements may also rarely be found as evaporites.

Some evaporites are of importance in building and in decorative work. In this context they may be regarded as monomineralic rocks.

Alabaster

Gypsum, hydrated calcium sulphate ($CaSO_4 \cdot 2H_2O$) has a hardness of $H = 2$, that is, it may be scratched easily with a finger nail. It, and the closely allied mineral anhydrite ($CaSO_4$) named from the Greek 'without water', are commonly found interbedded with shales, marls and limestones and may occur as persistent beds over considerable distances.

Gypsum occurs in a number of varieties. One form, found filling some veins, consists of fine, parallel, fibrous crystals with a silky lustre. It is known as satin spar and has been used for necklace beads and other ornaments. The variety selenite, named, because of its pellucid appearance, after Selene, goddess of the Moon, occurs as colourless transparent or whitish translucent flat, tubular crystals. An unusual type of gypsum which is widely known because it is sold as a tourist souvenir, is the Desert Rose. It is found only in arid areas and is apparently formed by the evaporation of ground waters drawn by capillary action to the surface. It consists of clusters of platey crystals. The crystals typically contain sand grains and commonly assume complicated shapes to resemble whatever the observer wishes to imagine. At one time Desert Roses were thought to be petrified flowers.

Alabaster is the name used for gypsum in its massive, fine-grained granular compact form, which is suitable for carving. This is the variety which has been used widely for building, monumental, gemmological and artistic purposes.

Thick beds of gypsum are found in many areas including North and South America, continental Europe, particularly Spain, and Great Britain. Italy is now the major supplier of the variety alabaster. The alabaster is mined in the Volterra district as ovoid masses up to a metre and a half in diameter from limestones interbedded with marls. It is cut, then commonly artificially stained and polished at Pisa, Florence and Volterra. It is made into table lamps, ash trays, statues and other knick-knacks. Because

thin slabs of alabaster are translucent they have been used as windows in the Mediterranean area from an early date. One of the most famous examples of alabaster windows are those in Galla Placidia's Mausoleum in Ravenna. They are yellow orange in colour and are the only source of indoor light.

At one time British alabaster was much sought after and was extensively wrought. Gypsum and anhydrite occur in many areas in Great Britain.[66] It is possible to collect pieces of the variety alabaster, which may be suitable for carving, from any of the places where gypsum crops out. For example, the pink Welsh Alabaster found in thin bands along the coastal cliffs of Glamorgan in Wales can be carved. Two places renowned for the supply of good quality block alabaster are Fauld, Staffordshire and Chellaston, Derbyshire. At Chellaston the Tutbury Gypsum beds were once worked on a large scale. The Fauld mine now supplies only a limited quantity.[67] At Fauld the mineral is found in a series of beds, not all of which are worked. The bed which is worked consists of discontinuous lenticular masses, several metres in diameter and about 2.5 metres thick, which are separated by marl. The thick nodular beds are known as 'floors'. The smaller masses are called 'cakes'.

The purest form of alabaster is white and translucent, but traces of ferric oxide produce light brown, orange- and red-coloured veins, bands and patches. Alabaster has been used in Great Britain since the earliest days. The second rim of the arch of the Norman west doorway of Tutbury Church, Staffordshire, dated 1160 is made of it, as is an effigy of a cross-legged knight in the parish church of Hanbury, Staffordshire dated about 1280 to 1300. Alabaster altar pieces, panels and other pieces were produced in quantity and generally were painted.[68]

Since about 1400 vast amounts of alabaster have been supplied from Tutbury, Chellaston and elsewhere to 'the factory at Nottingham'. There alabasterers were employed to carve effigies and panels. Nottingham was particularly known for its plaques of the head of St John the Baptist. The first reference to this industry dates from 1367 and mentions an alabaster altar-piece.[68]

Nottingham was an important centre for international trade. Mediaeval altar-pieces were exported from there to Iceland, Italy, Spain and elsewhere. The fame of British alabaster spread rapidly. In May 1382 King Richard II allowed Cosmato Gentilis, Pope Urban II's collector, to export four alabaster images. British alabaster was so sought after that blocks were exported. The industry suffered a blow during the Reformation when images of 'stone, timber, alabaster, or earth, graven, carved or painted' had to be defaced or destroyed. The production of effigies for tombs was excepted. The use of alabaster for building is magnificently seen in the so-called Marble

(a)

(b)

(c)

Figure 4.80 (a) Alabaster, richly gilded and painted, forms the bulk of a monument (part of the inscription on which reads 'The Marble Selfe Doth Weepe') in the church at Amersham, Buckinghamshire; (b) intricately carved alabaster forms the canopy above the High Altar, Peterborough Cathedral; (c) balustrade of staircase in alabaster supporting a marble handrail. National Liberal Club, London

Hall of Holkham Hall, Norfolk, and for the twenty 25-feet high columns of Kedleston Hall, Derbyshire. The alabaster for these columns was quarried at Red Hill near the confluence of the River Soar and the River Trent. Each column is made up of three blocks which are so well matched that the joints are not easily distinguished. Jacob Epstein's sculpture *Consummatum Est* (1937) is a direct carving in alabaster. The uses of alabaster are well recorded, see for example Cheetham[68] and Dimes.[69]

Gypsum easily loses and gains water. When heated the water is driven off and the resulting powdered product is Plaster of Paris. When water is added, gypsum is reformed and sets as a rigid mass.

Plaster of Paris is named from its early use in France. Extensive beds of gypsum up to 100 feet (30 m) thick were worked, notably at Montmarte, then to the north of Paris. When Henry II of England visited Paris in 1254 he was much impressed with the fineness and whiteness of this plaster and he introduced it into England. Soon after English sources of gypsum were exploited. A plaster made from calcined gypsum was used in the pyramids of Egypt, over 4000 years ago.[70]

Gypsum is used extensively in plaster and mortar and is also added to Portland cement to delay the setting time.

Marmo di Castellina is alabaster which has been placed in water, gently heated nearly to boiling point and cooled. The translucency of the alabaster is deadened to resemble, it is claimed, fine Carrara marble. As such it was sold to tourists. At one time many carvings sold to tourists in Mexico as jade were made from alabaster which was dyed green.

The use of large blocks of alabaster for structural purposes is familiar to many because it is mentioned by the tourist guides at the Palace of Knossos, Crete. Gypsum is also used in the process of burtonization of beer. Therefore, it may be appropriate that the balustrades of Messrs Bass's offices in Burton-upon-Trent are recorded as being of alabaster.

Bitumens

Bitumens are a series of substances, essentially mixtures of hydrocarbons, with a wide variety of names including asphalt, tar, pitch and bitumen. They have the general formula of C_nH_{2n}, but most hydrocarbons are mixtures of different series usually with impurities. Surface seeps, tar pools, and asphalt lakes occur relatively commonly. Their source is mostly a matter of speculation. They appear to have been left behind by the evaporation of the more volatile hydrocarbon content and thus are sometimes described as residuals. Hydrocarbons are invariably generated and accumulate in sedimentary rocks.

The peculiar deposit of elaterite, at Windy Knoll, near Castleton, Derbyshire, is known to generations of geologists. The natural bitumen seep in the Coalport tar tunnel, near Ironbridge, Shropshire is now a tourist display. The Athabaska Tar Sands,

North-West Territories, Canada, are well known. The 114 acre (46 hectare) Pitch Lake near La Broa, Trinidad has been used since at least the time of Sir Walter Raleigh (*Figure 4.81*).

In Mesopotamia and Palestine bitumens were used in the production of mortar. Bitumen mortars, bitumen cements and cements made with pitch are known. The bitumen acts as a bonding agent. Apart from its use for caulking ships, bitumen, or asphalt, has been used for paving and for roofing. Bitumen has been found used as a mortar in the river walls of the old Palace of Westminster, London. Modern asphaltic concrete is produced by mixing stone fragments with a precisely measured amount of bitumen.

Coal, Cannel Coal and jet

Coal is a sedimentary rock of organic origin; it is the result of the accumulation of plant material which was altered to greater or lesser degree. Coal is largely made up of carbon, oxygen and hydrogen. Beds of coal have closely spaced vertical jointing known as the *cleat*, with a less well developed jointing at right angles known as the *end*. This joint pattern leads to the development of the familiar cube-shaped pieces of coal when the coal is extracted.

Unlikely as it may seem, coal has been used as a decorative material. Occasionally large blocks of coal are secured and they have been carved into intricate objects displayed during miners' fêtes, village open days and the like. They have little, if any, practical use. A cube of coal with faces three feet (0.9 m) square sits atop a column in Newcastle, New South Wales, Australia, a monument to the development of the South Maitland coalfield. The Coal Seat, in Osborne House, Isle of Wight, is the ultimate fanciful conceit. In addition to its brittleness the danger of damage by fire is immediately apparent.

Cannel Coal is dense, lustreless, blackish and typically shows concoidal fracture surfaces. Under the microscope it is seen to be composed largely of spore and pollen remains, small resin bodies and fragments of leaf cuticles. It is considered to be a drift coal. It ignites easily and burns with a very smokey yellow candle-like flame (cannel is Scots dialect for candle). Recent examination revealed that a small section of the original floor in the Lady Chapel of Lichfield Cathedral amazingly was laid lozengy of Cannel Coal and alabaster. Such a floor is thought to be unique. (Personal communication by M. Stancliffe.)

Jet is a lustrous black substance which is easily worked and which will take a high polish. In Great Britain it is found particularly in the Upper Liassic age Jet Rock Series in the cliffs at Whitby, Yorkshire.

Figure 4.81 'Pitch' from The Pitch Lake, Trinidad, used by Sir Walter Raleigh, today is packed in cardboard barrels and mostly exported. (Courtesy of Mrs J. Hay)

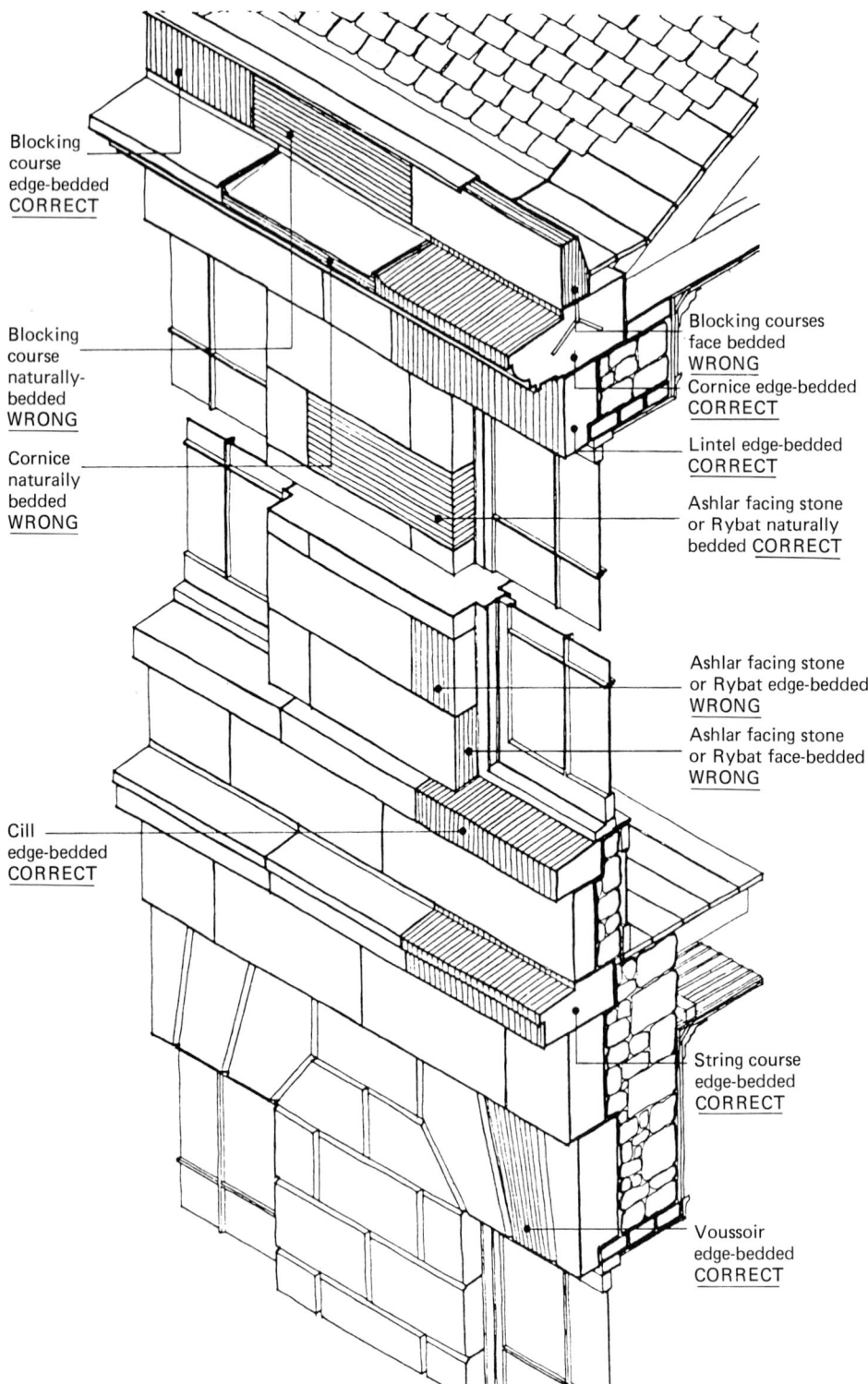

Blocking course edge-bedded CORRECT

Blocking course naturally-bedded WRONG

Cornice naturally bedded WRONG

Cill edge-bedded CORRECT

Blocking courses face bedded WRONG

Cornice edge-bedded CORRECT

Lintel edge-bedded CORRECT

Ashlar facing stone or Rybat naturally bedded CORRECT

Ashlar facing stone or Rybat edge-bedded WRONG

Ashlar facing stone or Rybat face-bedded WRONG

String course edge-bedded CORRECT

Voussoir edge-bedded CORRECT

Figure 4.82 The placing of a sedimentary stone into a building. The bedding planes should be at right angles to the thrust imposed on them. (From reference 75)

It occurs as sporadic lenticular masses and is derived from pieces of drifted wood buried in isolation which did not pass through a peat phase and thus were not coalified, but underwent decomposition and retained their cellular structure.

Jet was known in the Bronze Age. The Romans thought very highly of it and they established a jet workshop in York. It has since been widely used for personal adornment and jewellery. It was very popular in Victorian times for mourning jewellery.

Much folklore is attached to jet and it is said to protect against the evil eye, against serpents and dogs. It cures toothache, hysteria and epilepsy. It is also a love token and if a woman was given water into which jet had been dipped and she remained continent she was pure. It shatters during acts of infidelity. Proof of these properties has yet to appear in scientific literature.

Special considerations

Placing stone 'in bed'

The bed and the bedding plane are unique characteristics of sedimentary rocks. A block of stone from a quarry can be placed in a building in one of three attitudes in relation to the bedding (see *Figure 4.82*).

There is now no doubt that stone will resist weathering far better if it is 'in bed' than if it is oriented in any other direction. In effect the thrust on the stone should be at a right angle to the bedding, (see *Figure 4.82*) and this also seems to apply to having the stone the right way up. In many sedimentary stones the bedding is immediately apparent, but in stones taken from rocks which are massively bedded and wide-jointed the bedding direction may be difficult to determine by eye. Therefore, the way-up of the stone should be marked on each block removed from the quarry face and the mark should be maintained on the stone until it is finally fixed. The disastrous consequences of ignoring the bedding are all too easily seen (*Figure 4.83*). Even when stones are markedly cross-bedded way-up criteria should still be applied. The phrase 'built on cant' is used particularly in Scotland for stone which has been placed with the natural bed in a vertical position. It was noted that this stone wastes very quickly.[71]

The importance of placing blocks of building stone 'in bed' was recognized by the Romans when they built Rome. Blocks of travertine, an excellent building stone when laid on its bed, were sometimes set the wrong way and had speedily to be replaced '. . . the rostra in the Forum are an example'.[72] The lesson seems to have been forgotten. Many times a stone is thought to be unsuitable or of poor quality or to decay easily because due consideration was not paid to the bedding planes of the stone.

Freestone

Any stone, specifically those taken from sedimentary rocks, that can be freely worked in any direction is commonly referred to as a freestone. The term does not give any indication whatever of the nature of the stone. When used in the southern part of Great Britain, a freestone will almost certainly be a limestone, while in the Midlands and northern England it will be a sandstone.

Incompatible stones

Although different types of stones for building may be mixed with impunity, associations of some stones used without due regard to architectural detailing may lead to associative decay. This applies especially to limestone and sandstone association. If a limestone in a building is placed above a sandstone, it will normally be found that the sandstone will decay.

Limestone is essentially calcium carbonate, which is only slightly soluble in pure water. However, water which contains carbon dioxide, which most rain water does, will dissolve calcium carbonate to form calcium bicarbonate, which only exists in solution. Thus when rain falls on the limestone surfaces of building stone some calcium carbonate is dissolved into the water in the form of the bicarbonate, which is unstable. When it reaches the sandstone below, the rain water is absorbed, and, as the water evaporates, calcium carbonate is redeposited within the interstices. The grains of the sandstone are forced apart and the stone disintegrates. This process does not operate when sandstone is used above a limestone because the silica grains of the sandstone are virtually chemically inert. Associative decay has been noted widely in Bristol, which is sited in an area where the Pennant Grit and Carboniferous Limestone were both readily to hand.

If there is no alternative but to use the two types of stone, careful architectural detailing should endeavour to ensure that rain water is thrown clear of the sandstone.

Soiling by wax

Sandstones, many limestones and marbles are absorbent. Surfaces of these stones which are subjected to constant touching, rubbing or smoothing will absorb grease from human hands, sometimes to a significant degree. The wax will oxidize and darken on exposure to air, as will all polishes.

Most igneous and metamorphic rocks, because of their close, tight-grained nature do not suffer. Normally it is only the surface which is dirty. Integral

(a)

(b)

(c)

(d)

(e)

Figure 4.83 (a) The blocks of Portland Limestone from the Isle of Purbeck used for a seawall at Hotwells, Portsmouth are laid with due regard for the bedding; (b) further along the wall, one of parapet stones has been laid with its bedding planes horizontal, and as a consequence has failed; (c) blocks of Bath stone forming the parapet of a wall on the roof of St Pancras railway station were laid with bedding planes horizontal; (d) markedly false-bedded stones should be laid to observe way-up criteria, Old Red Sandstone, Goodrich Castle, Herefordshire; (e) current bedding in Coal Measure Sandstone used for the York City Art Gallery is emphasized by layers of small mica flakes along the bedding planes. The stone is correctly positioned to fulfil its function in the structure of the building. (Photos (a) and (b) courtesy R.H. Roberts)

Figure 4.84 The castle walls of York were built of Millstone Grit and of Magnesian Limestone. The topmost five courses are of sandstone, with eight courses of limestone below. No associative decay is seen. However, the next nine courses of sandstone below are badly decayed because rainwater, charged with calcium bicarbonate from the Magnesian Limestone above, is able to soak into the sandstone. Note that the lowest courses of limestone are unaffected

Figure 4.85 Traditionally, visitors to the inner area of the Temple at Angkor Wat, Cambodia (now Kampuchea), gently stroke the Apsaras (statues of the guardian women). The ingrained deposit of wax from human hands shows the favoured areas. (Courtesy of E.A. Jobbins)

handrails to stairs may appear appreciably darker than the adjoining stone and this may not necessarily be regarded as a desirable feature. Architectural detailing should take account of this factor.

Statues in museums, which are not regularly cleaned, show those areas favoured by the visiting public; it provides an illuminating study. In the past, some stone structures were painted or polished. The oil of the paint or the wax may well have penetrated to some depth. Although it may be possible to clean the pigment from the surface of the stone it is not possible to remove the wax or oil from any depth. Paint was used on the White House in Washington, DC, USA. It has penetrated several centimetres and now cannot be removed without removing the surface of the stone.

Effects of fire

Little detailed study has been made on the effects of fire and heat on a range of building stones. Normally the other materials burn to leave stonework still standing although it may be weakened by the destruction of other structural elements. The immediately apparent effect is a reddening of the stone, but not all reddening of stones is due to fire. Red coloration at the base of the Parthenon in Athens, Greece, once was thought to be due to fire. The effect of fire is dramatically demonstrated in Hafod Chapel, near Devils Bridge, Dyfed, Wales, and in the central tower of Tewkesbury Abbey, Gloucestershire. The reddened bases of the columns of the aisle in Gloucester Cathedral still witness the ferocity of the 'mighty fire' of 1122 AD.

Stone does not burn, with the obvious exceptions of coal and allied material, but it is damaged by the burning of other substances. The rate of heating is an

Figure 4.86 Fire-reddening and surface spalling on an external wall of Westminster Hall, London resulted from the fire of 1974. (Photo: John Ashurst)

important condition; temperatures of about 1000 °C may be reached within an hour in a not particularly vicious fire. By comparison a Bunsen burner flame reaches about 500 °C. The spallability of the stone determines whether small flakes, a few millimetres at the most, will spall off. Overall, the thermal expansion of rocks is very small.

The coefficients of linear expansion (α) given by Kaye and Laby[73] are: granite, $6-9 \times 10^{-6}$, marble, $3-15 \times 10^{-6}$, slate, $6-12 \times 10^{-6}$, sandstone, $5-12 \times 10^{-6}$ and Portland Stone, approximately, 3×10^{-6}. The coefficients are all of a similar order and about the same as those for porcelain and glass.

The coefficient of linear expansion may also be expressed more directly in millimetres per metre per degree C. Typical figures[60] are:

Name of stone	Type	Locality	mm/m °C
Bianco p.	Marble	Carrara, Italy	0.0029
Bianco venato gioia	Marble	Carrara, Italy	0.0063
Cipollino apuano	Marble	Lucca, Italy	0.0077
Potoro macchia fine	Calcareous breccia	La Spezia, Italy	0.0050
Travertino ascolano striato	Travertine	Ascoli Piceno, Italy	0.0050
Rosso antico d'italia	Serpentinite	Genova, Italy	0.0061
Verde issorie	Serpentinite	Val d'Aosta, Italy	0.0058
Granito rosa baveno	Granite	Novara, Italy	0.0075
Sienite balma	Syenite	Vercelli, Italy	0.0042

In Great Britain the range of temperature from solar gain that might be expected in stone cladding, depending on its type and colour, is from -20 °C to 65 °C. Taking Cipollino Apuano as an example and using the worst possible case temperature difference: $85 \times 0.0077 = 0.6545$ mm expansion per metre of stone.

The thermal conductivity of rocks is minute. Reports of stone being 'red-hot' can be dismissed as sheer invention. Stone may be regarded as the ideal fire-proof natural material. Laboratory tests on limestone containing iron oxides show that intense heating causes the limestone to pass through a cycle of colours including pink, purple, grey and cream. It is not possible, however, to use the colours as an indicator of temperature because too many variables are involved. The colour will depend on the type of stone and its mineral composition, which may vary substantially from one part to another.

With a fairly pure limestone with little other mineral matter and with practically no iron oxide minerals the calcium carbonate will dissociate according to the reaction:

$$CaCO_3 + heat \rightarrow CaO + CO_2$$

calcium + heat → lime + carbon
carbonate   dioxide

Depending on specific conditions dissociation will occur at about 900 °C (1652 °F).

Further reactions may occur. If firemen's hoses are played onto the dissociated limestone:

$$CaO + H_2O \rightarrow Ca(OH)_2$$

lime + water → slaked lime

Other reactions are now possible, for example:

$$Ca(OH)_2 + H_2SO_4 \rightarrow CaSO_4 2H_2O$$

slaked lime + sulphuric acid → gypsum
(acid rain)

or:

$$Ca(OH)_2 + CO_2 \rightarrow CaCO_3 + H_2O$$

slaked lime + carbon → calcium + water
dioxide   carbonate

The likelihood of all of these reactions occurring is remote. In any event, because of the low thermal conductivity of stone any of these effects would be purely on the surfaces of the stone, much of which will not have been exposed directly to heat. However, the surfaces which are affected may be important. For example, the fire inside Westminster Hall in 1974, which was quenched with large amounts of water, left the eleventh century wall surface with a thin superficial layer split from the face. In some areas this layer was fragmented.[74]

In laboratory tests, limestone heated to 900 °C throughout passed through an unstable stage. The cooled specimen eventually fell into a white powder after several days in the atmosphere. Other specimens heated to 1085 °C and to 1250 °C remained stable for several weeks before they disintegrated.

Other chemical effects

Instances are known of limestone ribs, bosses, string courses and the like in a church decaying and becoming unsafe. No immediate cause was found but in the past the church was lit by acetylene lamps.

When acetylene (C_2H_2) is burnt, carbon monoxide (CO), carbon dioxide (CO_2), and water (H_2O) are produced. Within a closed building acidic vapours, particularly carbonic acid, which is very much like an industrial smog, will be concentrated. This undoubtedly would have a deleterious effect on the limestone over the years. Acid gases may have a number of effects:

$$CaCO_3 + H_2SO_4 (=H_2O + SO_2) \rightarrow CaSO_3$$

calcium + sulphuric acid → calcium
carbonate   sulphite

or: $$CaCO_3 + O \rightarrow CaSO_4$$

calcium carbonate + oxygen → calcium sulphate

Cautions

Repair, restoration and replacement of stonework may destroy other important evidence. The reddening of stone used in ancient buildings may be of historical and of archaeological significance, and may help to date the development of the building. Care must be taken, however, to determine whether the fire-reddened stone has been re-used from earlier building.

The displacement of drums of stone making up columns of buildings may be evidence of an earthquake. It provides not only data for the architectural behaviour of a type of construction but also evidence of an event which is of both geological and archaeological importance.

It may be of great interest to maintain damaged stonework. The pock marks in the Portland Stone of the front of the Geological Museum, Exhibition Road, London are an emphatic reminder of the effect of German high-explosive bombs on masonry. The pitted giant monolithic granite columns of St Isaacs Church Cathedral bear grim witness to the 900-day siege of Leningrad, USSR. The grooves worn by wheels in the slabs forming the roadway, which is part of the Roman Wall, at Housesteads, Northumberland tell more about life at the time than does unworn stone. In these instances history has been impressed upon the stone rather than lying within it.

Figure 4.87 The drums of the columns of Pentelic marble have been displaced by earthquake activity at the Temple of Hephestos, Athens

References

1. Harris, P.M., *Mineral Dossier No. 17. Sandstone*, HMSO, London, 1977
2. Penoyre, J. and Penoyre, J., *Houses in the Landscape*, Readers Union, Newton Abbot, 1978
3. Watson, J., *British and Foreign Building Stones*, University Press, Cambridge, 1911
4. Smith, E.G. In Rayner, D.H. and Hemmingway, J.E., eds., *The Geology and Mineral Resources of Yorkshire*, Yorkshire Geological Society, 1974
5. Crane, T., *Newcastle Stone*, Ealing Publications Ltd., Maidenhead, 1979
6. Anon., *Edinburgh Weekly Journal*, November 1923 *quoted in* Craig, G., On Building Stones used in Edinburgh; their Geological Sources, Relative Durability, and Other Characteristics, *Trans. Edin. Geol. Soc.*, **6**, 1893
7. Craig, G. On Building Stones used in Edinburgh; their Geological Sources, Relative Durability, and Other Characteristics, *Trans. Edin. Geol. Soc.*, **6**, 1893
8. Wray, D.A., Stephens, J.C., Edwards, W.N., and Bromehead, C.N., 'The Geology of the Country around Huddersfield and Halifax', *Mem. Geol. Surv. G.B.*, HMSO, London, 1930
9. Mills, P., 'York Stone Paving', Letter in *The Times*, 13 January 1975
10. Clifton-Taylor, A., *The Pattern of English Building*, Faber and Faber, London, 1972
11. Pevsner, N., *The Buildings of England: County Durham*, 2nd edn, Penguin, Harmondsworth, 1983
12. Elsden, J. and Howe, J.A., *The Stones of London*, Colliery Guardian Co. Ltd., London, 1923
13. Simpson, I.M. and Broadhurst, F.M., *A Building Stones Guide to Central Manchester*, University of Manchester, Manchester, 1975
14. Whittow, J.B., *Geology and Scenery in Scotland*, Penguin, Harmondsworth, 1977
15. Lawson, J., *Building Stones of Glasgow*, Geological Society of Glasgow, Glasgow, 1981
16. Kent, Sir Peter, *British Regional Geology: Eastern England from the Tees to the Wash*, HMSO, London, 1980
17. North, F.J., *Limestones: Their origins, distribution, and uses*, Thomas Murby & Co., London, 1930
18. Nairn, I. and Pevsner, N., *The Buildings of England: Surrey*, 2nd edn, Penguin, Harmondsworth, 1971
19. Thurrell, R.G., Worssam, B.C., and Edmonds, E.A., 'Geology of the Country around Haslemere'. *Mem. Geol. Surv. G.B.*, HMSO, London, 1968
20. Dines, H.G., Buchan, S., Holmes, S.C.A., and Bristow, C.R., 'Geology of the Country around Sevenoaks and Tonbridge', *Mem. Geol. Surv. G.B.*, HMSO, London, 1969
21. White, G., *The Natural History of Selborne*, J. Fisher ed., Cressert Press, London 1947
22. Larwood, G.P. and Funnell, B.M., eds., *The Geology of Norfolk*, Paramoudra Club, Norwich, 1970
23. Anon., *Merstham Firestone Quarries: an interim account*, Croydon Caving Club, Carshalton, 1976
24. Osborne, B.E., 'Early Plateways and Firestone Mining in Surrey; an interim report' *Croydon Natural History and Scientific Society*, **17**, Pt. 3, Feb. 1982
25. Sowan, P.W., 'Stone Mining in East Surrey' *Surrey History*, **1**, No. 3, Phillimore, Chichester, 1975

26. Appleby, J.W., *Hertfordshire Puddingstone*, St. Albans Museum, 1978

27. Davies, A.M. and Baines, A.H.I., 'A Preliminary Survey of the Sarsen and Puddingstone Blocks of the Chilterns', *Proc. Geol. Assoc.* **64**, Pt. 1, 1953

28. Nairn, I. and Pevsner, N., *The Buildings of England: Sussex*, Penguin, Harmondsworth, 1965

29. Clifton-Taylor, A. and Ireson, A.S., *English Stone Building*, Gollancz, London, 1983

30. Dimes, F.G., 'What is Onyx?' *Stone Industries*, **12**, No. 5. Sept/Oct 1977

31. Whittow, J.B., *Geology and Scenery in Ireland*, Penguin, Harmondsworth, 1974

32. Watson, J., *British and Foreign Marbles and Other Ornamental Stones*, University Press, Cambridge, 1916

33. Ford, T.D., 'The Black Marble of Ashford-in-the-Water, Derbyshire', *Liverpool and Manchester Geol. J.*, **2**, Pt. 1, 1958

34. Whittow, J.B., *Geology and Scenery in Ireland*, Penguin, Harmondsworth, 1974

35. Donovan, D.T. and Reid, R.D., 'The Stone Insets of Somerset Churches' *Proc. Somerset Archaeological and Natural History Soc.*, **107**, 1963

36. L.S.C. and F.S.W. *The Stones of Wells Cathedral*, Wells Natural History and Archaeological Society, Wells, n.d.

37. Bainbridge, C., 'Cold comfort for the village of slate', *The Times*, 9th August 1975

38. Purcell, D., *Cambridge Stone*, Faber and Faber, London, 1967

39. Green, G.W., and Welch, F.B.A., 'Geology of the Country around Wells and Cheddar', *Mem. Geol. Surv. G.B.*, HMSO, London, 1952

40. Purcell, D., *The Stones of Ely Cathedral*, 2nd edn., The Friends of Ely Cathedral, Ely, n.d.

41. Arkell, W.J., *Oxford Stone*, Faber and Faber, London, 1947

42. Howe, J.A., *The Geology of Building Stones*, Edward Arnold, London, 1910

43. Perkins, J.W., Brooks, A.T., and Pearce, A.E. McR, *Bath Stone: a quarry history*, University College Cardiff and Kingsmead Press, Bath, 1979

44. Lang, J., *Rebuilding St Paul's after the Great Fire of London*, Oxford University Press, London, 1956

45. Arkell, W.J., *The Geology of the Country around Weymouth, Swanage, Corfe and Lulworth*, *Mem. Geol. Surv. G.B.*, HMSO, London, 1947

46. Simpson, I.M. and Broadhurst, F.M., *A Building Stones Guide to Central Manchester*, University of Manchester, Manchester, 1975

47. Brown, P.R., Rudkins, G.F., Wheldon, P.E., 'Portland Stone', *Chartered Civil Engineer*, January 1954

48. Edmunds, F.H., and Schaffer, R.J., 'Portland Stone: Its Geology and Properties as a Building Stone', *Proc. Geol. Soc.*, **43**, Pt. 3, 1932

49. Crane, T., *Newcastle Stone*, Ealing Publications Ltd., Maidenhead, 1979

50. Allan, J., *Restoration and Archaeology in Exeter Cathedral*, Devon Archaeology No. 1, 1983

51. Leach, R., *An Investigation into the use of Purbeck Marble in Medieval England*, Privately Printed, R.A. Leach, Devon, 1978

52. Thurrell, R.G., Worrsam, B.C., and Edmonds, E.A., *Geology of the Country around Haslemere*, *Mem. Geol. Surv. G.B.*, HMSO, London, 1968

53. Worssam, B.C., *Eight Centuries of Stone*, Eagle Printing Works, Cranbrook, n.d.

54. Marsden, P.R.V., *A Ship of the Roman Period, From Blackfriars, in the City of London*, Guildhall Museum Publication, n.d.

55. Jukes, Brown, A.J., 'The Cretaceous Rocks of Britain', Vol. III, The Upper Chalk of England, *Mem. Geol. Surv. G.B.*, HMSO, London, 1904

56. Fowler, J., *The Stones of Sherborne Abbey*, Friends of Sherborne Abbey, n.d.

57. Males, P.A., 'Mexican Onyx and other Marbles'. *Australian Lapidary Magazine*, February 1974

58. Dunham, M. and Dunham, K.C., 'The Stone of the Neville Screen in Durham Cathedral, *Durham University Journal*, March 1957

59. Honeyborne, D.B., 'The building limestones of France', Building Research Establishment Note, Department of the Environment, 1978

60. Catell, M. *et al.*, *Italian Marble—Technical Guide*. F. Lli Vallardi Editori, Milan, 1982

61. Lundbohm, H., *Några öpplysningar om Sveriges stenindustri*, Stockholm, 1888

62. Wilson, E., 'Swedish limestone paving in 17th and 18th century English buildings', *Post-Medieval Archaeology*, **17**, 1983

63. Anon., *Rochas Ornamentais Portuguesas*. Ministério da Indústria e Energia, Direcção-Geral de Geologia e Minas, Lisbon, 1982

64. Anon., *Coventry Cathedral*, Reprinted from Shell—BP News, The Staff Magazine of Shell-Mex and BP Ltd.

65. Shadmon, A., *Stone in Israel*, Ministry of Development, Natural Resources Research Organization, Jerusalem, 1972

66. Notholt, A.I.G., and Highley, D.E., *Mineral Dossier No. 13, Gypsum and Anhydrite*, HMSO, London, 1975

67. Anon., *Natural Stone Directory* 7th edn, Stone Industries, Ealing Publications, Maidenhead, 1987

68. Cheetham, F.W., *Medieval English Alabaster Carvings in the Castle Museum, Nottingham*, The City of Nottingham Art Galleries and Museums Committee, Nottingham, 1973

69. Dimes, F.G., 'Alabaster—soft option for sculptors', *Stone Industries*, **14**, No. 6, July/August 1979

70. Watson, J., *Cements and Artificial Stone*, Heffer and Sons, Cambridge, 1922

71. Anon., 'The Architectural Use of Building Materials, *Post-War Building Studies No. 18*, HMSO, London, 1946

72. Bromehead, C.E.N., 'Geology in Embryo (Up to 1600 AD', *Proc. Geol. Assoc.*, **56**, Pt. 2, 1945

73. Kaye, G.W.C., and Laby, T.H., *Physical Constants*, Longmans, London, 1959

74. Anon., 'Resins for Repair', *Stone Industries*, **19**, No. 2, March 1984

75. Davey, A. *et al.*, *The Care and Conservation of Georgian Houses*, 3rd edn. Butterworths, London, 1986

5

Metamorphic rocks

Francis G. Dimes

Introduction

Metamorphic rocks are formed by the crystallization or recrystallization of pre-existing rocks at elevated temperatures or at elevated pressures or both beneath the Earth's surface. The original constituent materials of the rocks, which may have been formed under widely different conditions, are rearranged mechanically or chemically, usually with the development of new minerals. During metamorphism the original rocks lose many, if not all, of their original characteristics. Any pre-existing rock may be metamorphosed. Thus there are many types of metamorphic rocks. The common types are given in *Table 2.3*. Most of the metamorphic rocks used in commerce are the product of regional metamorphism. By far the most widely used are slate and marble. However, one stone which is the result of thermal metamorphism is of interest both from a geological and from a visual point of view.

Thermal metamorphic rocks

Ematita Granite, known also as Verde Ematita, Madreperla, or Labradorita, is from the Andean Cordillera, north of San Juan, Argentina[1]. It is a high grade metamorphic rock, described as a cordierite-silimonite-phlogopite-plagioclase-quartz rock. Blue-grey to greenish in colour it has been used particularly for Marks and Spencer shops in Northampton, Sheffield, Cardiff and in the eastern end of Oxford Street, London. A striking example of its use is for St Peters' Hill House, Carter Lane, London.

Regional metamorphic rocks

Schist

Schist is one of the most abundant of the metamorphic rocks. Much of Scotland, for example, is underlain by it. The aligned arrangement of platy and other elongated minerals commonly gives a structure known as schistosity. The alignment of the platy minerals appears to the unaided eye as a marked layering.

Many varieties of schist exist. They are named after distinctive minerals which may be present, for example, garnet, chlorite, graphite and talc. By far the most common type is mica schist. Mica schists commonly have a second mineral. Garnet-mica schist and hornblende-mica schist are also common. Biotite mica is an important constituent mineral of most schists. Because of the ease with which schist will part along the lamination it has only been used locally for building. However, some quartzites of the stone trade are schists in strict geological definition. They differ from other quartzites in that a laminated structure is produced by aligned planes which are commonly of mica flakes.

Otta Slate, from Norway, known also as Rembrant Stone (or Quartzite) and as Pillaguri Slate after the mountain peak near which it is quarried half-way between Oslo and Trondheim. It is a garnet-hornblende-biotite-muscovite-quartz schist. It is blue-black in colour. The mineral hornblende appears as needle-like streaks up to 2 inches (5 cm) long. The garnets appear as small red spots. Some of the stone may be found without hornblende. The stone can be polished and a peculiarly fascinating three-dimensional appearance is obtained. The top

(a)

(b)

Figure 5.1 (a) Slabs of Otta Slate clad columns at Tenter House, Moorgate (Cippolina marble in background); (b) needle-like hornblende crystals and red spots of garnet are responsible for the characteristic appearance of the schist. Rutherford House, George Street, Manchester

layers of the quarry, where the schist has been exposed to the weather, yield rust-coloured slabs. The stone has been recently used in Britain; the Nationwide Building Society, High Holborn, London is an example. It was also used for Bergen Hospital, Norway, for floors, risers, and treads in Unilever House, Rotterdam, Holland and for Klöcknen-Humbolt-Deutz AG, Cologne, Germany.

Barge Quartzite also known as Sanfront Stone or as Italian Quartzite, is a mica-quartz schist from Mount Bracco, Italy, in which the quartz content may be as high as 95 per cent or more. Grey, gold, amber and olive colours are available. Many modern examples

of its use are found, usually for flooring or for cladding. Examples include the Bear and Staff public house, Charing Cross Road, London, Radiant House, Gas Company, Liverpool and facings of Tower Block and Bridge, Shell House, London SE1.

Gneiss

A gneiss is a foliated rock normally composed of feldspar, quartz, biotite or muscovite mica or both and sometimes hornblende. The minerals are arranged alternately in fairly large-scale, roughly parallel layers known as gneissose banding. This tough, massive and, in some instances, decorative rock has been used locally for building purposes. Because its mineral composition and appearance is similar to some granites, gneiss usually is sold as granite. Alps Grey Granite, from Switzerland, is a biotite gneiss, which is white and dark-grey to black in colour. Pink Parys Granite is a gneissose granite from Parys, Transvaal, South Africa. It was used for the spectacular cladding on Irongate House, Dukes Place, London (*Figure 5.2*).

Quartzite

A quartzite is produced when a sandstone is metamorphosed. The constituent grains of quartz are recrystallized to an interlocking mosaic of quartz as distinct from quartzites of sedimentary origin. Mica flakes are commonly present, occasionally with other minerals.

Alta Quartzite or Altazite, with some varieties known as Crystalite, is a silver grey-green somewhat micaceous quartzite. It has been quarried since 1919 from the mountains around Alta Fjord, Norway, well inside the Arctic Circle. It has been widely used since then for paving and steps. The floor of the Chapel of the Daughters of the Cross, Stoodley Knowle, Torquay, Devon and of The Weald Inn, Burgess Hill, Sussex provide contrasting examples. The Driver and Vehicle Licensing Centre, Swansea, South Wales is another example of its use.

Diamant Quartzite (Diamantzite, or Allied Quartzite) shows a variation of colour from white, through grey-blue to beige-ochre. It is also used for paving and steps. It is quarried in Namaquland, South Africa and, like most quartzites, is tough and hard-wearing. Mica is found along marked planes resulting in a very smooth cleavage. The stone could be classified with some justification as a schist. A fine example of its use is seen in St Joseph's Oratory, Montreal, Canada. It paves the British Telecom Monarch telephone exchange, London, and may be seen in the Nationwide Building Society, Edinburgh. Safari Quartzite, from the Transvaal, South Africa is a similar stone.

Figure 5.2 Granite from Parys, Transvaal, South Africa, used for Irongate House, Dukes Place, London, is strongly deformed and now shows gneissic structure

Slate

Slaty cleavage, the characteristic feature, imposed upon a clay during the processes of regional metamorphism may be of variable thickness (see *Figure 2.6*). Some slates are produced from fine-grained sediments which are not clay in strict sense. The thinner that a slate can be cleaved, the finer it is reckoned to be. The original bedding may sometimes be seen as coloured bands running at a different angle to the cleavage surface. Slaty-cleavage may be parallel to the original bedding, but normally it is not. The pattern of quarrying is determined by the cleavage. In North Wales the cleavage way is the direction along which the slate will most easily split. The pillaring way is more or less at right angles to the cleavage. In the Lake District the terms backs and ends are used. 'A back runs with the natural cleavage of the slate .... and an end close to right angles'.[2] The name slate has also been used for manufactured roofing tiles which are not true slates. Because slate can be cleaved readily and smoothly into thin or thick sheets, and is impervious and virtually chemically inert, it is widely used for roofing, stair treads, flooring, cladding, table tops and acid tanks among other things.

Slate is derived from completely or virtually sand-free sediment, which may have contained a considerable quantity of fine-grained volcanic ash. Individual crystals cannot be seen by the naked eye. The stone is compact and non-porous. It may be almost any colour from nearly white, through grey, blue, green, red and black.

Because slate, which is microcrystalline in nature with highly developed slaty-cleavage, is generally composed of particles less than 1 micron (0.001 mm) in diameter, it is difficult to study in petrographic thin section. Normally X-ray, electron microscope, thermal and chemical techniques must be employed. Consequently an analysis of the slate, unless the requirement is strictly defined, may prove to be costly. In general terms slate is a complicated network of sub-microscopic scales of clay minerals, which are mostly varieties of mica with other platy minerals.

Platy crystals of the green mineral chlorite (a hydrated silicate of aluminium, magnesium, iron; $(Mg,Al,Fe,Mn)_6(AlSi)_4O_{10}(OH_8)$ are commonly responsible for the green colour of many slates. Hematite (iron oxide, Fe_2O_3) gives many slates their red colour and graphite (carbon, C) disseminated through the stone is responsible for the intense black of many slates.

The platy crystals have a marked parallelism, which leads to the development of planar cleavage. The more nearly parallel the orientation of the crystals, the better developed is the slaty cleavage. The planes may be only microns apart. Apart from pyrite and calcite, which are sometimes present, slate minerals are insoluble and resistant to acids. Thus slates do not weather very much through the years.

In Great Britain, which once was a large slate producer, slate is found chiefly in Scotland, the Lake District, North Wales and Cornwall. Vast reserves exist to meet any foreseeable future demand.

Scottish slates

Ballachulish Slates from the Scottish Highlands were worked as early as 1761 but are not now in production. They are blue-grey to black in colour. At one time, a mottled green and purple coloured slate was sold with the trade name Tartan. Some horizons were noted for containing perfectly formed cubic crystals of the brassy-coloured mineral pyrite (iron disulphide, FeS_2), which were known locally as diamonds. Unfortunately pyrite, particularly when exposed to the natural elements, decomposes to form the mineral melanterite ($FeSO_4 \cdot 7H_2O$) which is normally found as a white, powdery efflorescence. Because melanterite like all secondary minerals occupies a greater volume than the pyrite, slate containing pyrite frequently is disrupted. In many instances crystals fall out of the slate to leave characteristically cubic-shaped voids. However, this does not have any effect on the structural strength of the slate in use.

Only about 2 to 5 per cent of the slate quarried is recovered for economic use as is evidenced by the massive tips seen around the workings. The tips at Ballachulish were known to the many motorists patiently waiting to cross Loch Leven on the ferry. The land renewal scheme at Ballachulish is a model of site reclamation. The former 63-acre site was once an eyesore. Other slates in Scotland were quarried in the past, some on a large scale such as the Macduff Slates, Grampian. However, they were rather thick[3].

The Island of Easedale, Strathclyde was famed for its slate quarries. The slates from this island were exported to the Inner and Outer Hebrides. They were also used for the re-roofing of Iona Abbey. Characteristically the slates are blue-grey in colour and, like Ballachulish Slates, may have brassy-coloured pyrite crystals.

Slates from the Lake District

The Lake District is a major producing area for slates. There are two main sources. Perhaps the better known are those which were generally known in the past as Westmorland Green or Lakeland Green. Some of these slates were, in fact, quarried in the former counties of Lancashire and Cumberland.

The history of their origin is but one of the fascinating stories of geology. During Ordovician times (439–505 million years ago) a massive outburst of volcanic activity blew vast quantities of ash, lava and pieces of the existing country rocks into the air. The rock sequence produced in this way is known as the Borrowdale Volcanic Group. The fine-grained ashes settled in the waters of the surrounding seas as a mud which consolidated into the volcanic ash rock known as tuff. During the Caledonian mountain building episode (around 400 million years ago), tuffs were subjected to regional pressures and were metamorphosed into slates.

The Westmoreland Green or Lakeland Green slates, which are generally green in colour, are produced from two main areas. One area is around Honiston. The second is around Coniston, along the Broughton Moor, Coniston, Tilberthwaite and Langdale belt.

Broughton Moor, Buttermere, Cumbria Green, Elterwater, Kirkstone Green, and Spoutcrag are names which the different green (olive, light sea, pale barred, silver-grey, hailstone and rainspot) slates are sold by the different producers.

Green slates from the Lake District have been widely used in Great Britain and they are also known world-wide. They were used on Mullard House, Tottenham Court Road, London, the Observer building, Queen Victoria Street, London, Hotel Leofric, Coventry, and ICI Research Laboratories, Alderly Edge, Cheshire. In Longridge House, Manchester, they make a 'splendid display....Many of the panels reveal stratification ... and small scale faults'[4]. The Bank of New Zealand, Christchurch, New Zealand; and the 3.5 acres (1.4 hectares) of cladding on the Canadian Imperial Bank of Commerce, Imperial Square, Montreal, Canada provide eye-catching examples abroad.

These slates were used for roofs across the country; for example on the roof of the Geological Museum, London (1935) and the adjoining British Museum (Natural History), which was partly re-roofed after the 1939–1945 war. The architectural use of Lakeland Green and other slates for copings, cappings and walls should not be overlooked.

Burlington Slate and Brathay Slate also are from the Lake District. The muds (geologically known as the Brathay flags) from which they were formed were laid down during the Silurian and were metamorphosed during the Caledonian mountain building episode. The slates are black to blue-grey in colour, and Brathay Slate has small amounts of the brassy-coloured pyrite.

Burlington Slate has been worked for over 300

(a)

(b)

Figure 5.3 (a) Lakeland Green slate clads the chapter house of Coventry Cathedral; (b) sedimentary structures may be seen in Lakeland Green slate slabs cladding The Observer building, Queen Victoria Street, London

years from quarries at Kirkby-in-Furness, Cumbria and may be seen cladding John Dalton house, Manchester (*Figure 5.4*). Slate steps and thresholds, beautifully polished by wear through the years, can be seen on old houses in Kirkby. Burlington Slate was also used for the Police Headquarters, Preston, Lancashire, the Strand underpass, London and the offices of Kalamazoo, Ltd., Birmingham. It has also been much used overseas, for example for the Congress Hall, Berchtesgaden, Germany, the State Library, Berlin, the Dupont Office Building, Delaware, USA and the Kaiser Office Building, Oakland, California, USA. Twenty-eight thousand 18 inch × 10 inch (46 × 25 cm) slates roof the church in the industrial town of Skellefteå, Sweden, on the Gulf of Bothnia, 125 miles (200 km) south of the Arctic Circle.

Brathay Slate is from near Ambleside, Cumbria. The quarry was worked originally during the reign of Queen Elizabeth I. It too has been widely used in Britain and abroad. In Britain it may be seen in The Standard Bank, St James's House, Manchester, an office block, Pilgrim Street, Newcastle-upon-Tyne, a shop in High Street, Newcastle-under-Lyme and the Lufthansa office, St Ann's Square, Manchester. Abroad it was used for the Unilever Ltd. Office, Vlaardingen, Rotterdam, the New Town Hall, Esslingen, West Germany and St Nicholaus Church, Eindhoven, Holland.

Welsh slates

At one time, Wales produced more slate than all the other slate producing areas in Great Britain put together, nearly four-fifths of British output. Welsh slate has been quarried since the Roman occupation.[5] 'Welsh slate is possibly the best in the world . . . it tends to be more durable in urban areas owing to the very low calcite content'.[6] The major producing areas in North Wales are around Corwen, Blaenau Ffestiniog, around Corris and along a belt extending from Nantlle to Bethesda. The slates are quarried or mined from rocks of Cambrian age (Nantlle, Penrhyn), Ordovician (Ffestiniog, Aberllefenni, Corris) and Silurian (Llangollen, Corwen) age. A much smaller amount was produced in the neighbourhood of Myndd Prescely, Dyfed, South Wales. There slates of Ordovician age were used at least as early as the thirteenth century. By the end of the sixteenth century they were being widely used and sent to many places including 'dyvers partes of Ireland'.[5] In colour they range from olive-green to silvery-grey, including a deep and characteristic purple colour.

The massive tips in North Wales stand as mute witness of the scale of former slate workings. The narrow belt of slate from Bethesda to Nantlle is of

Figure 5.4 Burlington Slate, a markedly black coloured slate from Kirby-in-Furness, was used with a riven surface (along the line of slaty cleavage) for John Dalton House, Deansgate, Manchester. The line of cleavage is more or less at right angles to the original bedding which can be picked out on some slabs. (Courtesy Dr F.M. Broadhurst)

Cambrian age. Perhaps the two best known workings are the famous Penrhyn and Dinorwic quarries. Several beds, locally known as veins, with poor slate and sandy beds between them are worked. The slates are mostly reddish-purple in colour with some blue and green. The house in Nantlle where Edward I stayed when he visited copper mines at Drws-y-Coed was roofed with slates from nearby Cilgwyn quarry. Slates of Cambrian age also have been quarried to the north-west of Arenig from the Dolgelly Beds. These are noticeably black in colour, but because of disseminated iron pyrites weather to a rusty brown colour. This meant they were not commercially acceptable.

By far the best slates come from around Blaenau Ffestiniog where Ordovician age slates may be obtained in very thin sheets because of the fineness of the cleavage. They were sometimes called Port-madoc Slates because they were mostly shipped from that port in the past.

Portmadoc Slates are very fine-grained, dark blue, blue-grey and sometimes intense black in colour. The Llangollen belt around Corwen yields slates of Silurian age which are dark grey-blue and paler blue-grey in colour. Much of the material from this belt, however, cannot be finely cleaved and large slabs, or flags, rather than slate in strict definition are obtained. Many of the beds split more easily along the bedding than along the direction of cleavage.

The identification of slates used for building and particularly for roofing presents complex problems, partly because few slates have been microscopically studied and compared. The determination of prove-nance is of more importance in the historical and in the archaeological context. The traditional use for slate is for roofing. It was the predominant material used in London. However, it is also used for other architectural purposes and increasingly cladding (*see Figure 5.6*).

The use of Welsh slate for roofing can be traced back to Roman times. It was used for mediaeval castle and ecclesiastical building through Tudor times to the present day. In extremely exposed areas it was not unusual to coat the roof with tallow whitewash, which eventually became so thick that it may be difficult now to see that the roof is of slate.

Slate from Penrhyn Quarry was used on St Asaph Cathedral, Clwyd, in the early seventeenth century. When 'after some 250 years, the roof was stripped owing to the failure of the timber, the slates were in such good condition that they could be used again'.[5] The Assembly Hall of the Blaenau Ffestiniog School (1936) shows the use of block slate for building. Welsh Slate has been extensively used. Some examples include the floor of St Bartholomew's Church, St Albans, Hertfordshire, and cladding tunnels on the Newport-Monmouth road. At Montparnasse Station, Paris, several thousand square metres of Welsh Red Slate was used to clad the pillars and the façades. The Environmental Museum, Llanberis, Gwynedd provides a magnificent example of the use of slate for building (*Figure 5.5*). At one time whimsical names were used for different sizes of slates not only in Wales but also elsewhere, including Collyweston, where they were applied to tilestones. Short Hag Hattee, Chits, Batchlers, Long twelves (which were 16 inches (40 cm) long) are some. More amusingly, many were named after the degrees of the aristocracy, including Lady, Countess, Duchess and Princess. During the period 1790–1830, Ladies cost 8 shillings, Countesses 13 shillings and Duchesses 23 shillings per hundred. Mr. Leycester, a Welsh Circuit

(a)

(b)

(c)

Figure 5.5 (a) The large scale of the slate quarry at Penrhyn, Bethesda, Gwynedd may be judged from the size of the quarrymen and the mechanical digger. Slate from this quarry was used for the Environmental Museum, Llanberis, Gwynedd (b) and for internal flooring and walling of the CEGB pumped storage scheme in the old Bethesda Quarry, Gwynedd (c). (Courtesy R.H. Boyle)

Figure 5.6 Modern shop front of slate slabs (otherwise unidentified) in Jermyn Street, London

Judge in 1839 incorporated the names into a poem part of which read:

> This countess or lady, though crowds may be present,
> Submits to be dressed by the hands of a peasant;
> And you'll see when her Grace is but once in his clutches
> With how little respect he will handle a duchess[7].

Leicestershire slates

In the Charnwood Forest area of Leicestershire, irregular outcrops of Precambrian rocks occur. The Swithland Slates, which form part of the succession, are mainly of siltstone grade and consist of white mica, quartz, chlorite and accessory opaque minerals. The slates are purple (blue-grey) and green-grey in colour and provide a remarkable contrast when graded slates are laid over the otherwise uninteresting red brick buildings of west and south Leicestershire[8]. They were quarried from an early date for roofing material. They do not, however, cleave as well as Welsh slates and when Welsh slates became readily available in the last century, the quarries in the Swithland Slate declined. Nevertheless, Swithland Slates are an attractive roofing material, so much so, that until recently, the roofs of old buildings were pillaged for their slates[9].

Figure 5.7 After some 150 years, the inscription on the headstone of Smithland Slate in The Churchyard at Rothwell, Northamptonshire, still remains crisply legible

Because of their fine grain and because they withstand the ravages of weathering, slates have been widely used for tombstones. Swithland Slate may be found widely distributed throughout Leicestershire and adjoining counties and many headstones over two hundred years old still retain crisp, readily readable inscriptions (*Figure 5.7*).

Cornish slates
Slates from south-west England were used from early times and were also exported to continental Europe. They have been found on many medieval sites in southern England and they were shipped to Brittany and to the Netherlands[10]. In 1187 800 000 slates were shipped from Devon to the King's Buildings, Winchester, Hampshire. In 1436 a Southampton man was granted a licence to ship Devon slates to Mont St Michel 'in satisfaction of a ransom'.

The belt of rocks which crop out between Launceston and Tintagel, Cornwall, has been quarried for slates on a large scale. The slates are of Upper Devonian age and are the geologically youngest slate produced in Great Britain. They are fine-grained, smooth, with a noticeable sheen, grey, green and rustic in colour. They are commonly very finely black-spotted. The spots are probably caused by small amounts of the mineral manganese. Slates of Devonian age also were quarried along the south coast of Cornwall[10]. The use of slates from south-western England has been plotted along the south coast of England and its hinterland to Dover and Canterbury where they have been found in mediaeval contexts by Jope and Dunning[10]. Of all the slate quarries undoubtedly the most renowned is Delabole, in north Cornwall. This huge hole, 'prob-

(a)

(b)

Figure 5.8 (a) Slate from Delabole Quarry, Delabole, Cornwall–'The biggest slate quarry in the world'–was used widely, particularly in Southern England, and also was exported; (b) the public house in the village is hung with slate from the quarry and is named after tools used by the quarrymen

Figure 5.9 Local slates of Devonian age were used to clad this cottage in Ashburton, Devon

ably the biggest slate quarry in the world', has been worked for at least 400 years and is now about 500 ft (150 m) deep. Slate from this and other quarries in these Devonian beds was used as slabs for walling, often with decorative effect. It was also used for cladding, for example on the picturesque slate-hung houses of south-west England (*Figure 5.9*). The quarries also provided roofing slates which were commonly crudely and disagreeably covered with a cement slurry. Local examples of these uses abound. Delabole Slate was used on the Victoria and Albert Museum, South Kensington, London and on Truro

Cathedral, Cornwall. Padstow Church, Cornwall was re-roofed with them[5]. There is a demand for Delabole and other slates for restoration work. Interestingly, part of the cargo of the ship *James Matthews*, sunk in 1841 off the east coast of Australia, is of slates believed to be from Delabole.

Imported slates

Although excellent quality British slate is readily available and can satisfy the domestic requirement, slate from abroad which is 'cheaper, but also inferior'[5] has been imported. The early part of the Highbury housing estate, Cosham, Portsmouth, Hampshire, built in the 1930s, was roofed with French slates. By the 1950s trouble was reported with these roofs. The later parts of the estate used slates from North Wales (Personal communication, R.H. Roberts).

Slate is imported principally from France, Belgium, Spain, Portugal and Italy. Recently the greatest amount has come from Spain followed by Portugal and then Italy. In Great Britain there is a big market in second-hand slates, which some authorities have reckoned are probably more used than the total current output of the slate quarries.

France has a long tradition of slate working, particularly in the Ardennes, where records indicate that slates were being produced before 466 AD. These slates are Cambrian in age and are remarkably similar to the Cambrian slates quarried in North Wales. As in the Welsh slates various colours may be found including green, blue, purplish and red. Slate from the Ardennes was certainly exported to England 50 to 60 years ago, but the records of its use appear to have been lost. Some specimens may well have been determined as North Wales slate. A green slate, probably from Fumay, was found at the deserted mediaeval village at Hangleton, Derbyshire[10]. Ironically, in recent years the French have complained

(a)

Figure 5.10 (a) Slate roofs of cottages in Wadebridge, Cornwall may be found covered with cement slurry;

(b)

(b) slate roof of house in Tonyrfail, Glamorgan coated with bitumen and slag chippings

(a)

(b)

(c)

Figure 5.11 Whilst slate from the mine at Chiavari, Italy, is still cleaved by hand for the production of billiard table beds (a), it is planed by machine to ensure a flat surface (b). The production of cills, skirtings and kerbs is almost entirely automatic (c)

about the amount of British slate being imported to re-roof historic buildings which were formerly roofed with Ardennes slate.

Slate also was produced in the Province of Anjou and the renowned grey slates were used for the Palace of Versailles. They are now replaced with slates from Spain or, sadly, with asbestos and cement tiles.

Spain has a vigorous industry and Spanish slates are currently being imported into Great Britain. Many historically important buildings in France are roofed with them, for example the cathedrals at Amiens and Liège.

Although Italy is inevitably associated with marble, slate also is worked. Italy claims to be one of the largest producers of clear, black slate. Production is concentrated almost entirely in the Province of Leguria. The underground quarry at Chiavari in slate of Ordovician age is one example. In addition to a large output of cills, tiles, hearths and skirtings the works produce 2000 to 3000 billiard table beds a month. Most of these are exported to the USA where the cost of a real billiard table is obviously not regarded as mis-spent.

Marble

Few countries do not produce marble, although many of the commercial marbles are limestones. The terms marble and limestone are wrongly and commonly confused. Limestone is a sedimentary rock. Marble is a *metamorphic* rock made up mostly of calcite ($CaCO_3$). In a marble the calcite is recrystallized to produce an interlocking granular mosaic of roughly equal-sized calcite crystals (*Figure 5.12*). Calcite is the name given to calcium carbonate when it is in crystal form. The recrystallization removes any of the original sedimentary structures and fossils. No true marble will have fossils. Non-calcareous mineral matter present in the original limestone will also be metamorphosed and new kinds of mineral assemblages will be created. Some marble is produced by thermal metamorphism but by far the greater amount is the result of regional metamorphism. Considerable temperatures and pressures are involved. As a result, the mosaic of calcite crystals shows a rough alignment which may not always be visible to the naked eye. It can commonly be seen on the gross scale and marble sometimes shows a rough schistosity (*Figure 5.13*). The length of time that the rock is subjected to metamorphic processes determines the coarseness of the grain size; the longer the time the coarser the grain size that may be expected. The process is aided by active pore fluids. In marble it is aided by carbon dioxide.

The granular structure of marble is often called sugary and viewed from some aspects a cut surface may look like sugar in the mass. As marble weathers, the bonds between the grains of calcite are loosened and the surface assumes a sugary appearance known as saccharoidal weathering. This feature may be used, with care, as one of the criteria used to decide whether a stone is a marble or a limestone. A limestone and a marble will weather in different manner. Because of the interlocking mosaic of calcite grains marbles have a very low porosity.

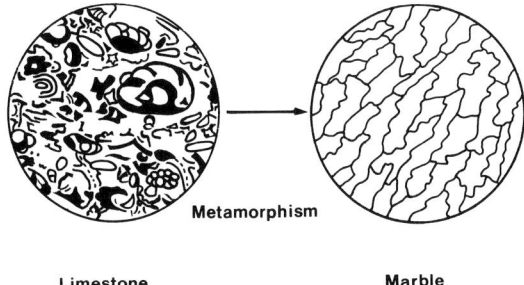

Limestone   Metamorphism   Marble

Figure 5.12 A limestone (here containing small fossils), when subjected to the processes of metamorphism is recrystallized to an interlocking mosaic of evenly granular calcite crystals

Figure 5.13 Schistosity, a characteristic feature of metamorphic rocks, is not normally seen in marble. However, it is shown on the large scale at Carrara, Italy, where it is picked out by vegetation

A pure marble, which is entirely or nearly of calcium carbonate, is a monomineralic rock. It is white in colour. Because the calcite crystals which make up the rock are normally transparent, slabs of marble up to about 1.2 inches (30 mm) thick may appear translucent.

The limestones which were metamorphosed to marbles usually contain other mineral matter and it is this which produces the colour seen in marble. It may be either evenly distributed or may give a blotchy, mottled look to the stone. It may also appear as veins. Some marble is highly coloured; black, grey, green, pink, red, and yellow marbles are common.

Serpentine (or serpentinous) marble, also known as ophicalcite, is a general name for marble containing a greater or lesser amount of the mineral serpentine. A serpentinous marble is characteristically streaked with the vivid green of serpentine.

The chemical equation for its production is[11]:-

$$2CaMg(CO_3)_2 + SiO_2 = Mg_2SiO_4 + 2CaCO_3 + 2CO_2$$

Dolomite + Quartz = Olivine + Calcite + Carbon dioxide

Water, if present, reacts with the olivine to form:

$$5Mg_2SiO_4 + 4H_2O = 2H_4Mg_3Si_2O_9 + 4MgO + SiO_2$$

Olivine + Water = Serpentine (removed in solution)

The water, which will be in the condition of a supercritical gas at the temperatures and pressures involved, is a hydrothermal fluid and is a very effective solvent and transporter.

Marble has acquired a reputation as a prestigious building and decorative material and was once even regarded as fit spoils of war. The statue of King George II standing in the middle of the Hospital Square, Greenwich, London was 'sculptured from a single block of marble seized from the French by Admiral Rooke'[12].

The choice of marble as a decorative stone as distinct from its use as a stone for cills, thresholds, cladding and other general building purposes, is based on colour. Panels of highly coloured and decoratively attractive marble may be seen hung on walls, rather as paintings would be. Marble was much used for fireplaces. Even if the limestones, cut, polished, and sold as marbles are discounted, the number of true marbles to choose from is large.

British marbles

In the British Isles, marbles are relatively rare rocks and most of them are only of geological interest. A few have acquired a greater than local importance.

Iona Marble, from the Isle of Iona, Strathclyde, Scotland is a serpentinous marble, white with green to yellowish-green streaks, bands and mottlings. At one time the outcrop of a vertical band 20 to 40 feet

(6–12 m) thick and about 100 yards (91 m) long was extensively quarried. Considerable quantities were sent to Leith and London[13]. Records of its use are regrettably sparse. Traditionally it is said to have been used for the old altar of Iona Cathedral (Abbey) and probably it was used similarly elsewhere in ecclesiastical buildings. A slab was sent to Johannesburg, South Africa, for the headstone of Lord Walter Campbell, a son of the Duke of Argyll. The marble may be seen in the pavement in St Andrews Chapel, Westminster Cathedral, London. A panel of Iona Marble which has religious significance is inset into the fantastic travertine cladding of the chancel of the Church of St Mary, Studley Royal, Yorkshire. Other examples of Iona Marble may have been confused with Connemara Marble, which it closely resembles.

Skye Marble, from the quarries near Torrin, on the Isle of Skye in Scotland is one of the few examples of a thermally metamorphosed marble. Limestone of Cambrian age was altered by an igneous intrusion of Tertiary age. The marble was worked briefly between the two world wars for statuary marble but because of many small igneous intrusions and extensive shattering of the rock, it mostly was worked for crushed rock and agricultural lime. There appear to be no records of its use for building or for decoration, but there are many white marble chip drives leading to cottages and houses both on the island and on the nearby mainland.

The Island of Tiree, Strathclyde, Scotland is composed mostly of metamorphosed sediments from which the highly decorative Tiree Marble once was quarried. This marble is unusually pink and is full of spots and clots of a dark green mineral, coccolite (a granular variety of diopside, $CaO.MgO.2SiO_2$). Although it is recorded as a 'well known ... ornamental stone'[14] there appear to be no records of its use.

In Glen Tilt, near Blair Atholl, Tayside, Scotland a limestone, which is locally thermally metamorphosed was worked as the Glen Tilt Marble. It was esteemed for decorative work and was used for wash-hand stands and other items of furniture. It is a white marble with green blotches and streaks, which closely resembles Mona Marble from Anglesey. Because it is not well known it is likely that examples of its use are confused with Mona Marble.

Connemara Marble, from a number of quarries including Lissoughter, Derryclare and Streamstown in Co. Galway, Eire, is a metamorphosed dolomitic limestone of Precambrian age. It has a greyish groundmass in which varying amounts of light to dark green serpentine occurs as twisted and interlocking bands. In block the stone can range from almost white to nearly completely dark green. The stone had many names including Galway Serpentine, Irish Green, Irish White (a very light coloured variety), Recess Marble (from near Recess, Co. Galway) and Lissoughter Marble.

The marble has been used for decorative purposes from early times particularly for ecclesiastical work. Two fine columns of it stand at the entrance to the Chapel of St Wilfred, Brompton Oratory, South Kensington, London. It was used for wall panels in St Anselm's Church, Mayfair, London. It appears in the chancel pavement of Bristol Cathedral and occurs in Truro Cathedral and in Peterborough Cathedral. It was also used widely elsewhere.

Imported marbles
Because of the comparative rarity of marble in the British Isles as well as its limited range of colour, the geological difficulties of working and the remoteness of the quarries, marble has been imported since at least Roman times. There is little doubt but that much of it was chosen purely for its colour; *opus tesselatum*, *opus sectile* and *opus alexandrinum* depend on colour contrast for their effect.

It is also worth recalling that Roman Rome was a glistening city of marble. In addition to local sources, which were developed comparatively late, some 500 foreign marbles have been identified in the ancient city. However, many of these are in fact limestone.

Italian marble
Italy claims first place in the production of marble. The main producing areas are listed on p. 122. Without doubt the most widely known locality is Carrara in the Province of Tuscany. It is particularly known for the pure white, and to some, characterless and boring, marble. The marbles (metamorphosed Jurassic limestones) of the Apuan Alps which surround the production area around Carrara where most of the quarries are found, may be grouped as follows:

1. Statuario (Statuary Marble)
   a. First Statuary (white statuary), virtually pure white, fine-grained marble;
   b. Second Statuary, marble with some grey markings;
   c. Vein Statuary, marble with noticeable grey veining and grey areas.
2. Bianco Chiara (or Blanc Clair); white marble with only a few grey markings.
3. Bianco Chiara Venato (Bianco Venato, or Blanc Veine), white marble with stronger greyish markings which may have a distinct vein pattern.
4. Bardiglio (or Bleu Tarquin, Turquin, or Italian Dove), a blue-grey marble.

Commonly it is very difficult to distinguish between Second Statuary and Vein Statuary marble. Statuary marbles which are more heavily veined may be called Bastard Statuary. It may be difficult to distinguish Bianco Chiara from Vein Statuary marble.

Figure 5.14 Ornamental fountain in grey veined marbles (Second Statuary with Arabescato in rear), Carrara, Italy

Figure 5.15 Banking hall floor of Sicilian marble (white, grey veins and patches), Kilkenny 'marble' (black) and Bardiglio marble (grey), Dublin. (Courtesy J. Redmill)

Many names have been given to stone from individual quarries which differ in the pattern and strength of the figuring but are very similar to stone from adjoining quarries: '...certain marbles which owe their naming to pure fantasy...'[15]. Arabescato is white with grey markings. Parona is white with veinings of grey colour. Tulanto is described as white with a few grey lines which are not prominent. Sicilian has a white ground-mass through which run light grey veinings.

Only on the British market is the name Sicilian applied to general types of Carrara marble which are white with irregular greyish veinings and cloudy masses. In Italy these marbles would be known as Bianco Chiara. At least 1000 tons of Sicilian Marble was used for the Queen Victoria memorial facing Buckingham Palace, London. Marble Arch, London, also built of it.

The Carrara area has also produced some markedly coloured stone. Fior has a violet-coloured ground-mass, and Red Carrara is reddish. Bardiglio Marble (Bardilla, Blue Turquin, Blue Fleuri) is one of the most important coloured types from Tuscany. It is best known in Britain as Italian Dove. It is dove-coloured (grey) with darker grey veins and bands. To some it appears drab. It is close-grained and hard wearing and has been used for flooring and paving as well as for decorative purposes. Many fireplace surrounds are made of it.

Carrara Marble is very widely used. The twelfth century Cathedral of Pisa and the Campanile (the 'Leaning Tower') are made of Luni Marble, which was known to the Romans as *Marmor Lunense*. When the Romans developed local marble quarries they founded a camp, named Luni, near the present town of Carrara in 177 BC. The use of marmor lunense was first cited by the historian Velleius Patercolus in the first century BC, on the occasion of the construction of the sumptuous home of the prefect Mamurra on Mt. Celio.'[15] It was Augustus who inherited a city of brick and left it a city of marble.

Greek marble

Not even the briefest review of marbles can ignore Greece. It produces the classic white marbles, Parian and Pentelic, as well as the highly coloured Skyros Marble. Parian Marble, from the Island of Paros, is considered by some to be the finest white marble in the world. Parian porcelain was named because it was considered to resemble the marble from the Island of Paros. Most of the island is of marble which was quarried from galleries driven into the sides of Mount Marpesian. The marble has a translucent appearance and, particularly in fresh faces, some of crystals reflect light with a sparkling play of colours, known by the Greeks as Lychnites. It was worked in the sixth century BC and was widely used by the Greeks for roofing, for example on the Parthenon on the Acropolis in Athens. Later the Romans quarried large quantities and the stone was widely used for building and sculpture. Pieces of the marble have been recovered from archaeological sites in Great Britain. Parian Marble was also used in the modern context. Watson[16] records its use in Draper's Hall, London (1898–1899).

Pentelic Marble, argued by some to rival Parian, is quarried from Mount Pentelikon in Attica. Classically the stone is known as *Marmor Pentelicum*. It is available as white or blue stone and was known commercially as Stavatovouni. White Pentelic (or Pentelicon) may be white or may have cloudy markings. The cloudy markings may contain finely disseminated iron pyrites in crystal form. Commonly the stone has a delicate, soft light golden cast, which is better demonstrated than described. This characteristic feature can, however, be used as a diagnostic feature for determination.

Pentelic Marble is the stone that was used for the Propylas which was built by Pericles 437 BC, and for the many other buildings in Greece. It is renowned for its use by Phidias for the Parthenon (447–438 BC). It was also used in Euston Tower, London, and for the interior floors and walls of the National Westminster Bank, King Street, Manchester. The Ceremonial Staircase to the Council Chamber, County Hall, London includes the marble. The Norwich Union Building built in 1905 on the corner of St James's Street and Piccadilly, London, is one of the first London buildings on which the marble was used. This listed building was not comprehensively cleaned and restored until 1980. This was done only because 'severe corrosion [of the structural steel members] had pushed the stones from position .... The Pentelikon marble was sound, apart from one course at fourth floor level which showed signs of movement caused by more rusty steelwork'[17].

Skyros Marble, from the Isle of Skyros in the Aegean Sea, is a markedly colourful stone. In general it has a white ground with strong orange, reddish, golden-yellow to brown and to violet veins and markings. Because of the variation in the veining and markings, specimens of this marble, in isolation, may look widely dissimilar. It is highly decorative and was used extensively for the late-lamented Lyons Corner Houses. It may now be seen in the offices of Canadian Pacific, Cockspur Street, London.

French marble

France has been a source of marble since Roman times. Most of the marbles are coloured. Some white statuary marble is found in the Pyrenees. The classic stone is Campan. Campan is not completely metamorphosed and the white calcite is crystalline, but the matrix is not (see p. 122).

Turkish marble

Asia Minor, principally Turkey, has supplied marble since the earliest days. The Romans used much marble from this area. White marble was taken from the Isle of Marmara. This stone was called *Marmor Proconnensus* after the classical name for the island. A fine, even-grained pure white statuary marble was obtained in addition to coarse-grained varieties. It was used in the Church of St Sophia in Istanbul, Turkey. Pieces of marble found on Roman sites in Great Britain have been identified as Marmara. A white marble with purple veins, widely known as Pavonazzetto, from Docimio, north of Synnada, Phrygia, was one of the first marbles imported into Rome. Other marbles from Turkey are known. The identification of a sample as Turkish White Marble probably from the Balikesir-Erdek district, was part

of the evidence used to determine that the Worksop Giant was one of the missing pieces of the main frieze of the Great Altar of Pergamon[18].

Scandinavian marble

Norway exploits only a small amount of the marble available. Breche Rose (Norwegian Rose, Norwegian Pink) has a pleasant white and pink colour and is brecciated. It is deservedly popular for decorative purposes and was used for part of the altar of the Chapel of St Augustine in Westminster Cathedral.

Sweden, like Norway, has much marble but only a little of it is worked. The most important is called Swedish Green in Britain. It is known to have been quarried since 1650. It is a Precambrian ophicalcite and is quarried in the Norrköping area, in Southern Sweden. It is greyish-white with twisted bands, streaks or patches of green to brown. It was used for the floor of the Regimental Chapel, Manchester Cathedral, where it is matched with Roman travertine, and in the Coliseum Theatre, London. It may also be seen in the main entrance hall floor of the Victoria and Albert Museum, London. It is sometimes confused with Connemara Marble, a similar type of stone, which it may resemble.

American marble

Vast quantities of marble exist in the United States of America and Canada. Some American marbles are widely known. Examples include Georgia marble which is white, silvery grey, grey to black and white

Figure 5.16 The Washington Monument, Washington DC, was faced with three types of marble: Texas Marble (Maryland) below, then a band of four courses of Lee Marble (from Lee, Massachusetts), followed by Cockeysville Marble (Maryland). The band of Lee Marble separating the two others may be easily distinguished

Figure 5.17 The Lincoln Memorial, Washington DC, built to a plan resembling the Parthenon on the Acropolis, used a white marble with faint grey markings from West Elk Mountains, Colorado

In the nineteenth century many mass produced pieces of statuary were made to stand in the gardens and the centre of ponds or fountain lakes of the *nouveau riche*. This is the origin of the name water marble. However, the name is not an indication of the type of stone used. Catalogues of these pieces were issued and they could be ordered from stock.

Although marble is commonly and popularly regarded as a luxury material, in those parts of the world where it is the stone of the country, it is used wherever stone is needed. For example, in part of South Africa, a pure white marble was used for pig sties.

and Tennessee marble which is grey and pink to brown. Texas Marble, from Maryland, Lee Marble, from Massachusetts, and Cockeysville Marble from Maryland, are white to pale grey. They were all used for the Washington Monument in Washington DC (*Figure 5.16*). Use of marble is so extensive that the USA also imports large amounts of marble from other countries. Much marble from Carrara, Italy as well as travertine from Italy is used in Washington DC. The marbles and other principal building stones used for many of the public buildings in Washington DC, have been excellently and comprehensively described in *Building Stones of our Nation's Capital*[19].

Marble from Australia and New Zealand
Australia has an inexhaustible supply of marbles. Those from New South Wales, Queensland and South Australia are particularly well known. At one time about forty different types came from New South Wales, where quarrying began some 185 years ago. However, some of these are limestone in strict geological classification. White, black and other coloured stone is found. They may be seen used for public buildings and monuments in Sydney, Adelaide, Melbourne and elsewhere. The stones were offered on the English market in the early part of the twentieth century but they do not seem to have been used, except for Australia House, London.

Kairuru Marble, a white, coarse-grained marble quarried in New Zealand, was used in Wellington. A light-grey variety may be seen in the interior of Parliament Buildings, Wellington. Other marbles also have been used locally.

Water marble
The homogeneous varieties of marble have long been a favourite of the sculptors and many famous works have been chiselled from it.

References

1. Caminos, R., 'Some Granites, Gneisses and Metamorphites of Argentina', *Spec. Publ. Geol. Soc. S. Afr.*, **3**, 1973
2. Anon., 'Modern Slate Output in the Lake District', *Stone Industries*, **7**, September 1983
3. Read, H.H., *British Regional Geology, The Grampian Highlands*, rev. by A.G. Macgregor, HMSO, Edinburgh, 1948
4. Simpson, I.M. and Broadhurst, F.M., *A Building Stones Guide to Central Manchester*, University of Manchester, Manchester, 1975
5. North, F.J., *The Slates of Wales*, National Museum of Wales, Cardiff, 1946
6. Crockett R.N., 'Slate', *Mineral Dossier No. 12*, HMSO, London, 1975
7. Anon., 'Curious Facts About Slate', *Stone*, **28**, No. 3, August 1907
8. Penoyre, J. and Penoyre, J., *Houses in the Landscape*, Readers Union, Newton Abbot, 1978
9. Eastwood, T., 'Roofing materials through the ages', *Proc. Geol. Assoc.*, **62**, Pt. 1, 1951
10. Jope, E.M. and Dunning, G.C., 'The use of blue slate for roofing in medieval England', *The Antiquaries Journal*, **34**, Nos. 3, 4, 1954
11. Holmes, A., *Principles of Physical Geology*, Nelson, London, 1965
12. Oman, C., *Britain against Napoleon*, Readers Union, London 1943
13. Viner, D.J., *The Iona Marble Quarry*, Iona Community, Glasgow, 1979
14. Phemister, J., *British Regional Geology. Scotland: The Northern Highlands*, HMSO, Edinburgh, 1948
15. Anon., *Italian Marble Technical Guide*. Vallardi Editori, Milan, 1982
16. Watson, J., *British and Foreign Marbles and other ornamental stones*, University Press, Cambridge, 1916
17. Anon., 'Recut red Jasper is fit for a new life', *Stone Industries*, **15**, No. 4, May 1980
18. Haynes, D., 'The Worksop Relief', *Sonderdruck aus Jahrbuch der Berliner Museen*, **5**, 1963
19. Anon., *Building Stones of our Nation's Capital*. United States Department of the Interior, Geological Survey, Washington DC, n.d.

6

Determination of a sample

Francis G. Dimes

Introduction

The two commonest questions asked of a geologist by an architect are 'What stone is it?' and 'Where can I get some more?' They are not always easy to answer. Generalized descriptions of a rock as given in this book must not be used as a basis for the determination of a stone in a building. Unless a stone is seen to be taken from a quarry and placed in a building there is no absolutely certain way of determining its provenance.

Rocks are aggregates of minerals and the properties of a rock will depend on many unpredictable factors. The texture may differ from place to place because of a difference in grain size. A schist may appear to be an entirely different rock depending on which schistose layer is observed. The relative proportions of constituent minerals in a rock may differ from place to place. In short, because rocks are not homogeneous, laboratory determinations of their physical constants may not produce data of relevance.

General analysis

It is possible for the lithology of a stone from a building to be determined, for example whether it is a sandstone or a limestone. The determination of its provenance is by no means as easy. The reason is quite simple; similar environmental conditions of deposition lead to similar types of sediments being deposited. This results in similar types of rock. Commonly the best a geologist can do is to suggest a stone of similar lithology (e.g. sandstone or limestone), mineral content, colour and other characteristics. Because the sample is matched geologically the match will be a good one, although the stone may not look the same because the colour

is different. This is because there is a marked difference in appearance between new and old, weathered stone which disappears with time.

The geologist must have a specimen of the building stone in order to identify it. It follows that a piece of the stone must be removed from the building. Care should be taken to ensure that the sample is of sufficient size to be representative of the building stone as a whole. A small specimen may not show features which are characteristic of the rock. As large a sample as possible should be supplied. Although determinations have been given on pieces no larger than the little finger nail, the smaller a specimen, the less secure the determination. Whatever the size of the sample it should be truly representative of the stone under study.

The comments made about the sample relate only to the block of stone from which the sample was taken; it must not be blindly assumed that the comments may be taken to apply to all stone used in the building. It is helpful if the sample is clean. The geologist will also like to know if the specimen may be broken further so that a fresh surface may be examined. Archival evidence is the way to determine the provenance and name of the stone, but archives may not record the type of the stone in petrographical terms.

A few simple observations and tests may be sufficient to establish the nature of the stone *in situ*. Observation with a hand lens, magnification ×10 is standard, should provide some answers. With a hand lens it should be possible to determine whether the stone is granular, compact, crystalline, coarse- or fine-grained. It should also be possible to decide whether the stone is igneous, sedimentary or metamorphic. However, some igneous rocks may be very fine-grained, and the grain size may be too fine to be properly resolved with a hand lens. The surface of the stone may have been rubbed to a flour, or covered with dirt, wax, polish, varnish or just the grime of ages. This will mask diagnostic features. A pocket knife with a blade of hardness $H = c.5\frac{1}{2}$, used with caution will give an indication. Limestones will scratch but sandstones and most igneous rocks will not.

A carbonate will effervesce when tested with dilute hydrochloric acid. The effervescence indicates only that a carbonate is present but does not identify the carbonate mineral. There are several carbonate minerals, but since copper carbonate (e.g. malachite) is green and magnesium carbonate (e.g. rhodochrosite) is pink the test usually indicates that calcium carbonate (as limestone or as marble) is being tested.

Commonly, these simple tests will be sufficient to determine the nature of the stone. They will not give any indication of provenance, but experience may be a valuable guide. The architect should use this information to look for a geologically compatible stone. If the integrity of the geology of a stone building is maintained, all else will be well. However, for historical or archaeological reasons, the determination of provenance may be required. In many instances, however, it must be recognized that the geologist is 'best-guessing'.

More detailed analysis

An analysis of a stone is rarely required. What is an analysis and will it give a useful answer? The architect, restorer, or conservator should discuss the purpose of the enquiry with the geologist. The geologist should be given as much information as is possible because a seemingly minor item may be crucial from his point of view. When a specimen has been submitted a simple systematic series of tests are possible. The tests used will depend on the sample and what information is required.

1. Macroscopic examination using a hand lens
   i. What is the texture?
     a. crystalline
     b. granular
     c. other
   ii. What is the grain size?
     a. is it uneven?
     a. any contained pebbles?
   iii. Are there any notable minerals or grains?
   iv. Are there any fossils present? (If the surface of a stone is moistened, the moisture will enhance the fossil.
   v. Is the stone compact or friable?
   vi. What colour is it? (The *Rock Color Chart* is of use)
   vii. Has it a lustre?
   viii. Is it transparent or translucent?
   ix. Has it any particular type of fracture?

2. Physical tests
   i. What is the hardness and toughness?
   ii. Is it
     a. compact
     b. friable
     c. fresh
     d. weathered
   iii. What is its density, does it feel heavy? In fact, this is of little help.)

3. Chemical tests
   i. Does it effervesce?
     a. A lot
     b. Little (There will be little if any effervescence with dolomitic limestone.)

4. Chemical analysis
   i. Partial
   ii. Total
   Chemical analyses are generally of little use in this context. They may indicate the presence of particular minerals, for example, dolomite, or gypsum, but there are easier ways of determination.

5. Microscopic examination
   i. Study of a thin section of the stone
   Undoubtedly this is the most useful method, particularly for igneous and metamorphic rocks. It will certainly identify the type of rock, for example, granite, dolerite, or micaceous glauconitic sandstone. It will not determine the provenance, although the information gained will be of great help in suggesting it.

   Thin sections are slices of rock about 0.8–1.2 in (2 cm by 3 cm) mounted on a glass microscope slide and ground down to a standard thickness of 30μ (micron = 0.003 mm). At this thickness all the common rock-forming minerals are transparent in transmitted light except the iron-oxide minerals which remain opaque. The optical properties may be determined and the quantity and relationships of the minerals may be studied. Thus, the mineral composition can be determined. This is an important factor especially in fine-grained rocks.

6. Special tests
   i. X-ray diffraction
   This may be used to determine the presence of dolomite, calcite, gypsum and other minerals but normally easier methods are available. This technique is of value when only the merest scraping of the object is allowed.

7. Geochemical fingerprinting and isotopic study
   A programme of geochemical fingerprinting would undoubtedly enable identification and determination of provenance in nearly every

instance. The programme involves the collection of specimens, both laterally and vertically across every outcrop to create a reference collection of specimens. Then any submitted specimen is 'fingerprinted' and compared with the reference specimens.

Some work already has been undertaken in the field of isotopic study which has shown that, when used with other analytical methods, it offers great possibilities of matching samples to quarry location.[1,2] The Craigs report[1], '...the Athenians scatter fragments of Pentelic marble around the Parthenon each winter, in order to provide material for the insatiable pillage by tourists. This marble is from modern quarries and is isotopically distinct from that of the classical quarries'.

Geochemical fingerprinting and isotopic study require sophisticated equipment and highly trained scientists. These are costly.

References

1. Craig, H. and Craig, V., 'Greek Marbles: Determination of Provenance by Isotopic Analysis *Science*, **176**, 28 April 1972
2. Coleman, M. and Walker, S., 'Stable Isotope Identification of Greek and Turkish Marbles' *Archaeometry*, **21**, Pt. 1, 1979

7

Weathering and decay of masonry

David B. Honeyborne

Introduction

If stone masonry is exposed to the weather, some changes must inevitably occur, however well the property is being looked after. The changes might be aesthetically pleasing or distressing, of no physical consequence or structurally hazardous and the rate of change might be very low or quite rapid. The word *weathering* is used to refer to all such changes. In specific cases where significant loss of substance or form occurs, the change is referred to as *decay*.

This chapter deals first with the basic causes of the weathering of stone masonry, including changes brought about by living organisms. Attention is then drawn to the influence that some design and construction errors have on the weathering of the masonry. Finally, the advantageous and adverse effects of possible actions by those using or looking after stone buildings is discussed. Some technical details that might be of interest are placed in an Annex.

Basic causes of weathering of stone masonry

Those responsible for the conservation of buildings or monuments in which stone masonry is decaying or otherwise deteriorating will wish to understand what is happening, if only to satisfy their curiosity. But there is more to be gained than that, for such understanding might well help them to reduce the rate of deterioration by improving the ambient conditions in some way. Moreover, an analysis of what is happening might permit some definition of the micro-climate immediately surrounding the masonry. This would greatly assist in the selection of suitable replacement materials, should such drastic action prove to be necessary.

There are several causes for the deterioration of masonry and each has a recognizably different effect. Some lead to a loss of substance of the stone or mortar; others lead to a disfigurement or a disruption of the masonry, not necessarily accompanied by any loss of substance. While it is generally recognized that disruptions can arise from excessive load concentrations, settlements, uneven thermal expansions and similar physical phenomena, it is not so widely realized that forces arising from chemical reactions can also cause them. Disruptions that have a chemical origin are dealt with here. A very detailed review of the chemistry and physics involved in all these phenomena will be found in reference 1.

Deterioration caused by decay

There are three main causes of deterioration involving loss of substance. These are:

1. salt crystallization,
2. attack by acidic gases in the air,
3. frost action.

Salt crystallization

Salt crystallization is the most important because it is potentially the most damaging. It attacks porous materials irrespective of their chemical composition and often enhances the effects of the other primary causes of decay. Also, it will occur in areas virtually free from frost or acidic air pollution. This cause of deterioration will therefore be dealt with first.

Limestones and sandstones

Table 7.1 gives a list of salts that are most frequently involved in crystallization damage to masonry, and lists some common sources for each of them. The main sequence of events giving rise to such damage

Table 7.1 Salts that have been known to damage stone masonry and their sources

Type of salt	Common sources
Sodium sulphate	Clothes washing powders; soil, some types of fired-clay bricks; some processed solid fuels; by action of polluted* air on sodium carbonate.
Sodium carbonate (washing soda)	Clothes washing powders; many domestic cleaning aids; some proprietary cleaners for limestone-faced buildings; fresh concrete and cement-based mortars.
Magnesium sulphate (Epsom salt)	Some fired-clay bricks; rain washings from dolomitic limestone affected by polluted* air.
Potassium carbonate	Fresh concrete and cement-based mortars; fuel ashes and ash-mortars.
Potassium sulphate	Some types of fired-clay bricks; by action of polluted * air on potassium carbonate.
Sodium chloride (common salt)	Seawater; road and pavement de-icing salt; salt used for preserving meat etc; soil.
Potassium chloride	Soil.
Calcium sulphate	Many types of fired-clay bricks; limestone and dolomitic limestone affected by polluted* air; gypsum-based wall plasters.
Sodium nitrate (Chile-saltpetre)	Soil; preserved meat; fertilizers.
Potassium nitrate (saltpetre)	Soil; fertilizers; gunpowder.

*Pollution in this context means pollution by oxides of sulphur or sulphuric acid.

is as follows. A solution of a salt, or mixture of salts, in water is transferred by some means to the pores or fissures of the stone. Under drying conditions, the water evaporates and the salt is deposited on the surface of the masonry, within its pores, or in both positions. A salty *growth* or *florescence* appearing on a surface is known as *efflorescence*. Crystallization that occurs invisibly within the pores of the masonry is called *cryptoflorescence*. It is not unusual for both forms of florescence to occur together.

Efflorescence is usually regarded as unsightly, but is, in itself, harmless. In contrast, cryptoflorescence causes some pressure to be exerted on the walls of the pores or fissures within the masonry. The magnitude of the pressure will depend partly on the kind of salt involved and partly on the size and arrangement of the pores. The process is not completely understood (see Annex for further information). However, if the pressure exceeds the internal strength of the stonework, some degree of damage will occur. The damage might be on a

microscopic scale at first and cause no more than a slight loss of strength, but, after a sufficient number of cycles of wetting and drying, each leading to a redissolving and recrystallizing of the salts, a powdering of the surface will become visible. Occasionally, a large scale fragmentation takes place along some plane of weakness, but this is always accompanied by some powdering. Formation of powder is, therefore, the diagnostic characteristic of crystallization damage to masonry.

The dissolving phase of this damaging process need not always involve a direct wetting of the stone by liquid water. Many salts will absorb water from the air in sufficient amounts to dissolve if the relative humidity of the air becomes high enough. Conversely, they will lose water and recrystallize if the relative humidity falls low enough. Such salts are said to be *hygroscopic*. The relative humidity at which a salt or mixture of salts will just begin to pick up water from the air is known as the *equilibrium humidity* (EQRH) of the salt or mixture. *Table 7.2* gives the EQRH of a number of salts at a temperature of about 25 °C. The values may be different at other temperatures. There does not seem to be any accurate way of estimating the EQRH of a mixture of salts from the EQRHs of its components. Direct measurement in the laboratory appears to be the only satisfactory way of obtaining this.

A third way in which salt crystallization damage can occur is through changes of temperature. Some salt crystals, in contact with a saturated solution of that salt, will redissolve if the temperature rises sufficiently and will recrystallize if it falls again. Thus, once potentially harmful salts get into the pores of a stone, there are at least three ways in which crystallization damage might occur. This damage will continue to occur indefinitely.

The rate of decay induced by salt crystallization will depend not only on the types of salt involved

Table 7.2 The equilibrium relative humidity of a number of simple common salts

Salt	Chemical formula	EQRH* (%)
Magnesium chloride hydrate	$MgCl_2 \cdot 6H_2O$	33
Potassium carbonate hydrate	$K_2CO_3 \cdot 2H_2O$	44
Sodium nitrate	$NaNO_3$	75
Sodium chloride	$NaCl$	76
Potassium chloride	KCl	85
Sodium sulphate hydrate	$Na_2SO_4 \cdot 10H_2O$	89
Sodium carbonate hydrate	$Na_2CO_3 \cdot 10H_2O$	90
Potassium sulphate	K_2SO_4	98

*The EQRH of a salt tends to rise with a fall in temperature. The effect is more striking with some salts than others. Exceptionally, the EQRH reaches a maximum at some mid-range temperature. The values given have been rounded off and apply approximately in the temperature range 20–25 °C.

and the frequency of the crystallization cycles, but also on the resistance offered by the stone. Clearly, the smaller the proportion of pore space in a piece of masonry, the better will be its chance of surviving salt crystallization attack. However, it is an apparent anomaly that some limestones of quite high porosity (say 28%) resist crystallization attack better than many with porosities as low as 16%. The pore space of those limestones that resist attack are comprised mainly of relatively large diameter pores. Susceptibility to attack is related closely to the fineness of the pores and this can be of greater importance than total pore volume over quite a large range of porosities (see Annex).

Sandstones also vary in their resistance to salt crystallization and the size of the pores also plays an important part in determining their resistance. However, the relationship is not quite so clear-cut as it is with limestones.

For types of stone with equal resistance to salt crystallization, the damage caused by a fixed number of cycles of crystallization will vary with the type of salt involved in a manner that is not well understood. The salts listed in *Table 7.1* are broadly in order of decreasing aggressiveness. However, mixtures of salts often behave more aggressively than the constituents alone. A common example is the mixture of table salt (sodium chloride) and calcium sulphate which has particular relevance to the behaviour of limestones in heavily built-up coastal regions.

Marbles and granites

The porosity (i.e. the ratio of the volume of pore space to the bulk volume) of a freshly quarried block of marble or granite is normally much less than one per cent. With such materials, contact with an aggressive salt might be expected to have little or no effect, or at least to take centuries to cause significant damage. However, heating and cooling can cause partial separation of some of the boundaries between the crystals of the rock. The consequent increase in porosity and reduction in cohesive strength may then be sufficient to permit the occurrence of salt crystallization damage within the lifetime of an historic building or monument.

Porosities greater than normal are also found in granites in which some of the feldspar has been converted to a clay mineral of the kaolin type. During the late stages of the consolidation of a magma highly reactive and mobile fluids and gases are squeezed out of the mass. During the emplacement of the mass in south western England acid solutions moved along the joints. They altered the crystals of plagioclase feldspar into aggregates of kaolinite. This process is called kaolinization. Purified kaolinite is generally known as china clay. Under conditions less favourable to this process, the kaolinization is far from complete and the resulting mixture is of little use to those industries. It is equally unsuitable for most building purposes.

Sources of salts

Unfortunately, there are many sources of harmful salts and many ways in which they can be transferred into masonry. Some indication of this has been given in *Table 7.1*.

Buildings near the sea will naturally tend to pick up sea salt. This consists of a very large range of salts, most of which are present only in minute quantities[2]. The main constituent of sea salt is sodium chloride and this is by far the most significant in the context of stone decay. Coastal regions tend to have a higher than average relative humidity. Hence the EQRH of sodium chloride ($\sim 76\%$) will be exceeded often enough to ensure that stonework contaminated with seawater will suffer some crystallization attack even when it has not been rained on. The resulting decay will become apparent most quickly on the *inside* faces of mullions, transoms and tracery of windows, where the thickness of the stonework is less than in the walls. However, after long exposure, much of the *external* masonry may also show decay. In all cases, this will take the form of powdering. It will primarily affect those surfaces from which most drying occurs.

The winter salting of roads and paths to reduce risks to traffic and pedestrians from hazards of ice and snow can provide a source of sodium chloride close to buildings and other structures. Even if a building has a damp-proof course, splashing can cause contamination that might result in the decay of the stonework.

Meat preserving has also led to crystallization damage in the past. At least one mediaeval stone wall is still decaying as a result of the storage of salted meat against it more than 100 years ago. The stonework of one mediaeval kitchen in a college has been replaced because blocks of cooking salt (sodium chloride) were once stored against it.

Fired-clay bricks, stored in close contact with a masonry wall and left uncovered or built as a backing in direct contact with stone masonry that becomes very wet, can introduce sulphates of calcium, magnesium, potassium or sodium, according to the type of brick involved. Fresh concrete or cement-based mortars in contact with stone can introduce sodium or potassium carbonates, which will be converted to sodium or potassium sulphates by the sulphur-based acids in our polluted air.

Preparations containing caustic soda or caustic potash are marketed for cleaning the external faces of limestone buildings. These materials will also be converted to sodium or potassium sulphates by the sulphur-based acids in the air. An exceptionally skilled operator might be able to clean limestone safely using such aids, but, in practice, their use has led to much staining and crystallization damage.

Damage can also be caused to other types of stone by rain-washings from limestone or magnesian limestone that contain sulphates, and which has been attacked by sulphur-based acids in the air and thus contains sulphates. This will be discussed in more detail in the next section.

Decay caused by acidic gases in the air

Over most of the highly industrialized parts of the world, the air is polluted with small particles of carbon or tar products and with acidic, sulphur-based gases. These are produced by the combustion of solid fuels and oils by industry, transport and domestic heating systems. Various industrial processes put other particles into the air. These, along with transport vehicles, produce nitrogen compounds that almost certainly add to the thunderstorm production of nitrogen-based acids[3]. Air pollution is an important cause of decay in building stones in the industrialized world, but where pollution is low, the effects described below will be minimal.

Limestones and marbles

The particulate pollution makes buildings dirty and the tarry matter occasionally causes staining. The acidic pollutants greatly enhance the rate of acid-based decay of limestones. However, even if there were no man-made pollutants, the carbon dioxide naturally in the air and the sulphur-based acids that are released during the decay of sea-weeds would be sufficient to cause some decay of this type of building material, though the rate of deterioration would be very slow.

The main aggressor in acid attack is sulphur dioxide gas (SO_2). This gas is very soluble in water, and reacts with it to form sulphurous acid (H_2SO_3). Two reaction paths may then be followed in the attack on limestone[4]:

1. Sulphurous acid + oxygen from the air could produce sulphuric acid (H_2SO_4), which would then attack the limestone ($CaCO_3$) to give calcium sulphate ($CaSO_4$) and water (H_2O). The calcium sulphate then takes up water as it crystallizes as the mineral gypsum ($CaSO_4 \cdot 2H_2O$).
2. Sulphurous acid can directly attack the limestone to give calcium sulphite ($CaSO_3$), which then combines with oxygen from the air to produce calcium sulphate. This also crystallizes as gypsum.

The first of these paths is probably the one more likely to be followed, particularly under damp, foggy conditions. However, there is evidence that some reactions along the second path must take place because the presence of some calcium sulphite in the gypsum coating of exposed limestone surfaces has been reported[5,6]. In any event, the gypsum coating slows up the attack. What happens next depends on how often the affected stone is washed by the rain or sprayed with water during cleaning.

The slightly soluble gypsum is steadily removed from those parts of a limestone-faced building that are frequently washed by the rain along with any dirt that has been fixed to the limestone surface by the gypsum when it first crystallized. The limestone is thus maintained in a clean state, because it is being slowly eroded. Those external parts of a limestone-faced building that are sheltered from the rain behave very differently. When there is no rain-water to keep these parts clean, droplets of acid in the polluted air will continue to condense on them under foggy conditions. The acid will react with any unchanged limestone surface and bind any available particulate pollutants to that surface. Thus, these areas become darker and the skin on them becomes less and less permeable. In urban districts, where the particulate pollution is high, the surfaces often become black. In rural districts, where particulate pollution is normally low, they are sometimes only a rich brown, even after more than a century.

What happens to this virtually impermeable skin depends on the resistance of the limestone to weathering. The most durable limestones appear to be able to retain a dirty, inert skin more or less indefinitely. Less durable limestones behave differently. On these, occasional blisters will gradually form. Sometimes, the blisters are very flat and their limits are not easily discernible. More often, they have a clear form and develop until they burst. They often look so much like miniature volcanoes that the word erupt is used to describe their formation. The stone immediately behind the skin of the blister has decayed to a powder or a pack of lightly connected flakes. Much of this decayed stone will fall away in time, thus presenting a fresh limestone surface for further attack. As with crystallization damage, coarse-pored limestones prove the most resistant.

In magnesian limestones, the mode of attack is slightly different. The mineral dolomite is a chemical association of 45.7 % by weight magnesite ($MgCO_3$) and 54.3 % by weight calcite ($CaCO_3$). The compositions of the magnesian limestones vary over a wide range, but usually the proportion of magnesite is lower than it is in dolomite. Magnesian limestones are sometimes called dolomitic limestones, but this term can be misleading unless their composition closely approaches that of dolomite.

In rain-washed parts of a building faced with magnesian limestone, acids derived from the sulphur-based gases in the air will normally attack the stone surface and produce calcium sulphate and magnesium sulphate. The rate of attack varies from one type of magnesian limestone to another and is believed to be at a minimum when the ratio of magnesium carbonate to calcium carbonate approaches that of a true dolomite[7].

As with the simple limestones, the stone remains clean in the rain-washed areas and the solution resulting from the acid attack is carried harmlessly to the ground or is absorbed by the more sheltered parts of the stonework or by other porous materials. Where the solution is absorbed by sheltered areas, the calcium sulphate often forms a skin of gypsum, which incorporates dirt, as do the gypsum skins on simple limestones. However, the magnesium sulphate penetrates further and crystallizes behind this skin. In most cases, the gypsum skin forms blisters which eventually break open to disclose a powdered area beneath the skin. Removal of the powder reveals a deep cavern caused by the crystallization and recrystallization of the magnesium sulphate. This is known as *cavernous decay*. Dirt accumulation, blistering and cavernous decay in sheltered areas of stonework also occur in the absence of rain-water running down from overlying exposed masonry, if moisture often condenses on the surface when there is fog. The rate of attack and accumulation of dirt is much lower in rural districts. The resistance of magnesian limestone to blistering and cavernous decay varies from one type to another. The pore structure is only one of the controlling factors. For a discussion of the other factors see Annex (page 174).

Because marbles consist essentially of calcium carbonate, they initially undergo the same chemical reactions as limestones when they are in moist air containing sulphur-based acids. A skin of gypsum is formed that can incorporate some dirt particles. As with limestones, what happens next depends on whether or not the marble is in a position that is well washed by rain. In well washed areas the gypsum is dissolved, no dirt accumulates and the marble surface is gradually weathered away. But, since the surface is usually nearly free from pores, there is normally no secondary damage resulting from re-crystallization of gypsum. Hence, the rate of erosion is normally considerably less than that of limestone in the same environment, though polished marble will quickly lose its smooth surface.

In some circumstances, marbles decay more quickly and, although more research is needed, it appears that this is associated with considerable temperature variation. Excessive heating and cooling can result in movements at the boundaries of the calcite crystals which can lead not only to the bending of marble headstones that is sometimes to be seen in cemeteries, but also to an increase in the porosity of the marble. This enables recrystallization of the gypsum skin to occur below the surface. Weathering, often in the form of *sugaring*, then proceeds more quickly.

In sheltered areas of buildings in urban districts,

marble, like limestone, will acquire a dirty coating. However, so long as the surface of the marble remains relatively free from pores, the dirty layer will not become nearly so black as a porous limestone, nor will its surface develop unsightly blisters.

Sandstones, slates and granites

The majority of sandstones consist of grains of quartz (a crystalline form of silica, SiO_2), cemented together by silica in a less well crystallized form. Iron oxides or hydroxides are sometimes present in the cement and the quartz grains are sometimes accompanied by grains of feldspars and micas. Quartz-based sandstones are very resistant to the sulphur-based acids in the air, but they can become very dirty. They tend to be dirtier in the rain-washed areas than in the sheltered parts of buildings. In this sense their behaviour is quite different from that of limestones or marbles. Very occasionally, sulphur-based acids in the air will attack one of the iron compounds in a sandstone and temporarily convert it to a soluble form. This can then migrate to the surface of the stone, where lime, derived perhaps from mortar, reconverts it to a rusty-looking insoluble form. Such deposits can remain unnoticed beneath the soot layer until the sandstone is cleaned by a mechanical or chemical process.

A small minority of sandstones used for building in the United Kingdom are cemented by calcite (*calcareous sandstones*). *Calciferous sandstones* are defined here as sandstones which contain calcite that does not take part in the cementing process. Sulphur-based acids in the air readily attack calcareous sandstones. These sandstones weather more severely than limestones in regions of high air pollution because the dissolving of a small amount of calcite will release many sand grains. Where the stone is heavily rain-washed, the surface will steadily powder away. When the stone is not heavily rain-washed, the acids attack some of the calcite converting it to the more soluble gypsum. Some of the gypsum is drawn towards the surface in solution and redeposited as the moisture dries out again. This produces a weakened layer roughly 4 mm below the surface of the stone which blocks the pores of the surface layer. As the temperature varies, the unrestrained gypsum expands or contracts about 1.7 times as much as sandstone. Changes of temperature will therefore create stresses that tend to break the gypsum-rich layer from the underlying sandstone. In time, these layers will peel off. The effect may be seen on the south wall of the old (bombed) Cathedral Church of St Michael, Coventry. A striking example of attack by acidic gases on calcareous sandstone on the mainland of Europe is at Strasbourg Cathedral[8].

Some sandstones are cemented with dolomite. In general, these withstand an acid-polluted atmosphere better than calcareous sandstones, particularly when there is a lot of cementing material present. This is probably because dolomite is much less readily attacked by acids than calcite. When a dolomitic sandstone seems to respond like a calcareous sandstone, the cement probably contains calcite as well as dolomite. It is usually the calcite that has been attacked by the acid.

Calciferous sandstones, where calcite plays no part in the cement, behave very like calcite-free sandstones, providing there are no complicating factors like the presence of clay. Sandstones containing substantial amounts of clay are known as *argillaceous sandstones* and have very poor resistance to weathering agencies. They tend to lose strength when wetted and dried, whether or not the air is polluted by sulphur-based acidic gases.

All sandstones, even those in which the grains are cemented by silica, are to some extent susceptible to salt crystallization attack. One common source of trouble is the calcium sulphate washed from limestone in urban districts by rain. Where sandstones are exposed to the washings they usually decay sooner or later. This is an indirect attack on sandstone by sulphur-based acidic gases in the air.

Closely allied to the attack by acidic gases on calcareous sandstones is the attack by such gases on some types of roofing slates that contain up to 13% calcite. Sulphur-based acidic gases in the air dissolve in rain-water and are held by capillarity 'between the lap', that is, in the overlap between adjacent slates in a roof. They form acids which attack the calcite in the slate, thus weakening it. The gypsum formed by this reaction causes further weakening by crystallization attack, so that in time the surface of the slates between the lap can be easily scratched by the finger nail. Eventually, the fixing holes become so enlarged that the slate slips from its position.

Another kind of slate contains pyrite (iron sulphide) in an unstable form, with some calcite. Rain-water alone is able to cause decay of this type of slate by reacting with the unstable pyrite. This forms a sulphur-based acid, which then attacks the calcite causing the slate to crumble. This type of slate will deteriorate on exposure, even if the air is virtually free from sulphur-based pollutants. Its use was abandoned many years ago because it failed even as a barrier to water when used as a damp proof course.

In complete contrast, acidic pollutants in the air are unlikely to cause any significant decay of granites used for building.

Two special cases

Two special cases of acidic air attack on stone deserve mention; stone exposed near the sea, and contour scaling.

It has been observed that limestones that are not much affected by acidic gases in inland cities, or by sea salt in crystallization tests in laboratories, can suffer serious decay when exposed to mild air pollution by sulphur-based acids in coastal regions. The effect is believed to occur because gypsum, the normal result of acid attack on limestones, is more soluble in water which contains common salt (sodium chloride), which is the main constituent of sea salt. In consequence, the crystallization damage caused by gypsum in the presence of sea salt is much greater than when gypsum alone is involved.

Important examples of this phenomenon have occurred in the Portland Stone used for the War Memorial at Southsea, Hampshire and the National Library of Wales, near Aberystwyth, Dyfed. Most of the blocks affected were of a quality that would have been expected to give good service in London and other large cities. In both cases, analysis revealed that the only soluble salts present were calcium sulphate and sodium chloride. Laboratory tests subsequently confirmed that stone is more affected by a crystallization test employing a combination of the two salts than by either of them on its own.

Contour scaling is a phenomenon first recognized in the United Kingdom about 1955, but not publicly reported until 1965[9]. In this form of decay, a crust of sandstone breaks away at an approximately constant depth of between 5 and 20 mm (0.2–0.8 in.). The crust follows the man-made contours of the block, rather than any of the natural bedding planes. The effect is most striking when it occurs in mouldings.

It was first thought that it could be explained in terms of *moisture rhythm*. This occurs when the stone is wet by rain, and water penetrates to a depth, which is a characteristic of the stone. Subsequent drying brings small amounts of the cementing material towards the surface. If continued over many years this cycle would result in a weakening of the structure at approximately the maximum depth of penetration. Even silica, the cement in the most durable sandstones, is sufficiently soluble in water for this mechanism to operate over a long period of time. In apparent support of this view, the examples found were always in buildings at least 35 years old and usually much older.

However, it was later discovered that in the few cases that were carefully examined, the detached surface of the sandstone had become completely blocked with gypsum. It was then supposed that the separation of the affected layer occurred as a result of fatigue failure of the stone just behind the choked layer. This was thought to arise because changes in temperature would affect the choked layer differently because of the high coefficient of thermal expansion of gypsum. The fact that the failures occurred as often in stonework fully exposed to the sun as in stonework that was in the shade raised doubts. It was also thought that the tendency of the unchoked stone to expand when wet and contract when dry would be sufficient to develop the necessary shear forces to lead to fatigue failure[10]. The problem was then to explain how the stone became wet and dry in view of the impermeability of the outer skin.

The presence of gypsum in the samples was not easy to explain because the sandstones were virtually free from calcite or other sources of lime that could be attacked by acidic gases in the air. However rainwater occasionally contains a very dilute solution of calcium sulphate. It was assumed that this arises as a result of a reaction between sulphur-based gases and particles of lime or limestone that escape from the stacks of lime and cement works and can be carried very far from the sources. The fall-out of calcium sulphate formed in this way could explain the presence of calcium sulphate in the pores of the sandstones in question. The fall-out would not be detected on bricks or limestones because these are contaminated with calcium sulphate in any event.

Therefore, on the assumption that the choking of the surface pores of some sandstones leads the development of contour scaling, the phenomenon appears to be related to air pollution.

Decay caused by freezing

Frost attack differs from attack by salt crystallization and air pollution in two striking ways: frost damages only those parts of a building that can become frozen when very wet; and the damage appears dramatically, in the form of cracking. Cracking can result in the production of a few large fragments of stone or many small pieces, but frost attack never reduces the stone to a fine powder or produces blisters. Its effects are thus distinctive from those of salt crystallization or to attack by sulphur-based acids.

Because frost damage will not occur unless a stone is very wet, it is seldom if ever seen in plain walling between damp-proof course and eaves. Instead it tends to be confined to features with surfaces that will catch the rain, or water from some other source. Copings, cornices, sills, string courses and window hoods are the features usually affected. Tops of plinths and steps are occasionally affected but many builders and architects now take care to ensure that such features are constructed from frost-resistant stone.

Broadly speaking, frost damage to stonework takes one of two forms, illustrated in *Figures 7.1a* and *b*. The commonest form involves the separation of a wafer or lens-like piece of stone from the most exposed surface of the block. This will normally be the top surface, but it can be the outermost surface when the block is part of a string course or sill. The break usually occurs at right angles to the line of maximum thermal gradient and the separating piece moves in the direction of greatest heat loss (*Figure*

7.1a). Sometimes, the separation is sufficient for ice to be seen between the separating pieces. The ice often appears to consist of a number of minute columns aligned along the direction of movement. Sometimes the appearance of separate columns is an illusion caused by lines of very small air bubbles trapped in the ice. Frost damage of this kind usually leaves the affected blocks disfigured, but otherwise functional. Many similar attacks can occur before they cease to serve any useful purpose in the building.

In the second and less common form of attack, the block of stone is often rendered useless, apparently in one single action. As shown in *Figure 7.1b*, cracks can radiate in many directions and a block can be reduced to several smaller blocks. As might be expected from the form taken by the damage, this kind of decay is associated with multi-directional cooling of the stone. It is much more likely to affect coping blocks, cornice blocks and balusters, which are very exposed to any cold winds and to clear night skies, than it is to affect sills, string courses and the like, which are much more shielded by the rest of the building.

The effects of frost damage are different if the stone has very marked weaknesses along its natural bedding planes. This can distort the pattern of radiating cracks that develop in the second form of frost damage and it might be mistaken for frost damage of the first kind.

The pore structure of a stone plays an important part in determining its resistance to frost. The fine-pored types of stone being more susceptible than the coarse-pored types. Pore structure has a similar effect on the resistance of stone to salt crystallization and acidic gas attack.

Causes of frost damage

Damage to metal water pipes caused by the freezing of the water in them is well known and the mechanism involved is well established, even if some of the details are not entirely understood. Under very cold conditions, ice starts to form within a pipe at the position where the temperature first falls to the freezing point of water ($0\,^\circ\text{C}$; $32\,^\circ\text{F}$). This ice eventually forms a plug, trapping water between this point and a tap or valve. Sometimes water is trapped between another plug of ice formed at a second point.

At normal pressures, ice occupies about 9% more volume than the water from which it was formed. If the water cannot be pushed away to make room for this increase in volume, the pressure inside the pipe must rise. *Figure 7.2* shows the relationship between the pressure on the water and the temperature at which it will be converted to ice. As the pressure rises, the freezing point falls. The maximum pressure

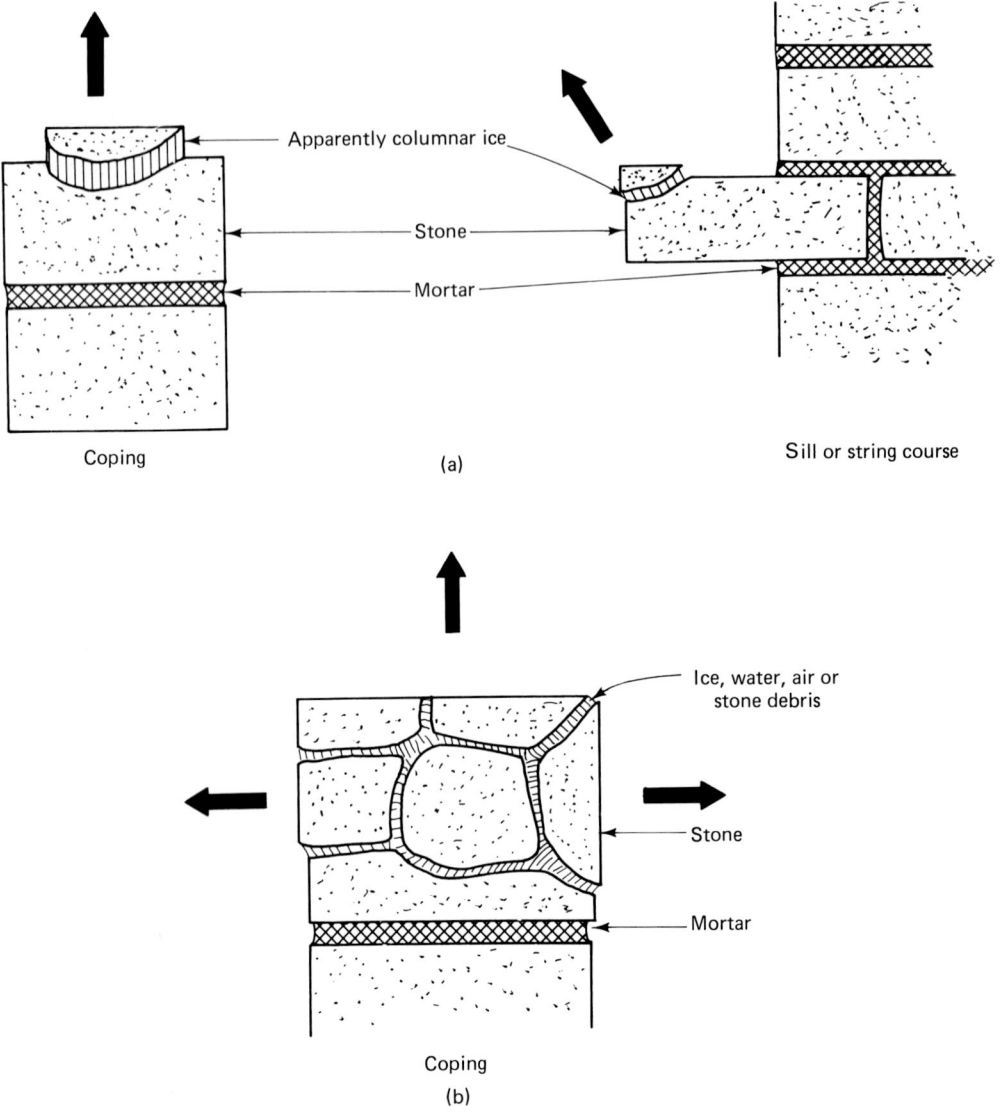

Figure 7.1 Forms of frost attack on stone (a) cross-section through blocks of stone showing examples of the common form of damage. Broad arrows show the direction of heat loss. (b) Cross-section showing an example of the less common form of frost damage

that can be developed by ice forming from water in a confined space of this kind is $207.4\,\mathrm{MN/m^2}$ (2047 atmospheres) and the temperature needed to achieve this is $-22\,°\mathrm{C}$ ($-7.6\,°\mathrm{F}$). At lower temperatures a different kind of ice forms, which occupies less volume than water, so the pressure would fall again. However, pressures far below this maximum are sufficient to burst all normal water supply pipes made of metal.

It is tempting to assume that all frost damage to

stone occurs in the same way. For this to happen a block of stone would need to be frozen on all sides to produce an ice casing. The ice casing would have to trap water, and this water would then need to be frozen. It is just conceivable that this might happen to copings over balustrades but not to copings over solid walls, parapets, sills and other water-collecting features, where special circumstances are required before water can become trapped. However, the water held in the pores of a coping block on a wall

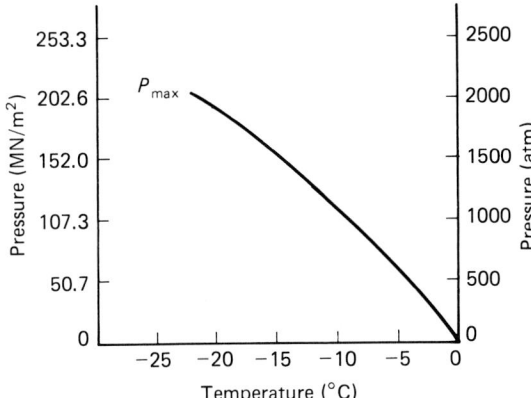

Figure 7.2 Pressures which may be developed by freezing completely enclosed water. P_{max} (= 2047 atm = 207.4 MN/m^2) is the highest pressure that can arise in this way. At lower temperatures a form of ice crystallizes out which occupies less volume than the water from which it is formed. It contracts on further cooling. The crushing strength of porous stone is usually in the range 7.5–56 MN/m^2. The tensile (bursting) strength is usually much lower. Reliable values of bursting strength are not available. Basic numerical data are taken from reference 2.

and in the top of the wall itself might freeze completely during several days of frost and then be covered by a coating of snow. Sunshine might melt the snow, which will help keep the stone very wet, and the ice in the block might partially melt but the bottom of the block will remain frozen. A very severe night frost might then case the top and upper parts of the sides of the block with ice, trapping the water that was thawed the previous day. Freezing of the trapped water could then cause a shattering of the block.

An alternative method by which shattering pressures might arise entails the formation of an ice casing on all faces but the bottom of a block of stone. If very rapid freezing of the remainder of the water occurs, the advancing ice front would force water through the pores of the bottom part of the stonework. If these pores were very fine, they would resist this flow very strongly and sufficient hydraulic pressure to shatter the stone may develop. This theory is attractive, because it explains why fine-pored stone is more susceptible to frost than coarse-pored stone.

The commoner form of frost damage (*Figure 7.1a*) has a different cause. It is related to the frost heaving of soils described by Stephen Taber[11] and the thermodynamical considerations discussed by D.H. Everett[12] and J.M. Haynes[13]. A more detailed discussion is given in the Annex (pages 174–177).

Everett[12] considered a wet, porous body subjected to severe cooling from one face only. If, as a result of this cooling, ice forms in a relatively large pore connected, on its warmer side, to a source of water through smaller pores, ice crystals will continue to grow in the larger pore so long as there is an unrestricted supply of water and no great pressure is exerted on the ice. However, if the ice is confined by the roof of the larger pore, pressure will begin to rise and, if nothing gives way, ice will begin to grow down the finer pore *after a certain critical pressure is reached*. While growth down the finer pore occurs there will be no further increase in pressure. For the sake of simplicity, let the larger pore be cylindrical, with a radius R and the smaller pore be cylindrical, with a radius of r. The maximum pressure that can develop in this case would be $\sigma(1/r - 1/R)$, where σ is a constant[12]. This maxi-mini pore system acts as if it were a miniscule jack of precisely limited lifting power. If many of these jacks act in unison along a plane within the stone, it is likely that fracture will occur, particularly if the stone has been weakened by previous attacks. This is a possible explanation for the lifting of wafers or lens-like spalls of stone from copings and the like, in the commonest form of frost damage. This theory also helps to explain why fine-pored stone is more susceptible to this kind of frost attack than coarse-pored types.

Taber[11] found that ice lenses grow initially in sandy or silty soil fed by water from fine-pored clay soil below. The direction of lens growth is determined by the direction of heat flow. No lens forms if all the soil below is sandy and hence coarse-pored (this is of particular importance in the designing and siting of cold stores). Everett's theory[12] fits these facts well, for it requires there to be a considerable difference between the magnitudes of $1/r$ and $1/R$ for large heaving pressures to be developed.

Only if stone is very wet will it suffer frost damage. If water is trapped by a coating of ice, pressure will be transmitted the moment more freezing occurs and the ice–water system begins to expand. If the casing has trapped a mixture of air and water, the easily compressible air will be able to accommodate some of the increase in volume of the ice–water system and, hence, further freezing. If there is much air present, all of the water present might be able to freeze without giving rise to sufficient pressure to cause damage. Where water is not encased by ice, but is being rapidly forced through a narrow escape area, the presence of air between the ice front and the escape area might also be sufficient to prevent the development of damaging pressures. When the frost heave mechanism is operating, the pores supplying the growing ice lens must be full of water. If air is present the growth of ice will cease and pressure will not be maintained.

It often happens that a frost attack will leave a

stone apparently unharmed, but internally weakened. In fact, it is usual for most types of stone that are eventually damaged by frost to suffer several weakening attacks before showing visible signs of damage. Stone that is visibly damaged after being caught in a very wet condition by a single frost is quite exceptional.

Unlike crystallization damage, which can affect all classes of porous stone, frost damage occurs much more often in limestones and magnesian limestones than in sandstones. In long term tests blocks of stone measuring $100 \times 50 \times 50$ mm were exposed standing on end in trays that became filled to a depth of 50 mm each winter. The results after up to 22 years exposure at Garston, Watford, Hertfordshire, England were: limestones failed, 63.5%; sandstones failed 8% (ref. 14). Later unpublished results showed sandstones to be even more resistant.

Marbles, slates and granites

The types of marble, slate and granite normally used for building have porosities that are too low for them to be susceptible to frost attack. The porosity of marble, particularly statuary marble, can be significantly increased by prolonged heating and cooling. It is conceivable that increases of this kind might be sufficient to make the marble susceptible to frost attack, but this has not been observed. It is also conceivable that slates containing calcite that have been softened by acidic gas attack might become susceptible to frost attack, though such slates would be doomed in any event. Partially kaolinized granite might well be attacked by frost if used in susceptible features of a building, in the same way that it might be attacked if it became contaminated by soluble salts. Such types of granite are sometimes used because they are easily accessible, but they are really unsuitable for use externally in buildings.

Deterioration caused by staining

While the word decay implies a loss of substance, the word staining implies an undesirable addition of some material to the masonry. Most staining of masonry involves metal corrosion, but other factors are also important.

Effects of tarry pollutants

The blackening of stonework is caused by particulate air pollutants which consist of carbon and associated tarry matter. In particularly sheltered parts of limestone walls, these pollutants become cemented on to the wall by gypsum, formed as a result of chemical attack on the limestone by sulphur-based acids. Because gypsum is slightly soluble in water, any dirt that adheres to rain-washed areas of limestone is regularly removed, but, in the semi-sheltered areas, a heavy black deposit accumulates. If this remains untouched for many years, the tarry matter builds up in the pores of the stone to such an extent that any eventual removal of the sooty matter by artificial washing leaves the stone with a tarry, light brown stain. The stain becomes intensified as the limestone dries out. On stone that was originally pale in colour, this can be rather disfiguring.

Sandstones behave rather differently. The particulate pollutants are very firmly held by the sandstones even where the stone is washed by the rain. Artificial washing with water will not remove them. Tarry matter penetrates the pores of sandstones quite deeply. Artificial washing using special cleaning agents is possible, but tarry stains tend to remain. Fortunately, the average sandstone is darker than the average limestone and the staining is less obvious and more readily accepted.

Rain washings from limestones

Although rain washings from the exposed parts of a limestone building are normally deposited in more sheltered parts on the same kind of stone, they may be deposited on darker porous material, such as another limestone or a sandstone or brickwork. Deposits on the same kind of stone normally do not result in unacceptable staining. However, pale-coloured stains on a darker limestone can be disturbing and stains on sandstones or brickwork can be very disfiguring. They can also cause crystallization damage, unless the stones or bricks are highly resistant.

Effects from rising damp

Soil and subsoil often contain small amounts of coloured matter, derived from the decomposition of organic materials, that are sufficiently soluble in water to be capable of staining stone quite unpleasantly. When a building has no damp proof course, or has a defective damp proof course, the base courses often become stained. The effect is more striking, the paler the colour of the stone. When soluble salts are present, as they usually are in soil water, efflorescence will occur and pitting or powdering might add to the unattractive effect.

A similar problem is often found in porous stone retaining walls that have not been provided with any means of keeping the soil water away from the stone.

Effects from mortars containing hydraulic lime or Portland cement

Many types of limestone contain small amounts of organic matter that do not cause any staining, unless they are brought into contact with a highly alkaline solution. A possible contemporary source of this contamination is the effluent from washing powders which form highly alkaline solutions.

There are numerous records of the staining of stonework by alkaline solutions leached from fresh mortars based on Portland cement or hydraulic lime. The phenomenon was first recognized early in the present century by investigators searching for an explanation of the appearance of brown stains on Indiana limestone (see ref. 15). The stain is always brown and most noticeable on the paler coloured limestones.

Rich Portland cement mortars are unlikely to be used in the conservation of stone buildings, but hydraulic limes are often thought to be suitable. If hydraulic lime mortars are to be used with fresh stone, it would be advisable to carry out a staining test.

Effects from copper and its alloys

Copper is used externally on buildings for lightning conductors, flashings and the external skin of domes. After many years exposure to town air, copper acquires a stable patina, consisting of copper sulphate ($CuSO_4.3Cu(OH)_2$). Copper exposed near the sea acquires a patina of similar appearance, but which consists of copper chloride. In the interim stages of patina formation some copper is washed away, presumably as a dilute solution of copper sulphate or copper chloride. On contact with limestone or mortar, this alters to a less soluble, blue-green basic copper salt, which remains on the mortar or stone as a stain.

Analogous staining occurs on the stone pedestals of figures made of bronze or gun metal. Gun metal is an alloy of copper and tin; other forms of brass may contain additional ingredients. Elimination of the bluish-green stains is tedious, but not impossible. The methods are described in Chapter 11 in volume 2.

Effects from iron and steel

Rust, formed by the action of water and the atmosphere on iron and steel, produces the worst kind of staining on stonework. Rust is virtually insoluble in water, and it is not completely understood how it can be deposited on masonry some distance from the exposed iron or steel. What is well known is that the stain produced can be more intense than any other common stain on masonry and is more difficult and sometimes impossible to remove. Hence every reasonable effort should be made to avoid its occurrence.

Railings that have been left unpainted for some time after insertion, or have been maintained by an insufficiently frequent painting cycle, are a common source of rust staining. Neglected cast iron gutters, rain-water pipes, or their fixings are another. Old scaffolding poles, left where rain can run off them on to masonry, are a third source. Neglected iron or steel window bars are a fourth source. Buried cramps or dowels of steel or cast iron, that have been left unprotected in stone for a long period and have caused the stone to split are a fifth group. Cramps and dowels will not rust if they are set in a thick pad of mortar so long as the mortar retains its original high alkalinity and is free from sodium chloride. Both lime- and cement-based mortars lose this alkalinity in time as the carbon dioxide gas naturally present in air penetrates the pores of the masonry and neutralizes it. Any sulphur-based acids in the air will go further and gradually render the mortar acid. This will drastically increase the rate of corrosion of the metal and hence the production of rust.

An interesting example of the development of rust stains on stone occurred on the porphorytic granite facing of an important building in London some years ago. A granite which had been cut into slabs by a steel frame saw was coated with sulphuric acid to remove the specks of iron from the saw that had become embedded in the stone. As a result of production difficulties, a few slabs were inadequately rinsed with water to remove the acid. After installation, rust stains appeared on these slabs. Laboratory examination showed that a solution of iron sulphate ($FeSO_4$) was being held in minute fissures in the surface of the granite and was gradually working its way to the surface. On contact with limestone, lime or cement dust on the surface, rust was immediately formed[16].

Other causes of deterioration

There are a number of examples of deterioration caused by inanimate matter that do not fit into the above classification. These are discussed below.

Wind erosion

The idea that wind, carrying sand particles, can erode and shape large rocks in desert regions so catches the imagination that people often point to stone in buildings in Britain that has become furrowed in a spectacular manner as examples of wind erosion. However, it seems doubtful that wind erosion occurs to any extent in any building in Western Europe.

The buildings cited are nearly always ruins, cloisters or projections of buildings in arches or alleys. Wind passes at increased velocity over such features. In nearly all cases, the stone is a limestone which will accumulate calcium sulphate because of air pollution, or a sandstone in a coastal region. Hard driven rain will wet the stones thoroughly; and dry wind flowing past will dry them rapidly. These conditions favour salt crystallization attack. This, almost certainly, is the explanation for what has happened. The shaping is caused by the variation in drying rates with wind speed, which is higher where there is any narrowing of the gap. The additional furrowing seen in some sandstones is caused by the different resistance to crystallization attack shown by adjacent thin beds in the stone. There is no reason to postulate wind-blown sand as an important agent of decay. In fact, geomorphologists are now emphasizing the importance of salt crystallization in desert rock weathering[17,18].

Heating and cooling and wetting and drying

Stone slabs can be heated on one side so rapidly that parts of their surface will break away from the cooler, underlying mass. Flame-texturing of granite and dense limestones depends on this principle. The surface temperature involved is far higher than any likely to be reached by stone exposed to the sun. Nevertheless, it is theoretically possible for temperature gradients set up in stone by the heating effect of the sun to lead to surface decay, if repeated often enough. No decay purely from this cause has been recorded in buildings in Britain.

However, a closely related effect is known to cause trouble in marbles. Although marble is essentially composed only of one mineral, calcite, each calcite crystal expands along one crystallographic axis when heated and contracts along the other two, and thus behaves rather like a conglomerate of different minerals when heated. If heated to 300 °C and cooled a number of times, white Carrara marble will lose virtually all its strength. Kessler[19] found that a sample of marble, heated to 150 °C and cooled a number of times acquired a small permanent set after each cycle and started to bow. The effect is thought to be due to slippage of calcite crystals relative to one another. The bending of marble headstones and marble mantelpieces seems to be due to the same phenomenon.

General considerations suggest that a related effect must occur in granites because its three main constituents, quartz, feldspar and mica, have distinctly different coefficients of thermal expansion. On long heating and cooling, there appears to be sufficient micro-cracking at mineral boundaries to make the otherwise resistant granite susceptible to crystallization damage. Hockman and Kessler[20] carried out many heating and cooling and wetting and drying experiments on North American granites and concluded that the damaging effects may contribute to the deterioration of granites in monumental structures, but that they were probably not the cause of any deterioration of granites in normal buildings.

Heating and cooling probably also play an important part in the development of blisters on limestones once a sulphate skin has formed as a result of attack by sulphur-based gases in the air. The thermal expansion of gypsum is very much greater than that of limestone; the ratio is five to one[21]. Thus, it seems reasonable to assume that such differences should lead to a separation of the sulphated layer during a heating phase.

Wetting and drying is an inevitable part of the process leading to salt crystallization damage to stonework, even if the wetting phase sometimes involves water vapour rather than liquid water. Wetting and drying also accounts for the destruction of slate containing calcite and unstable pyrite. However, the part it plays is a subsidiary one. There is a widespread belief among building material technologists and geomorphologists that wetting and drying plays a considerable part in causing the decay of porous stone or the disintegration of porous rock. Porous stones expand when wetted and contract on drying. The theory is that fatigue failure must eventually occur, because of the shear forces that will frequently arise along any plane separating the wet from the dry material. This mechanism may account for contour scaling but, apart from this, the decay or disintegration of unconfined stone or rock can not be attributed to wetting and drying alone.

One of the more spectacular effects of heating and cooling or wetting and drying is when a wall of porous material is built under cool, dry conditions between two substantial abutments and its temperature or its moisture content later rises considerably. The attempt of the wall to expand may generate stresses severe enough to cause the masonry to bulge or even to crack diagonally, so that one part can oversail the other. Under extreme weather conditions, the wall will normally be either cold and wet or hot and dry. In consequence, thermal movement and wetting and drying movement tend to counteract one another, and little harm is done. Only

Table 7.3 Approximate thermal and moisture movement of masonry materials

Material	Thermal movement 0/000 for 10°C	Dry to wet movement 0/000
Porous limestones	0.028	0.083
Marble and dense limestones	0.038	0
Granite and other igneous stones	0.10	0
Slate	0.11	0
Sandstone	0.11	0.67
Concrete (dense)	0.11	0.33

exceptional hot and wet conditions cause trouble. If the wall is built of virtually pore-free material such as slate, only the temperature change will be significant and there can be no off-setting effect. *Table 7.3* gives the thermal and moisture expansions of some relevant building materials.

Fire

Broadly speaking, a building fire can have four relevant effects on stonework: blackening, shattering, decomposition and oxidation. Blackening is a result of the deposition of carbonaceous or tarry matter derived from the thermal decomposition of wood, or woollen, cotton or synthetic organic materials within the building on relatively cool parts of the structure. Blackening has no directly damaging effects on stone, but the processes used to remove it may well cause some damage, particularly if tarry matter has deeply penetrated porous limestone or sandstone.

Shattering of surface layers of stone is likely to occur when the flames heat up a previously cold surface very rapidly. The surface of marble is likely to 'sugar' under these conditions and the surface of granite may show some disintegration because of the many grain boundaries that separate different types of minerals with different coefficients of thermal expansion. Sandstones tend to suffer more than limestones when their surfaces are rapidly heated, probably because their main component, quartz, undergoes a sharp crystalline change at 573 °C. Porous limestones behave well by comparison. The temperature of decomposition of calcium carbonate is reached at about 550 °C. Even then, decomposition is very slow until temperatures of over 900 °C are reached, when quick-lime is rapidly formed. Quick-lime does not necessarily fall away to expose fresh limestone to the flames. Experience in World War II showed that many burnt-out buildings constructed of limestone remained structurally sound and could be re-used after the walls were scraped and the floors and roofs reconstructed.

Oxidation as a result of a fire changes the colour of limestone. Small quantities of some iron compounds that either attract no attention or contribute to the acceptable appearance of the limestone before a fire, are converted by fire to a highly oxidized and stable form that imparts a very enduring pink colour to the stone. On pale stones, this is very noticeable. It sometimes provides an interesting reminder of a fire that occurred in mediaeval times, as, for example, at Tewkesbury Abbey.

Chemically induced expansions

Some expansions of building materials are caused by chemical changes in the masonry itself. This cannot happen unless there has been some error in design or construction, but even conservators can make mistakes.

The splitting of stone by the rusting of iron or steel is a chemically induced expansion. Access of air and water to the metal is necessary for this rusting to take place and its associated pressure to develop. Attempts in the past to prevent access of air and water to the metal by coating it with tin, zinc or some form of bitumen have all had their disadvantages. Tin, once scratched, actually accelerates the rusting. Zinc, in the form of hot-dip galvanizing of the whole piece of iron, is quite good. Its life-time is dependent upon the thickness of the coating and the degree of acidic pollution of the ambient air. At best, it will serve for a small fraction of the expected life of a monumental building. Covering with a thick coating of bitumen reduces the effectiveness of the metal-to-stone bond. The traditional method of setting iron in the stone with molten sulphur, which has often been used for railings, has been known to lead to cracking of the stone[22]. Undoubtedly, the best method of reinforcing stone or of fixing railings to stone is to use a non-ferrous copper-based alloy, or an austenitic corrosion-resistant steel for the areas of contact between metal and stone.

The practice of burying iron in stonework has continued up to the present century, despite the recognition of its associated hazards early in the fifteenth century and the additional warnings that were given in the sixteenth century[23].

To understand why serious difficulties sometimes arise with mortars made from magnesian lime, it is necessary to have an outline understanding of the manufacture of a building lime by burning and slaking and the hardening process that takes place when lime is used in a mortar. Normal lime mortars are made by heating ('burning') limestone (calcium carbonate) until it decomposes and loses carbon dioxide gas to form quick-lime (calcium oxide). When the quick-lime is added to water (slaked), it is converted to slaked-lime (calcium hydroxide). When the slaked-lime is used to make mortar and the mortar begins to dry out, it absorbs carbon dioxide from the air and is reconverted to limestone. If some magnesium carbonate is present, as in a magnesian limestone, the magnesium carbonate goes through an analogous process and forms magnesium oxide, which is changed to magnesium hydroxide on slaking. When this magnesium hydroxide is used in a mortar, it combines with carbon dioxide from the air and reforms magnesium carbonate. The resulting mortar contains both calcium carbonate and magnesium carbonate. The result is excellent.

However, the 'burning' of magnesium carbonate has to be done much more carefully than the burning of calcium carbonate. If 'burning' is incorrectly done, the magnesium carbonate is converted to magnesium oxide, but will not readily hydrate to form slaked-lime. The lime is then said to be 'dead burnt'. If the slaked-lime obtained from normal limestone and dead burnt magnesium oxide are used in a mortar, the mortar apparently hardens in the normal way. The normal slaked-lime is converted back to limestone, but the magnesium oxide remains virtually unchanged. If it remains so for the life of the building, there is no problem. However, if the mortar is kept rather wet, the magnesium oxide will very gradually change to magnesium hydroxide and then to magnesium carbonate over the course of many years. There is a considerable increase in volume when magnesium oxide slakes and hardens and, though such an increase is easily accommodated when the mortar is still in the plastic state, it cannot normally be accommodated once the calcium hydroxide has hardened. The result of this late hydration and carbonation is normally a bending or disruption of the masonry and, eventually, a complete loss of strength of the mortar. Under optimum conditions, magnesium oxide will increase in volume by 240% on changing to magnesium carbonate.

It is unlikely that any 'dead burnt' magnesium limestones are produced today. Trouble still occasionally arises with nineteenth century buildings in which magnesian lime mortars were used. The problem is summarized in *Figure 7.3*.

Chemical expansion can also be caused by a reaction between a solution of calcium sulphate and a Portland cement-based mortar that has already set. Some hydraulic limes may produce the same effect. The setting of Portland cement gives rise to a number of products including calcium aluminate. Under wet conditions, calcium sulphate will react with this material to form a mineral called ettringite (calcium sulpho-aluminate), which occupies much more volume than the components from which it is made. The result is a considerable and powerful expansion, which can cause serious cracking in masonry[24]. If the damp conditions persist, this chemical reaction can continue until the mortar has lost its cohesion, whereupon the already-disrupted masonry might disintegrate.

Ettringite expansion has been observed mainly in brickwork in which the bricks were heavily charged with calcium sulphate. The effects have also been observed in a screen wall of flint work, surmounted by a capping of under-fired, and hence rather salty, bricks, sited in a very exposed position. Because of the degree of exposure, the architect had specified the use of a Portland cement-based mortar. After

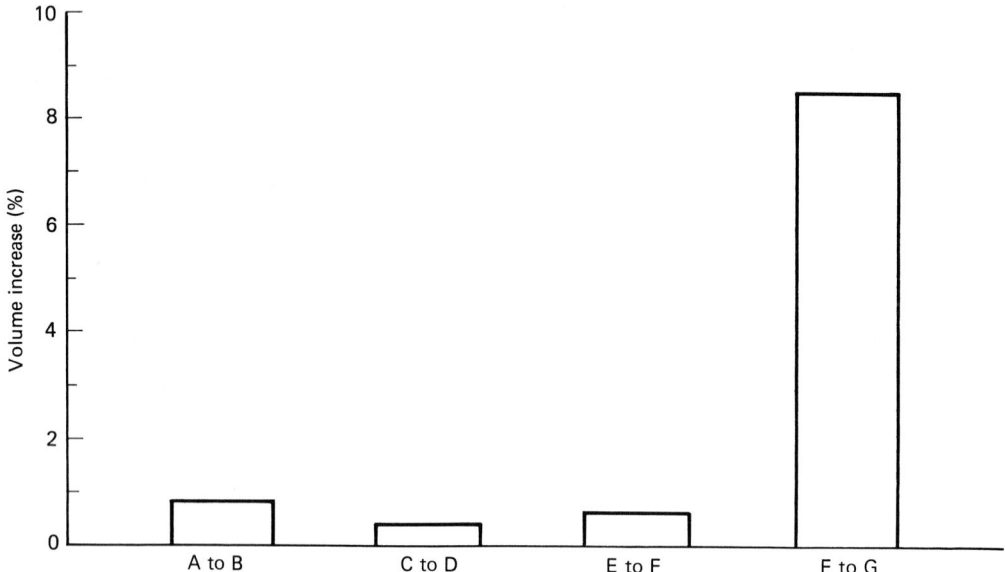

Figure 7.3 Theoretical volume increases in hardening of lime mortars. All mortars are composed of one part by volume slaked lime and three parts by volume sand. A ratio of one part by weight magnesium oxide to 2.48 parts by weight calcium carbonate is assumed. Less magnesium will give a smaller volume increase. Changes A to B, C to D and E to F occur mainly when mortar is in a plastic state. Change F to G takes place after the mortar is hardened, and may take decades. The risk of damage to the masonry is then much greater

about six months, the wall was leaning away from the wetter side, flints began to fall out and displacement of return walls became apparent. Almost complete rebuilding was essential. The use of bricks with a low soluble-salt content would have avoided the trouble. The simple use of a damp proof course between flintwork and the brick capping may have been sufficient and would have kept the flintwork drier.

Small amounts of calcium sulphate (gypsum) are deliberately added to Portland cement during manufacture to control the rate of setting because calcium sulphate acts as a set accelerator. Such additions do not cause disruptive expansions because any small expansion of the mortar in the plastic state is easily accommodated. However, if large amounts of calcium sulphate are added accidentally in making up a mortar for masonry the mortar will first set rapidly. The calcium sulphate then slowly acts on the set mortar to produce an extreme example of disruptive expansion. This mistake often arises because a particular kind of plaster based on calcium sulphate, Keene's Cement, has been inadvertently used with Portland cement for making up large batches of mortar. An error of this kind led to the disruption of a whole Gothic-style window in a matter of about three weeks and complete rebuilding was necessary.

Another form of chemical expansion involves certain concrete aggregates which contain a reactive form of silica that can swell in the presence of strong alkalis based, for example, on sodium or potassium. Alkali-reactive aggregates are rare in the British Isles and British Portland cements in the past have had alkali contents too low to cause trouble[25]. However, environmental protection pressures are forcing aggregate suppliers to look for fresh sources of aggregates, and alkali-reactive aggregates might come on the British market in the future. Moreover, the need for manufacturers to reduce particle emissions from their factories is causing a rise in the alkali content of British cements. In consequence, the risk of disruption caused by alkali-aggregate interaction in the British Isles is slowly increasing.

Disruption from this cause is more troublesome when the reactive aggregate is coarse than when it is finely ground. The minerals, not the whole piece of concrete or mortar swells and a swelling piece of aggregate in a non-swelling matrix will tend to crack the matrix. If all swelled equally, the total expansion might cause trouble, but there would be no disintegration. Thus the alkali-aggregate reaction can cause the collapse of structural concrete. If it occurs in a mortar, it will make repointing necessary and possibly cause some staining of stone round the joints but is not likely to lead to serious structural weaknesses in masonry. Therefore, it is not as serious a problem as sulpho-aluminate expansion.

Deterioration caused by living organisms

Certain plants, fungi, algae, lichens and bacteria have the potential to harm some kinds of stone or stonework. In some cases, the ability to cause serious damage has been well established; in others, it remains conjectural. The process by which deterioration might be caused varies considerably according to the type of organism involved.

Trees, climbers and creepers

It is a well-established fact that trees of some fast-growing species can progressively lower the average moisture content of clay soils and cause sufficient shrinkage to damage foundations of nearby buildings. Massive monuments are unlikely to be affected in this way, but smaller houses and the low parts of ruins are potentially at risk. Similar problems do not occur on fast-draining, sandy soils.

Sometimes, the seeds of a tree (e.g. Elder, *Sambucus nigra*) will germinate in soil or mortar dust that has collected in a cavity or ledge in the walls of an old building. As the tree's roots seek sources of moisture, ancient mortar will be further loosened and blocks of stone might eventually fall away if no action is taken to remove the tree. Ivy (*Hedera helix*) can be even more damaging, because its adventitious roots will eventually attack a multitude of weak points in the mortar system and an old tree will add very considerable weight to the weak parts of the wall. Schaffer[26] quotes parts of a poignant letter to *The Times*[27], in which Sir Martin Conway describes the partial destruction of Allington Castle, and the complete destruction of nearby Leybourne Castle by ivy. Evidence from old drawings and prints shows that this devastation was completed in about 100 years.

Growths of trees and climbers and creepers should be removed as quickly as possible, if damage to the structure is to be avoided. However, plants like Virginia Creepers and other *Vitis* species, which hold on to walls without the use of deeply penetrating adventitious roots, are probably not harmful. It is often argued that the leaf cover provided by such plants causes the wall to be moister than it would otherwise be. This is not necessarily harmful because the cover will shield the wall from heat loss by radiation so that frost attack is less likely to occur. Salt attack will also be reduced if the wall is kept moist for long periods because it is wetting and drying that causes crystallization damage. Admittedly, in an area of high air pollution, sulphur-based acid gas attack on damp limestone will be greater than on dry limestone.

Smaller flowering plants, ferns and mosses

Some smaller, flowering plants, such as Wallflowers (*Cheiranthus cheiri*) or the Ivy-leafed Toadflax (*Cymbalaria muralis*) and some species of grass, sometimes establish themselves on old walls. Their presence is an indication that soil-like dust is available for the plants to grow in. This may indicate that joints in the stonework should be repointed. These plants also indicate that some moisture is present. If the wall is unduly wet moss may be present. Ferns occupy an intermediate position as indicators, because some need damp conditions and others can thrive in moderately dry ones.

Algae

Algae form a group of plants that includes the sea-weeds. Freshwater forms, particularly green algae, readily colonize stonework that remains damp for sufficiently long periods of time. Because they contain chlorophyll, they are able to manufacture most of the food they require by photosynthesis and, under the right conditions, they can multiply rapidly. The green appearance imparted to the stone is often considered to be disfiguring. Bravery[28] makes the point that, while the algae alone might not be considered to be too unsightly, their appearance is made much worse in an urban environment when dirt readily becomes entrapped in the algal mass.

Bachmann[29] suggested in 1915 that acidic by-products of the algae will attack calcareous stones, but no quantitative evidence has yet been cited to show that algae cause any significant increase in the rate of decay of limestones.

Fungi

Fungi have no ability to manufacture their own food by using the energy of sunlight and hence they cannot live on stone, even if it is permanently wet, unless some organic food is present. The waste products of algae and bacteria, or the dead cells of these organisms, can provide such food. Decaying leaves and bird droppings are other sources.

Several workers have isolated fungi from decaying stone where nutrients are present. Lepidi and Schippa[30] have found fungal hyphae (the food-seeking threads of a fungus) extensively penetrating the decayed parts of a limestone and apparently burrowing into otherwise sound stone. Fungi can produce organic acids such as oxalic and citric acids[31,32]. Both of these acids can dissolve calcium carbonate, the main constituent of limestones. Hence fungi are potential contributors to limestone decay. But it has yet to be shown what proportion of the total decay of limestones is attributable to their activities.

Lichens

Lichens are an intimate association of fungi and algae, in which the fungal hyphae seek the water and salts necessary for both organisms and the algal cells manufacture organic food for both of them by photosynthesis. Thus, it seems likely that lichen are more important contributors to limestone decay than either type of organism on its own. It has yet to be demonstrated that their contribution is significant in comparison with the amount of decay caused directly by salt crystallization, acidic gas attack and frost action. This may be because most lichens are killed by even moderate levels of air pollution by sulphur oxides[33], though Lloyd[34] has reported the rapid colonization of pre-washed asbestos cement sheets in central London.

Lichens have also been known to attack sandstones and even basalts and granites[35]. The attack appears to be mainly on micas in the granites and Bachmann[36] believed it to be chemical in nature. However, there are also reasons to believe that the damage is often the result of surface stresses induced when the lichens shrink on drying after remaining wet for long periods[37]. Drying gelatine can attack glass in the same way[38].

Despite the generally attractive appearance of lichens growing on old stonework and the lack of conclusive evidence that they contribute significantly to stone decay, there is a general feeling among conservation experts that lichens should be removed and the stonework treated to discourage re-infection. Bravery[39] gives a detailed account of toxic treatments.

Bacteria

Bacteria are a group of living organisms that are so small that their presence is normally recognized only by the chemical and biological changes that they bring about. Thus, unlike lichens, algae, fungi and higher plants, bacteria do not significantly change the appearance of stone by their presence. If they play a part in the decay of stonework, it is because they initiate or augment the production of chemicals that can attack stone or mortar directly.

As early as 1911, Anderson[40] suggested that bacteria might play this kind of role. Since then, many biologists have isolated bacteria from decaying stonework and shown that they are species that could almost certainly have contributed to the observed decay. The groups of bacteria most likely to be involved are those that can oxidize sulphur or one of its compounds to form sulphuric acid[41–43], which attacks limestone directly, those that oxidize ammonia in the air to form nitric acid, which also attacks limestone directly[44,45] and those that pro-duce organic acids with the power to dissolve silicates[46-48]. However, in nearly all cases, little or no evidence has been produced to show that the decay caused by bacterial products is significant in comparison with the decay caused by salt crystallization, frost and the effects of air pollution.

From the practical point of view, those concerned with the conservation of stonework need take no more than an academic interest in the matter until it can be shown that the use of some bactericide can significantly decrease the rate of decay of stonework.

Birds and bees

Small birds can damage soft stone with their bills. In Britain, the species most commonly involved appear to be the Blue Tit (*Parus caeruleus*) and the House Sparrow (*Passer domesticus*) who appear to be seeking grit. They may also be seeking salt. The damage caused by their bills might not be very conspicuous on broad stretches of ashlar, but on carved features in soft stone it can become a matter for concern.

However, more damage is unquestionably done by the roosting and nesting of birds on masonry. Starlings (*Sturnus vulgaris*) and wild, feral and domestic pigeons are the main offenders. Decay is caused mainly by the accumulation of their droppings and nesting materials. These can form a compost, which breaks down as a result of bacterial action and releases acids which will attack limestone and calcareous sandstone. The compost also contains salts which might cause crystallization damage to any susceptible type of stone. This aspect has not been adequately investigated. Such troubles are likely to be most serious when the birds roost among statuary.

Mason bees, also, can harm stonework. The type involved in Britain bores holes in soft stone to provide a safe refuge for its eggs and grubs. The stones affected are mainly loosely bonded, possibly argillaceous sandstones. At one time, these creatures appeared to be active only in East Anglia, but more recently they have been reported from other parts of the country. A massive attack could result in highly disfigured stonework that is possibly so weakened that the stability of that part of the building is threatened. Such attack is, however, unlikely to make the stone more susceptible to frost, or to any other of the main causes of decay.

Effects of errors in design, specification or construction

Although it is a prime principle of conservation that the original should be changed as little as possible, there are occasions when errors in design, specification or construction of some part of a building lead to a degree of deterioration that begins to threaten the viability of the whole. If some alternative construction is essential for this part of the structure, it is equally essential to understand the reasons for what has happened, so that the original faults can be avoided in the remedial work.

This chapter is concerned with over-stressing that has a chemical origin. *Table 7.4* gives a list of design, specification and construction errors that can cause trouble.

Errors at the design stage

Water is involved in nearly all the processes that lead to deterioration or decay of building materials and a well-designed building will have arrangements for conducting the rain-water that falls on it harmlessly away from the building. If the building has no impermeable plinth or damp proof course, but depends instead on the good drainage of the soil on which it stands, it is better not to rely on simple shedding of rain-water. During heavy rainfall this may raise the water content of the soil around the building so that good drainage will become an insufficient safeguard and water and salts will enter the lower courses and cause damage by crystallization and general staining.

If the face of the building contains more than one kind of building material, damage might be caused before the rain-water reaches the soil. Water running over limestone on to brickwork or sandstone is likely to cause staining with subsequent crystallization decay unless the brick or sandstone is exceptionally resistant to the forces involved in the crystallization of the calcium sulphate that the rain-water extracts from the limestone. Conversely, rain-water flowing over brickwork on to limestone or sandstone is likely to cause crystallization damage to the limestone or sandstone as a result of the transfer of salts extracted from the brickwork by the rain-water. The effect will be significant unless the area of brickwork is very small compared with the area of the stone, or the bricks are exceptionally free from soluble salts.

The injudicious placing of corrodible metals such as iron or copper where rain-water can flow over them on to light-coloured stonework is likely to give rise to rusty-brown or greenish-blue stains that are impossible or extremely difficult to remove. The only iron-based metal that should be used in such circumstances is some suitable variety of corrosion-resistant steel. If this is unacceptable, the iron will need to be painted at regular intervals and the cost of maintenance might be high especially if the use of extensive scaffolding is required. The problem of preventing statuary in bronze or other copper-based alloys from causing bluish-green stains on the plinth of the statue or on other underlying stonework can

Table 7.4 Effect of errors in design, specification or construction

Error	Possible harmful effects
Design	
Design of building allows rain-water to flow over brickwork on to porous stone.	Crystallization damage to stone.
Design of building allows rain-water to flow over limestone on to brickwork or sandstone.	White staining and probable crystallization damage to brickwork and to sandstone.
Design of building fails to prevent soil water from entering stonework.	Stains and/or crystallization damage to stonework.
Design of building involves use of corrodible metals where rain-water can wet them and then run over stonework.	Staining of stonework; slight possibility of decay by crystallization attack.
Design of building involves use of iron or steel partially or completely but shallowly, embedded in stonework or mortar.	Cracking of stonework sometimes accompanied by rust staining.
Specification	
Specification of an unduly rich Portland cement-based mortar.	Alkali-induced staining of pale-coloured limestones; any crystallization damage occurs to stone rather than to mortar.
Specification of too dense a mortar (but not necessarily too cement-rich).	Any crystallization damage occurs to stone rather than to mortar.
Specification of stone of generally inadequate weather resistance.	General decay of stonework.
Specification of stone of adequate general weather resistance, but inadequate resistance to frost.	Failure of projecting features in stone unless they are protected by flashings of metal.
Specification of type of stone characterized by vents.	Usually no problem in plain walling; might lead to falls of stone from overhanging features or from fine, elaborately carved details.
Specification of stone characterized by soft seams.	Furrows in surface of stonework might appear early in the life of the building. Could be considered as 'character' but could lead to falls from overhanging features.
Specification of stone with shakes.	Question of aesthetics only; can adversely affect appearance; can provide 'character'.
Specification of stone with too high a permeability for cappings.	Undue rain penetration leading to staining or frost damage to underlying stonework.
Specification of unsuitable metal for cramps or dowels.	Staining or even disruption of masonry caused by volume of corrosion products.
Workmanship	
Unsuitable positioning of stone with shakes.	Aesthetic question only.
Use of blocks with soft seams in particularly exposed positions. (It is not always possible to distinguish these seams in unweathered stone.)	Unduly rapid erosion of the soft seams.
Failure to place a block of stone on its natural bed.	In general the consequences are not serious but if the bedding is strongly marked and the block is face bedded the rate of decay might be enhanced.
Bruising of stone during squaring up or carving.	Unduly rapid decay of affected surfaces where exposed to the weather.
Wrongly compounded mortar.	A whole range of consequences from rapid erosion of mortar to disruption of the masonry by expansion of the mortar.
Inaccurate positioning of cramps or dowels.	Cracking of stonework sometimes accompanied by rust staining.

sometimes be overcome by providing an inconspicuous metal tray beneath the statue that will collect rain washings and enable them to be led harmlessly away. The problem of avoiding staining of masonry by the copper of lightning conductors is one that has not been satisfactorily solved.

A more serious error is for the designer to include ironwork that is to be partially or shallowly embedded in stonework. The expansion accompanying the inevitable rusting almost invariably leads to the cracking of the stonework and to some degree of rust staining. It is better for the designer to plan for the use of corrosion-resistant steel in all such situations.

Errors in specification

A good design is often spoiled by inadequate specification of materials or components. It is an error to specify a type of stone that has inadequate resistance to the environmental conditions in the locality of the building. This could lead to unduly rapid deterioration of the external fabric. It is also an error to fail to allow for the fact that stone that is suitable for use in plain walling is not necessarily adequate for the harsher microclimate affecting projecting features such as copings, cornices and string courses in areas subject to frosts. Moreover, stone that is to be used in buildings near the coast must be of higher weathering resistance than stone that is just adequate for otherwise similar positions inland.

A type of stone that is characterized by the occasional occurrence of soft seams (seams of lower weather resistance) might be acceptable in plain walling if the furrowed appearance that develops is considered to give desirable character to the building. However, in buildings with much external carved work, development of furrows is usually an undesirable disfigurement. Such stone should therefore be specified only after cautious deliberation.

Similarly, stone containing vents, though often acceptable for plain walling, or walling with shallowly-cut decoration, will often prove to be quite unsuitable for stonework that is to be intricately carved because weaknesses along the vent planes will sometimes allow parts of fine decorative features to fall away.

If a permeable type of stone is specified for a building, the specification of a different stone, with slight or negligible permeability, should be made for features such as cappings. Otherwise, serious amounts of water might enter the underlying stonework and lead to staining, efflorescence or even penetration of water to the interior of the building.

It is as important to specify a suitable mortar or metal for use as a cramp or dowel as it is to specify a suitable type of stone. The specification of a mortar that is unduly rich in Portland-type cement is likely to result in alkali-induced staining of pale-coloured limestone. Moreover, the low permeability of such a mortar induces any salts present to crystallize in the stone rather than in the more expendable mortar. This can lead to crystallization damage to the stone. Similar damage can occur if the specification is for mortar that is rather dense, though not necessarily too rich in Portland-type cement.

Errors in workmanship

Even if the design and specification are beyond criticism, errors in workmanship can still cause serious trouble. They lead not only to defects in the building, but also to defects in the raw materials supplied to the building site. If, for example, mortar made with over-burnt magnesium lime is supplied due to an error on the part of the supplier the consequences can be severe and extensive damage can be caused to the masonry.

However, most errors of workmanship affecting a building occur on the building site. Some of them are aesthetic rather than material errors and have no effect on the life of the stonework. They reflect on the quality of the supervision rather than on the workman concerned. One example is the placing of a block of limestone with a shake in a position that is inappropriate in respect of the aesthetic appearance of the building. Because shakes are veins of calcite they do not detract from the strength of the block concerned or the masonry as a whole.

A materially more serious effect results from the use of a block of stone with a soft seam (even of poor weather resistance) in a very exposed position. Sometimes an expert mason can detect such seams in unweathered stone, but this is not always so. Where it is not possible, the mason cannot be blamed for inappropriate placing. Where the results of wrong placing could be serious, the use of stone types known to be subject to soft seams should be avoided until materials technologists have developed a reliable and non-destructive on-site test for them.

In most types of stone, the natural bedding is distinguishable and masons will normally place a block on its natural bed, except perhaps at cornices and other overhanging features, where joint-bedding may be used to reduce risk of frost damage. Problems arise at the corners, where a block that presents a joint-bed on one façade of the building must present a face-bed on the façade at right angles to it. Face bedding generally enhances the rate of weathering in the long term. It is a serious mistake for a mason to face-bed a block of stone unless it is well known that the type of stone can be safely face-bedded.

It is a more serious error of workmanship to bruise a stone during squaring up or carving by using too much force or dull tools. By creating microscopic fissures in the stone, bruising could lead to unduly rapid decay of the affected surface, particularly if the stone is to be used externally.

Inaccurate positioning of cramps and dowels is a fault of workmanship that could lead to fractures as a result of an increase in stress concentrations beyond the design level. If corrodible metal is involved, it could also lead to unduly rapid development of fractures resulting from the volume increase as the metal decays and to stains caused by the corrosion products.

Fixer masons need to be even more careful in preparing mortars than bricklayers because stone is generally more sensitive than bricks to mortars that are outside the intended range of compositions. Errors are most likely to occur with composition mortars which contain a hydraulic cement as well as lime and sand. Serious damage has arisen as a result of the use of a calcium sulphate-based plaster called Keene's cement.

Effects of behaviour of users and occupiers on the welfare of stone buildings

The owner of a stone building normally has responsibility for its welfare, but the owner is not necessarily the occupier and there can be other users besides the occupier. A cathedral building, for example, is owned by the appropriate church organization and used by those who conduct religious services and worship there, as well as those who visit the building to admire or study its architecture or to enjoy its historic atmosphere. All users will have some adverse effect on the building, but only the occupiers or regular users can reasonably be expected to exert a net positive benefit.

The effects of direct contact by visitors

For a building or monument that is visited by a very large number of people every year, the wearing down of paving and flooring materials by the passage of many feet is a well recognized hazard. In general, the damage is done by hard grit embedded in the soles or heels of shoes or boots. Damage will be greatest where people turn sharply[49].

In some circumstances, the damage can be minimized by arranging for people to have to take smooth curves rather than sharp turns. It may also be possible to lead the visitors along routes paved with hardwearing contemporary materials of no historical value. Eventually, it may be necessary to make it obligatory for visitors to wear slippers in some historic buildings. However, this is a matter of policy rather than of technology.

The rubbing of clothes against the fabric of a building can produce a polishing and staining of the surface. This is particularly noticeable in spiral staircases. Even granite can be affected in this way, but limestone and lime- and gypsum-based plasters are more quickly polished. In contrast, sandstones are relatively immune. Paler coloured materials naturally show staining more rapidly than dark ones. The staining is generally attributed to oil from woollen clothing. However, some of the staining might well be due to polishing in of dirt particles already on the surface.

Oil in the skin has a similar effect to oil from clothing and this can often be seen on stone handrails and on other carved features that people tend to finger out of curiosity. Some of the stains seen on marble, particularly white statuary marble, probably originate in this way. Oil stains of this kind will not lead to any deterioration of the building material and there is some evidence that the oil has a tendency to preserve stone. However, the stains are usually considered to be unsightly. The special techniques required for their removal are expensive and absorb funds that are usually needed for other conservation activities.

The indirect effects of visitors

Staining can be caused on marble counter and table tops by cigarettes that have been left smouldering in contact with them. A more widespread staining can occur as a result of a large number of people regularly smoking within a building. This has been established as being the most likely cause of otherwise unexplained staining of marble in at least one large building in London. There is no reason why tobacco smoke should not also cause stains on *porous* stone or brick surfaces, though such stains are likely to be noticed only if the surfaces are pale in colour. The removal of these stains from porous stone or brick would present grave difficulties. There is usually a ban on smoking in historic buildings because of fire risks and staining is another good reason why the ban should be maintained.

The presence of many people in a building alters the relative humidity of the air. The air exhaled in breathing will be much moister than the air inhaled. If a large number of people are involved, the relative humidity of the air in the building may rise sufficiently for condensation of moisture to occur on some of the colder surfaces. What happens to this condensed moisture depends very much on the nature of the cold surface on which it is formed. Moisture condensing on an impervious surface will initially be very pure and very reactive in a chemical sense. Although modern glass is unlikely to be significantly affected, mediaeval window glass, particularly that with a high content of potash, is likely to be slightly attacked. This process, often repeated, could eventually cause visible damage. Condensed water running down window panes can also cause damage to putty and to timber framing in the long run. If condensation runs over gypsum-based plaster, it can cause softening or the appearance of blisters on the plaster. If it runs into brickwork it can dissolve soluble salts in the bricks and may transfer them to other porous building materials which can be damaged if the salts crystallize when the water evaporates. Staining of the surface from which the evaporation takes place can also occur.

Condensation of moisture from the air can also occur directly on to porous materials. In the very finest pores condensation will occur at a slightly higher temperature, and hence more often, than it will on an impervious surface. In the absence of soluble salts, this is not likely to cause trouble. However, if soluble salts, particularly hygroscopic salts, which absorb water at relative humidities below those causing normal condensation, are present, they are likely to dissolve at the higher relative humidities brought about by visitors and to crystallize out again when the relative humidity returns to normal after the visitors have gone. If this cycle is repeated often enough, crystallization damage to the porous material can occur.

Effects of occupiers or regular users

The occupier or an informed regular user of a stone building of merit might reasonably be expected not only to avoid actions that might harm the fabric of the building but also to take positive action to help to conserve it. One of the simplest beneficial actions they might take is to ensure that all gutters, downpipes and other parts of the rain disposal system are free from blockage and are functioning correctly. This might be boringly obvious, but in practice it is often neglected. Rain-water, flowing where it was not intended to flow, will make some parts of the building wetter than normal. This can have many deleterious effects.

Areas that are normally dark because they are not much washed by rain will become paler as a result of the overflow. Correction of the fault will not cause the building to return immediately to its former appearance; the change might take years. If the overflow has given rise to more serious stains such as those caused by rust, it will be very difficult to put right. Extra water flowing over stonework might also lead to frost attack on those features that are normally not affected because their water contents never reach the critical value. Also the additional water might penetrate deeply enough into the stone to dissolve dormant salts within the structure. Under drying conditions, these salts could be brought to the surface where they may cause crystallization damage. Finally, the additional water may penetrate to the interior of the building and damage to wooden panelling, wall paintings, interior stonework and furnishings may occur.

If lead water channels become perforated penetration of stonework by water from defective guttering can occur without being accompanied by a gross overflow of water on to the exterior stonework. The perforation of lead channels by workmen wearing unsuitable boots or dropping hard metal objects such as scaffold poles can easily be prevented. However, water dripping on to lead from one point can eventually cause perforation, particularly if the rain-water has run over organic growths on the roof which might generate organic acids. Exposed lead normally survives because it quickly becomes covered by a protective film. Organic acids or constant dripping of water at one point can remove this protective film and permit penetration. Although this seems unlikely in view of lead's resistance to many other acids, it can be significant.

An occupier or frequent user of a building can also help to conserve it by preventing any tree, bush, creeper or other significant flowering plant from establishing itself on the stonework. Ivy is particularly harmful. Some lichens can slowly attack stone and their presence should be noted. Green algae might not do harm by themselves, but they are an indicator of persistent dampness, which should be investigated.

It is wrong to attempt to suppress an efflorescence of soluble salts that has appeared on the *inside* of stone window frames, mullions, or transoms by using a water-repellent treatment of any kind. These efflorescences usually affect windows facing seawards and the salt is usually sodium chloride. A palliative procedure is to treat the *outside* stonework of the window with a water repellent and to brush the efflorescence gently from the inside stonework until new efflorescence no longer appears.

It is also wrong to allow soil, solid fuel, stacks of bricks or bags of fertilizer to be placed in contact with a porous stone wall, particularly if they are in contact with stonework above a damp proof course or impermeable plinth. All are sources of salts of various kinds that will eventually cause crystallization damage to the stonework. For the same reason, it is wrong to use common salt as a means of removing any ice or snow lying in contact with the stonework. Any de-icing treatment of paths near the building should be carried out carefully, to avoid splashing salt solution on to the stonework.

Many household cleaning powders and cleaning grits contain salts that are harmful to porous stone and great care should be taken in cleaning stone floors, to prevent damage to the floors or to the walls which might become contaminated in the process. It would be ideal if special materials based on grits of appropriate size and detergents that are free from sodium, potassium and other alkali metals in any form were available. However, this is not the case. Laundry detergents are even more harmful and should not be used on stonework in any circumstances. For this reason, leaking drains that might allow discharge from domestic sinks or washing machines to contaminate stonework should be dealt with immediately. Treating stone with a solution of common salt on the grounds that it preserves meat, is a serious mistake.

Implements or stock materials, such as pipes that are made of copper, bronze or brass should not be left in contact with stonework for any considerable time, particularly in urban areas. This can lead to staining of the stonework. It should also be noted that an unwise choice of cleaning materials or of repointing mortar can lead to an increase in the rate of deterioration of the stonework.

Annex

Frost attack on stone

The work of Everett[12] and Haynes[13] attempted to explain the relationship between pore structure and resistance to decay in building stones. Their ideas are summarized below.

Fineness of pores

In the commoner form of frost attack, freezing is somewhat one-sided and the stone is not surrounded by a casing of ice. The effect of this type of attack may be stated *approximately* in the form of the equation

$$P_{max} = \sigma_{iw} \left(\frac{1}{r} = \frac{1}{R} \right) \qquad (7.1)$$

where P_{max} is the maximum excess pressure that can be developed during the slow freezing of water in a pore of radius R attached to a finer pore of radius r that has access to an *unlimited* supply of water that is free from any significant restraints on its movement. P_{max} is also the excess pressure at which ice will begin to grow in the fine pore (see *Figure 7.4a*). The constant σ_{iw} is the interfacial tension between ice and water, not the better known interfacial tension between water-saturated air and water.

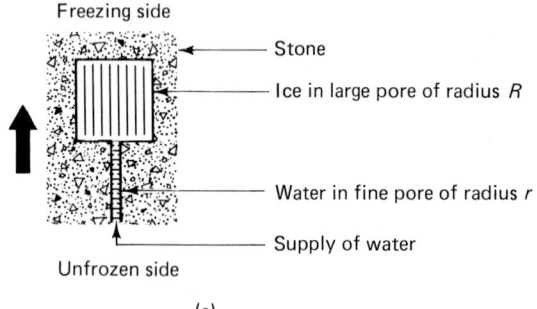

(a)

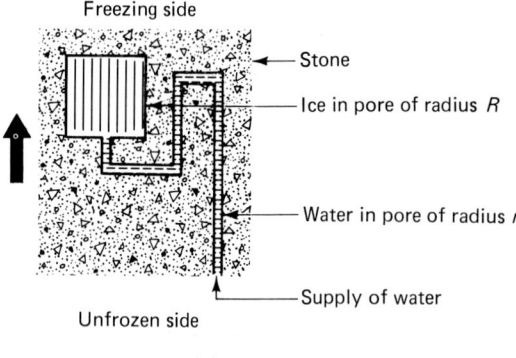

(b)

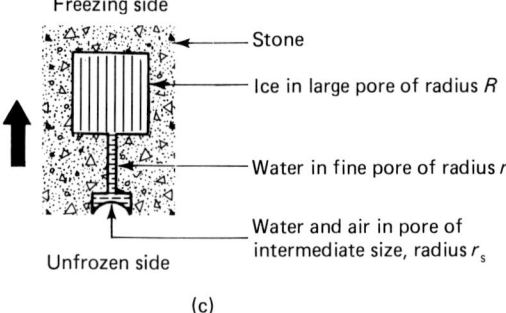

(c)

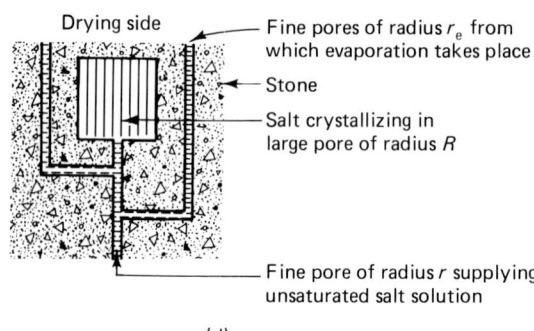

(d)

Figure 7.4 Everett's theory applied to frost and crystallization attack on stone (a) the simplest case of pressure development during one-sided freezing. Broad arrows show the direction of heat flow. The maximum pressure in the large pore is $\sigma_{iw} (1/r - 1/R)$. (b) water freezes at a lower temperature in small pores so the supply is not necessarily cut off if the small pore passes through the freezing region. The maximum pressure in the large pore is $\sigma_{iw} (1/r - 1/R)$. (c) effect of limited supply of water. Broad arrows show the direction of heat flow. The maximum pressure in the large pore is $\sigma_{iw} (1/r - 1/R) - \sigma_{aw}/r_s$. (d) pressure development by crystallization of salts caused by evaporation of water. As evaporation occurs, more solution feeds in from the pore of radius r and diffusion causes the solution in the large pore to become more concentrated and to attempt to form more crystals in the large pore. This further increases the pressure in the pore until the maximum possible pressure for that pore geometry is reached. This is $\sigma_{ss} (1/r - 1/R)$

The value of σ_{iw} is not known with certainty, but some experimental results[50] have indicated that it is about 0.032 N/m. The finer pore in the model need not be entirely on the warmer side of the freezing-point isotherm in the stone, because water in fine pores freezes at a lower temperature than water in wider pores. Hence a pore system of the kind shown in *Figure 7.4b* would still develop a pressure equal to $\sigma_{iw}(1/r - 1/R)$ before ice could begin to penetrate the finer pore. The open water in contact with the fine pore must be on the warm side of the freezing point isotherm. If it were situated on the cold side of the isotherm, it would freeze and cut off the supply of water before pressure could build up in the coarse pore.

It is clear from Equation 7.1 that potential excess pressure attributable to ice growth becomes greater as the fine pore becomes finer and the coarse pore larger. It would be unusual for any band lying along a freezing-point isotherm in a piece of stone to consist entirely of large pores fed by numerous small pores. A study of pore structure suggests that it is much more likely that the ratios of the radii of the coarse and fine pores will lie within the range 2 to 30. *Table 7.5* gives values of P_{max} computed for

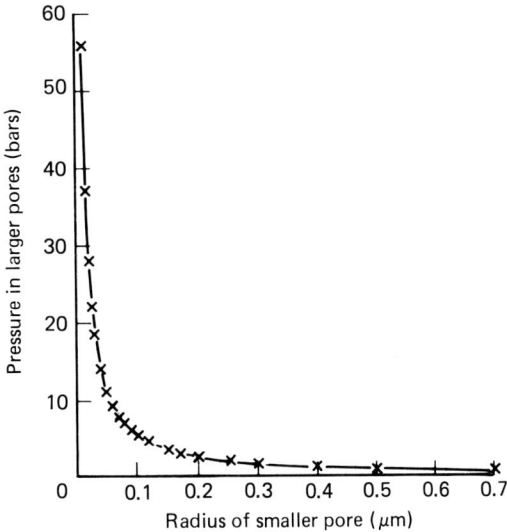

Figure 7.5 Theoretical pressure resulting from the freezing of water in a large pore connected to a smaller pore. The ratio of large and small pores was kept at eight

Table 7.5 The maximum pressure in bars (pascals $\times 10^5$) that can be developed in a pore of radius R connected to a smaller pore of radius r when water in the larger pore freezes. The pores are shown in μm. It is assumed that σ_{iw} = 0.032 N/m. σ_{iw} is the interfacial tension between ice and water. The small pores are assumed to have access to a free water supply

$r=$	$R=$ r	$2r$	$4r$	$8r$	$16r$	$32r$
0.01	0	32	48	56	60	62
0.02	0	16	24	28	30	31
0.04	0	8	12	14	15	15.5
0.08	0	4	6	7	7.5	7.8
0.16	0	2	3	3.5	3.8	3.9
0.32	0	1	1.5	1.8	1.9	1.9
0.64	0	0.5	0.8	0.8	0.9	1.0
1.28	0	0.3	0.4	0.4	0.5	0.5

values of R/r ranging from 2 to 32 and for values of r ranging from 0.01 to 1.28 μm. The effect of the ratio of the radii becomes relatively unimportant when R/r is greater than 8. *Figure 7.5* shows the effect of changes in the value of r on P_{max}, when the radii ratio is 10. P_{max} rises rapidly as r falls below 0.1 μm. Therefore the fineness of the pore structure plays a large part in determining its frost resistance under conditions of one-sided freezing where there is an adequate supply of water on the warmer side.

Water supply

If the supply of water is limited, Equation 7.1 must be extended:

$$P_{max} = \sigma_{iw}\left(\frac{1}{r} - \frac{1}{R}\right) - P_s \qquad (7.2)$$

where P_s is the negative pressure on the supply side. This is Everett's equation[12].

The pressure P_s could arise if all-round freezing cuts off the supply of water. If shortage of water causes the air/water interface on the warmer side to enter smaller and smaller pores:

$$P_s = \sigma_{aw}/r_s \qquad (7.3)$$

where r_s is the radius of the pores at the air envelope on that side, and σ_{aw} is the normal surface tension of water. This is also shown in *Figure 7.4c*.

This is why all-round freezing causes damage by a process that is distinctly different from that involved in one-sided freezing and why initial moisture content is so important in determining whether frost damage by one-sided freezing may occur.

Porosity

Under conditions of one-sided freezing, associations of coarse and fine pores can give rise to considerable local pressures. This acts like a miniscule jack. To cause damage there must be a sufficient concentration of jacks within the zone under attack to allow the development of a gross pressure that can overcome the cohesive strength of the stone. The probability of the occurrence of such a concentration is greater the higher the porosity of the stone. Moreover, the higher the porosity, the lower the amount of solid material within the zone and hence the lower the bursting stregnth of the stone.

In fact porosity is not the most important factor in determining frost resistance. Obviously, stone without pores cannot suffer frost damage, but even stone with a porosity of 40 per cent is not necessarily susceptible to frost attack. This is because the natural process that gives rise to porosity produces a fine pore system in the early stages and then proceeds by breaking down the pore walls, thus increasing the mean pore radius and hence reducing the number of jacks and the maximum pressure developable from each of them.

Salt crystallization attack

Because freezing is a crystallization process, Equation 7.2 may also be applied to salt crystallization attack on stone with only modest modification. Crystallization can take place as a result of cooling or evaporation of solvent (see *Figure 7.4d*). In both cases, the appropriate governing equation is:

$$P_{max} = \sigma_{ss} \left(\frac{1}{r} - \frac{1}{R} \right) - P_s \qquad (7.4)$$

where P_{max} is the maximum pressure that can develop in the larger pore, σ_{ss} is the interfacial tension between the salt and its solution, r and R are the radii of the small and large pores. P_s is the negative pressure in the finer pore caused by the entry of an air/water meniscus at the distant end due to shortage of water or salt solution or by the blockage of the distant end of the pore system by crystallization. At the beginning of crystallization attack, P_s will normally be zero.

In the freezing process, σ_{iw} will always be the same; in the crystallization process, σ_{ss} will vary with the salt involved. This explains why some salts are more aggressive than others. It is also clear from this theory why the coarser pored types of stone are generally more resistant to salt attack than the finer pored types. Unfortunately, in the absence of any experimental value of σ_{ss}, it is not possible to treat the problem quantitatively.

Acid gas attack on limestones

Everett's[12] theory does not directly apply to the attack on limestone, magnesian limestones, calcareous sandstones and calcareous slates by acidic gases in the air. Nevertheless, since the primary attack by these gases is normally followed by a crystallization attack, it has some relevance.

The good influence of coarse pores can be discerned more easily with ordinary limestones than with calcareous sandstones or magnesian limestones. This is because the loosening cause in calcareous sandstones by direct chemical attack on the calcium carbonate cement is so great that the effects of subsequent crystallization attack, which is influenced by pore size, is relatively minor. With magnesian limestones, the susceptibility to acid attack depends very much on their composition. It is lowest when the calcium carbonate/magnesium carbonate ratio is 1.19, as in the mineral dolomite. Variations in chemical resistance caused by variability in chemical composition tend to obscure the effects of pore coarseness on subsequent crystallization damage.

Blister formation on limestones

Attack by sulphur-based acids in the air can lead to the development of blisters on the surface limestones. Because this seems to occur mainly on limestones with finer-than-average pore structure, it is tempting to think that Everett's theory[12] is directly applicable and the blisters are forced up by crystals of gypsum growing in larger pores from supersaturated solutions fed through finer pores in which the gypsum cannot crystallize. However, the majority of limestone blisters are hollow beneath the skin, with no sign of crystals that could have forced the blister upwards. Instead, blisters appear to arise because the skin develops a larger surface area than the underlying stone. Hence, Scott Russell's explanation[21], that this occurs because the thermal expansion of gypsum is about five times as great as that of the unattacked limestone, seems sensible. Thus, when the temperature rises, the gypsum-rich surface skin will expand relative to the limestone below and cause a degree of shear failure. However, for a blister to continue to grow, it must not return to its original area on cooling. It has sometimes been thought that stone debris, formed as the crack extended, will prevent the skin from returning to its original position. However, the hollowness of most blisters on limestone belies this. Instead, the thermal expansion may enlarge some pores in the skin and allow the crystallization of more gypsum from the supersaturated solution held by the finer pores. The skin would thus increase in area and the blister bulge further away from the plane of the original surface with each significant cycle of heating and cooling. Everett's theory[12] may thus be invoked and the relationship between susceptibility to blister formation and the fineness of pore structure of the limestone may thus be explained. This process of blister formation has not been adequately studied experimentally in the past, but a new approach to this and to closely related problems is currently being made[51].

References

1. Amoroso, G.G. and Fassina, V., 'Stone Decay and Conservation' *Materials Science Monograph II*, Elsevier, Amsterdam, 1983
2. Dorsey, N.E., *Properties of Ordinary Water Substance*, p. 655, Reinhold, New York, 1940
3. Apling, A.J., Potter, C.J. and Williams, M.L., 'Air Pollution from Oxides of Nitrogen, Carbon monoxide and Hydrocarbons, *Warren Spring Laboratory Report LR 306*; Galloway J.N. and Likens G.E. 'Acid Precipitation: the Importance of Nitric Acid' *Atmospheric Environment*, **15**, 1081–1085, 1981
4. Serra, M. and Starace, G., *An Isotopic Method for Studying Absorption and Oxidation of Sulphur dioxide on Calcium Carbonate'*, CNR Centro di Studio Cause di Deperimento et Metodi di Conservazione delle Opere d'Arte, Rome, 1973
5. Kaiser, E., 'Skin Formation on Limestone', *Der Steinbuch*, **5**, 254, 1910; 'A Fundamental Factor in the Weathering of Rocks and a Comparison of the Chemical Weathering of Stone in Buildings and in Nature', *Chemie der Erde*, **4**, 342, 1929
6. Schaffer, R.J., 'The Weathering of Natural Building Stones', *Department of Scientific and Industrial Research Spec. Rep. 18*, pp. 28–29, HMSO, London, 1932 (available from the Building Research Establishment, Watford WD2 7JR, England)
7. Hull, E., *Building and Ornamental Stone*, p. 203, MacMillan, London, n.d.
8. Millot, G., Cogne, J., Jeannette, D., Besnus, Y., Monnet, B., Guri, F. and Schimpf, A., 'La Maladie des Grès de la Cathédral de Strasbourg', *Bull. Serv. Geol. Alsace Lorraine*, **20**, 131–157, Strasbourg, 1967
9. Anon. 'The Weathering, Preservation and Maintenance of Natural Building Stone, Part 1', *Building Research Station Digest*, **20**, Pt. 3, HMSO, London, 1965
10. Anon., 'The Decay and Conservation of Stone Masonry', *Building Research Digest*, **177**, Pt. 2, HMSO, London, 1975
11. Taber, S., 'The Mechanics of Frost Heaving', *J. Geol.*, **38**, 302–317, 1930
12. Everett, D.H., 'The Dynamics of Frost Damage to Porous Solids', *Trans. Farad. Soc.*, **57**, 1541–1551, 1961
13. Haynes, J.M., 'Frost Action as a Capillary Effect', *Trans. Brit. Ceram. Soc.*, **63**, 267, 1964
14. Honeyborne, D.B. and Harris, P.B., 'The Structure of Porous Building Stone and its Relation to Weathering Behaviour', *Proc. 10th Symp. Colston Research Soc. Bristol, March 1958*, p. 345, Butterworths, London, 1958
15. Huber, H. 'Staining and Efflorescence on Indiana Limestone caused by Moisture Seepage through Backing Masonry', *ASTM Proc.*, **28**, Pt. 2, 695–713, 1928
16. Department of Scientific and Industrial Research, *Building Research 1956*, p. 10, HMSO, London, 195
17. Evans, I.S. 'Salt Crystallisation and Rock Weathering: A Review', *Revue de Géomorphologie Dynamique*, **19**, 153–177, 1970
18. Cooke, R.W. 'Salt Weathering in Deserts', *Proc. Geol. Assn.*, **92**. 1–16, 1981
19. Kessler, D.W. 'Physical and Chemical Tests on the Commercial Marbles of the United States', *Technical Paper 123*, U.S. Bureau of Washington, 1919
20. Hochman, A. and Kessler, D.W. 'Thermal and Moisture Expansion Studies of some Domestic Granites', *US Bureau of Standards, Journal of Research*, **44**, 395–410, 1950
21. Scott Russell, A., quoted by Schaffer, R.J. Reference 6, p.32
22. Gaetani, L. de 'Cracking of Stonework by Cementing Iron Rods with Sulphur', *Giornale del Genie Civile*, 425, 1902
23. Rogers, F. *Specifications for Practical Architecture*, 2nd Edn. Crosby, Lockwood and Co., London, 1886. Quotes warning by Alberti (15th C) and de Orme (16th C)
24. See, for example, DSIR *Building Research 1952*, p.8, HMSO, London
25. Jones, F.E. and Tarleton, R.D. *DSIR National Building Studies; Research Papers 14, 15 and 17*, HMSO, London, 1951 and 1952
26. Schaffer, R.J., reference 6, p.76
27. Conway, Sir M. Letter to *The Times*, 11 May, 1929
28. Bravery, A.F. 'Preservation in the Construction Industry', in *Principles and Practice of Disinfection, Sterilisation and Preservation* (eds Hugo, Aycliffe and Russell), Blackwell Scientific Publications, Oxford, 1980
29. Bachmann, E. 'Kalklösende Algen', *Berichte der Deutschen Botanischen Gesellschaft*, **33**, 45–57, 1915
30. Lepidi and Schippa 'Some Aspects of the Growth of Chemotropic and Heterotropic Micro-organisms on Calcareous Surfaces', *Proc. 1st Int. Symp. Biodeter. Building Stones*, 143–148, 1973
31. Bachmann, E. 'The Phthalus of Calcicolous Lichens', *Berichte der Deutschen Botanischen Gesellschaft*, **10**, 30–37, 1892
32. Neculce, J. 'Some Aspects of Fungi in Stone Biodeterioration', *Proc. 6th Symp. Biodeter. and Clim.*, pp.117–122, 1976
33. Smith, A.L. and Hearing, G.G. 'Lichens', *Encycl. Britannica*, London, 1950
34. Lloyd, A.O., private communication to Bravery, reference 28, 1980
35. Lloyd, A.O. 'Progress in Studies of Deteriogenic Lichens', *Proc. 3rd Int. Biodegrad. Symp.*, (eds Sharpley, J.M. and Kaplan, A.M.) Applied Science, 395–402, 1976
36. Bachmann, E. 'The Relation Between Silica Lichens and their Substratum', *Berichte der Deutschen Botanischen Gesellschaft*, **22**, 101–104, 1904
37. Fry, E.J. 'A Suggested Explanation of the Action of Lithophytic Lichens on Rock (Shale)', *Annals of Botany*, **38**, 175–196, 1924
38. See, for example, *National Glass Budget*, **60**, 7, 1944
39. Bravery *loc. cit.*, reference 28
40. Anderson, T. 'The Decay of Stone Antiquities', *Museums Journal*, **10**, 100–106, 1911
41. Pochon, J. and Jaton, C., *Chem. and Ind.*, 25 Sept., 1587–1589, 1967
42. Jaton, C. 'Microbiological Aspects of the Alteration of Stonework of Monuments', *Proc. 2nd Int. Symp. on Deterioration of Building Stone*, 149–154, 1973

43. Paleni, A. and Curri, S. 'Biological Aggression on Works of Art in Venice', *Proc. 2nd Int. Biodeter. Symp.,* 392–400, 1972

44. Kauffmann, J. and Toussaint, J. 'Corrosion des Pierres: Nouvelles Experiences Montrant le Role des Bacteria Nitrifiantes dans l'Alteration des Pierres Calcaires des Monuments', *Corrosion and Anticorrosion,* **2**, 240–244, 1954

45. Jaton *loc. cit.,* reference 42

46. Duff, R.B., Webley, D.M. and Scott, R.O. 'Solubilisation of Minerals and Related Materials by 2-Ketogluconic acid-producing Bacteria', *Soil Sci.,* **95**, 105–114, 1963

47. Wood, P.A. and Macrae, I.C. 'Microbial Activity in Sandstone Deterioration', *Int. Biodeter. Bull.,* **8**, 25–27, 1972

48. Dumitru, L., Popea, F. and Lazar, I. 'Investigations Concerning the Presence and Role of Bacteria in Stone Deterioration of some Historical Monuments from Bucharest, Jassy and Vluj-Napoca', *Proc. 6th Symp. Biodeter. and Clim.,* p.67, 1976

49. See, for example, *Wear,* **10**, 89–102, 1967

50. Rennie, G.K. and Clifford, J. *J.C.S. Faraday 1,* **73**, 680, 1977

51. Price, C.A. and Ross, K. (Building Research Establishment, Watford), private communication, August 1982.

Illustrations of weathering and decay phenomena

Photographs on pages 179–184 © John Ashurst

1 Frost spalling of limestone

Detachment of lens-like pieces of stone in a saturated limestone viaduct record seasonal losses over many years. In the centre of the illustration is a frost spall which occurred the night before the photograph was taken and relates to water seepage through joints.

2 Fire damage to limestone

Of the several effects which fire may have on stone, shattering is the most obviously destructive. Rapid heating of previously cool surfaces will bring about the shattering illustrated here, after a fire following a bomb explosion. Rapid cooling of very hot surfaces, commonly brought about by quenching with water, will similarly encourage fracturing. The deeper tones in the photograph indicate areas which have undergone a colour change due to oxidation of iron compounds during the fire.

3 Marine salt damage to sandstone

Marine environments often provide ideal conditions for salt crystallization damage to take place. A ready source of salts (principally sodium chloride) and frequent wetting and drying cycles cause spectacular damage to the sandstones forming the sea wall defences of Berwick upon Tweed. Damage is most pronounced in the upper courses of the wall from which most drying occurs.

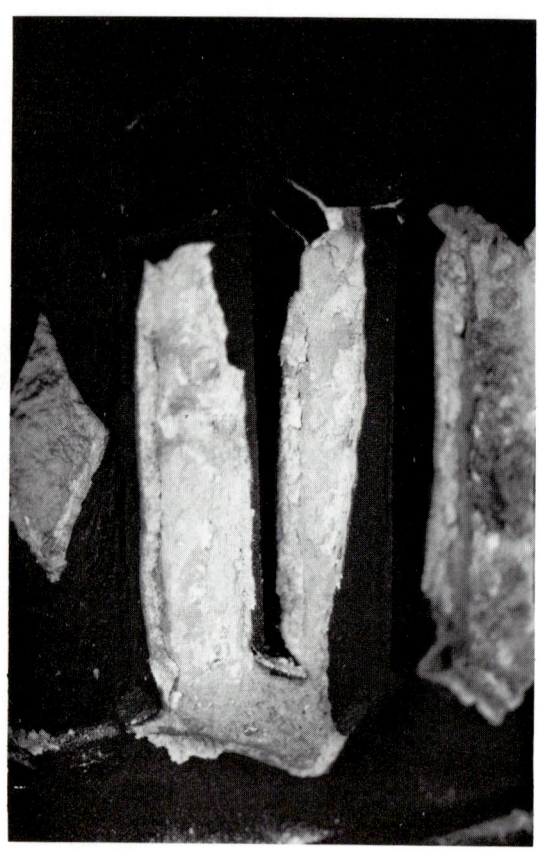

4 Calcium sulphate skin formation: washed and unwashed zones

Limestone which is regularly washed by rain, as indicated by the light coloured parapets, exposed ashlar and plinths in the illustration, often remains sound in spite of small-scale surface erosion. Sheltered zones, however, on which water sits in droplet form, are subject to the formation of skins of calcium sulphate, which become progressively darker and less permeable. In some cases, on the more durable limestones, these skins cause little problem. In other cases, the skin may split and blister.

5 Detail of splitting sulphate skin on Magnesian Limestone

Acid solutions derived from sulphur-based gases in the air attack the surface of Magnesian Limestone and produce calcium sulphate and magnesium sulphate. In sheltered zones, gypsum skins are formed but the magnesium sulphate penetrates more deeply and crystallizes behind the skin. The illustration shows a sheltered, blackened frieze of carved lettering on the Palace of Westminster, London, splitting and spalling.

6 Splitting and spalling of calcium sulphate skin on limestone

This recently cleaned limestone shows characteristic splitting and spalling of a calcium sulphate skin in a semi-sheltered position. The limestone is of moderate durability and had been exposed for about one hundred and fifty years.

7 'Cavernous' decay of Magnesian Limestone

Deep pockets in Magnesian Limestone created by crystallization and re-crystallization of magnesium sulphate. In this illustration the gypsum skin has largely disappeared.

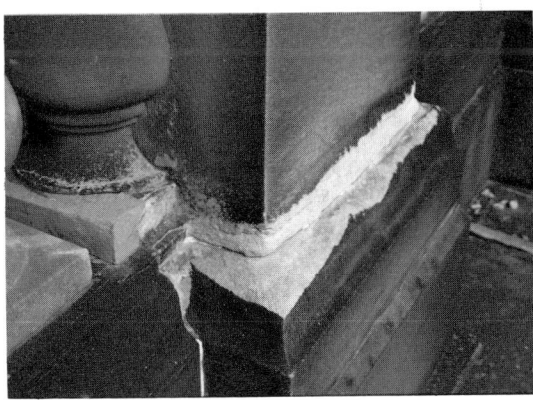

8 Acid attack on argillaceous sandstone

Sulphur-based acids in the air readily attack calcareous sandstones, argillaceous sandstones and, to a lesser degree, dolomitic sandstones. Heavily rain-washed areas powder away dramatically because the dissolving of a relatively small amount of cementing material (calcite, clay or dolomite) will release many grains of quartz. The illustration shows the deterioration of an exposed detail of argillaceous sandstone.

182

9 Contour scaling of sandstone

Blocking of the surface pores of sandstones appears to be
related to air pollution and to wetting and drying and
heating and cooling cycles. In some cases which have been
examined in detail, such as Tintern Abbey (Wales), shown
in the illustration, the detached crusts had become
completely blocked with calcium sulphate hydrate. The
crusts break away at a constant depth independent of any
bedding pattern.

10 Splitting from rusting iron

Wrought iron and mild steel fixings have caused enormous
amounts of damage to stone buildings. The splitting and
spalling of stone caused by the rusting of ferrous fixings is
a chemically induced expansion following access of air and
water to the metal. All renewals of such fixings should be
of stainless steel or non-ferrous metal.

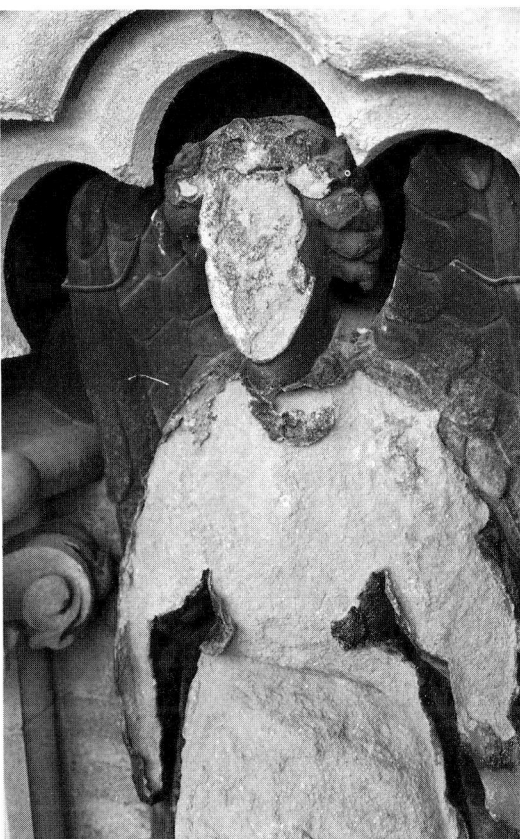

11 Weathering of 'soft' seams or pockets

Some sedimentary stones are characterized by the presence of readily eroded pockets of clay or sand or poorly cemented material. The illustration shows the critical effect produced by the weathering out of such a pocket in a limestone parapet at Gloucester Cathedral.

12 Face bedding of limestone sculpture

Decay of this sculpture on Wells Cathedral, Somerset, could have been avoided by placing the stone on its natural bed or on its edge (edge bedding). In general, sedimentary stones should be placed in the building in the same position in which they were laid down. Failure to carry out this practice can result in unnecessary deterioration (see also 13 and 14).

13 Failure of stones in an arch construction

Decay of these stones at Crowland, Lincolnshire, could have been avoided by placing the bed of the stone at right angles to the thrust of the arch.

14 Edge bedding of sandstone dressing

Edge bedding of this window jamb lining at Mount Stewart, Northern Ireland, is also inducing face bedding failure. Decay could be avoided only by natural bedding.

15 Structural disruption caused by climbing plants

Masonry ruins can be substantially colonized by trees, climbers and creepers, which can attach weak points in the walls by seeking sources of moisture. The illustration shows the displacement of large ashlar blocks at Corfe Castle, Dorset, by climbing plants. Ivy is notoriously destructive. Creepers which cling to the walls without the assistance of deeply penetrating roots are much less harmful, but when luxuriant can obscure the true condition of a wall.

Index